Freckles:
A Child's Life

Canada

*The Publishers acknowledge the financial assistance of the
Government of Canada through the Book Publishing Industry Development
Program (BPIDP) for our publishing activities.*

Library and Archives Canada Cataloguing in Publication

Trudzik, Ardith, 1934-
        Freckles : a child's life / Ardith Trudzik.

ISBN 978-0-88887-337-8

            1. Trudzik, Ardith, 1934--Childhood and youth.
    2. Alberta, Northern--Biography.   I. Title.

FC3694.25.T78A3 2007   971.23'1   C2007-902300-2

Permissions

I have made every effort to obtain permission to use excerpts from old
melodies, and found most to be in the public domain. I apologize for,
and promise to correct in a subsequent edition any error or omission.

Printed and bound in Canada on acid free paper.

Freckles:
A Child's Life

Ardith Trudzik

Borealis Press
Ottawa, Canada
2007

Acknowledgements

With thanks to my many friends for their help in writing
this book: Lily McCool, whose reliable and faithful commit-
ment included advice and typing; my sisters, Noël and Ruby,
for photographs and contributions; my brother Douglas
and his daughter Nancy, for their advice; Beatrice Nordli,
who remained steadfast throughout; Eunice Scarfe, who
nurtured my creativity; Mary Wright, for her wise judgement
that influenced the presentation; writing instructors and
writers-in-residence: Edna Alford, Di Brandt, Wayson Choy,
Mary Dawe, Katerina Edwards, Sally Ito, Myrna Kostash,
Margaret MacPherson, Alice Major, Jake McDonald, Shani
Mootoo, Gloria Sawai, Judy Schultz, Olive Senior, Shirley
Serviss; Dr. Lochan Bakshi, Joe Sobolewski and Mike Woyewada
for their advice; members of the Writers' Guild of Alberta for
critiquing: Sylvia Chetner, Jean Crozier, Dolly Dennis,
Kay Dier, Jenny Frost, Elizabeth Germain, Sue Marxheimer,
Florence McKie and Brenda Vilnoff; John Patrick Gillese, who
first inspired me to write; Linda Jenkins for editing; and Glenn
Clever and Frank Tierney of Borealis Press for creating a venue
for new Canadian writers and for choosing my manuscript.

To protect the privacy of my friends, I have used fictitious
names in this memoir.

www.ardithtrudzik.com

Table of Contents

ONE

Sad Christmas

I have a plain childhood and now I'm four years old. There is a great Depression in Canada. We live on a farm in northwestern Alberta, bush country. A range-line road runs north and south past our place, separating our farm from Granddad Ray's. Directly south of our house lies Grandpapa Black's farm. We're a close-knit family, close settled.

On a cold December morning Mummy bundles Noël and me into our homemade snowsuits and we walk the half mile to Granddad Ray's house, where he and Granny work on twelve huge turkeys that they have slaughtered this morning. Granny prepares the birds for sale—Christmas turkeys. Mummy comes to help.

Noël and I aren't much help, but Mummy never leaves us alone at our place during cold weather because our wood-burning heater sometimes spits sparks, which could cause a house fire. We stay in Granny's steamy kitchen, watching Mummy and Granny strip all the feathers from the turkeys and then singe the hair by holding each bird in turn over an open flame at the stove. Phew! The smell is awful. Next, with painstaking care, the two women pull all the pinfeathers. The meat is getting chilled, so those pinfeathers are tough to pull. Granny uses her sharp paring knife to slide right under each pinfeather for a better grip.

"Ouch! Now look what I done. Snicked my thumb!" Granny's thumb drips blood.

Granny has to finish the birds, so she pulls some adhesive tape off a roll to cover the cut. She doesn't take time to wash the wound. "I don't want no blood on the turkeys. It'll stain that skin. Granddad's taking these turkeys to town to sell. The money'll git more stuff for Christmas."

Three days later we visit and Granny draws Mummy aside to say in a low voice, "What do you make of this?"

Mummy's eyes grow round at the telltale red streak climbing Granny's arm, the lump under Granny's armpit. She squeezes the lump. "Is this sore? Why didn't you show Granddad? He could have come to get me."

Granny shakes her head. "Hush, child. It don't make no never mind."

"But this is serious," Mummy cries. "I'll get Papa's team and be right back. I'm taking you to the doctor. He comes to Mayerthorpe one day a week on the train. I don't know when he's due next, but we'll get there right away to wait for him. We'll rent a room."

Mummy borrows her dad's light team so they can make the trip fast. They drive off in the sleigh, planning to catch the doctor as soon as he sets up shop in a room at Hub Hotel.

Granny's flesh has blackened, filled with poison by the time the doctor arrives and lances her thumb. There are no antibiotics.

It is too late.

Granny lies in a pine box wearing pennies on her eyelids when Mummy drives the sleigh home. My two grandfathers carry that big box into Granddad's front room and settle it on four straight-backed chairs.

"We'd best start digging the grave," Grandpapa says. "The ground is frozen solid. I'll bring some coal to make a fire to thaw the ground on the plot."

"Bet that frost has gone down four feet deep," Granddad adds. "But that don't make no never mind. We'll git it dug."

Noël and I watch Mummy take a basin of warm water and a clean flannel to wash Granny's skin. She has a struggle to slide Granny into a pretty dress. Granny's stiff. Mummy fixes Granny's hair and arranges her turtle-shell comb to hold the thick brown curls. Mummy opens the window to keep Granny cool.

We hold Granny's funeral two days later, on Christmas Eve, 1938. Lots of neighbours come although it's cold, but Nan can't make it because she is crippled.

Daddy is very sad because Granny is his mother, and she won't get out of that box. He holds Granddad's arm to guide him as they stumble over clumps of clay beside a black hole dug near the corner of Granddad's farm.

Mummy gathers Noël in her arms and leans her over the box, which four neighbours now carry. "Kiss Granny goodbye."

Then Mummy pushes me forward, "Kiss Granny good-bye."

I press my lips to the still face. It doesn't feel like Granny's face. The skin is stiff and cold. It doesn't smell like Granny. It sure doesn't look like Granny. "That's not Granny," I scream. Chills run up my spine.

"Sh-sh. She's sleeping," a neighbour tells me.

"If that's sleep, I never want to sleep again! Wake up," I beg.

But her eyelids never flutter. Not even when Mummy takes off the pennies. Daddy nails the lid down. They use a long rope to lower her coffin into the clay, cold and deep, steep and dark. What a terrible place to sleep. I scream again, "Granny, wake up!"

My big brother Douglas is six years old and knows lots of things. "Granny's not really sleeping," he whispers. "She's dead."

Now I understand. Granny's dead. Dead like the rabbits Grandpapa shot in the willow bluff. Is that where I'll go when I die? I don't want to die. Not ever. Douglas pushes a clod of clay into my hand. I drop it down the hole. Plunk!

The funeral is a sad party. All our friends pat Granddad's arm and hug him. Mummy pours coffee from our wash-boiler cooking on the kitchen stove. She hands each person a cupful, and when all our cups are used, she fills clean jelly jars with the hot drink. Everyone is glad to have coffee to warm themselves after the grave-side service. A few women bring sandwiches, pickles and cakes. But I can't eat. I still feel a lump in my throat. I lie in the crib under the covers with Noël until the neighbours leave.

That evening Mummy allows each of us to open one Christmas gift—the gift that Granny bought. I am so excited, I rip off the brown paper wrapping and discover a doll-sized wicker set: davenport, two armchairs and a round coffee table all woven of colourful rattan.

"You must never play with these," Mummy tells me, with tears in her eyes, "because they're your last gift from Granny. She bought them just before she died, so you must save them as a keepsake." I don't know what "keepsake" means, but my heart sinks. I can't play with my new toys. I never had such precious gifts and I long to play with them. I wish Granny were still alive so I could play with my dolly set.

TWO

My World

*Granddad Ray holds Sandy; Noël, and Ardith in sleigh;
Ruby, Douglas, Mummy and Granny. 1938.*

I love to walk along the range line and stand on the hill, squint my eyes and see the road pointing straight as a pencil, getting thinner and thinner until it reaches south to the very edge of the earth. Then half turning myself and seeing this range line as it runs thinner and thinner in the opposite direction until, like a pencil sharpened on both ends, it meets the northern edge of the world. I am in the centre of this world. My world.

Today frosty clouds of breath warn me it is very cold, so I must hurry home. The kids will soon be home from school. My big sister Ruby, eight years old, is so clever that her teacher "skipped" her into grade three. She's as pretty as the lovely little girls shown in Eaton's catalogue—shiny blond curls, large

*Granddad Ray holds Ruby, Granny at original log cabin
on homestead. 1931.*

blue eyes and pearly white teeth. Nan says Ruby is precocious,
whatever that means, and chooses my big sister to stay with
her every day after school.

Douglas is our only brother, a thin boy, very smart, who
has finished grade one. He has soft sandy hair and solemn
hazel eyes. And he's very kind.

I'm next in line. I have freckles—freckles cover my face,
neck and arms. The kids all call me Turkey Egg because my
freckled face looks like a turkey egg. Mummy braids my red
hair so it won't fly up like a mad cat whenever I pull off my cap.
I'm tall and sturdy, and will start school next year.

Noël is the youngest, pretty and tiny; she's really cute.
She has a sweet face and big blue eyes. She's only two, but she
knows how to roll her eyes to get what she wants.

I walk up the lane and enter the house just as the potatoes sizzle and the smell of squab pie rises from the baking oven.

"Supper is ready," Mummy calls. "Squab pie and fried
tatties!"

With a quick rinse of hands in the tin washbasin, I dry
them by rubbing them across my flannel skirt and sink into my

place. Doug and I share one side of the table. I sit to the left, so that I don't bump into him. Ruby sits with Noël, helping her with her food on the opposite side of the table, leaving Mummy and Daddy each a side to themselves. Mummy settles briefly in her place, and we fold our hands as Ruby says grace:

> *Accept thanks from us, dear Lord*
> *For the food upon this table*
> *Prepared by loving hands, to strengthen us,*
> *So we may serve Thee faithfully.*

"Amen," we chime in and Mummy gets up to serve us. She takes each plate warming on the hob and piles crusty squab pie over a mound of crispy brown potatoes and sets the food before us: Noël, me, Ruby, Doug and, last of all, Daddy.

I close my eyes and smell the rich oniony steam of the squab pie. It smells better than it looks. I peek under the crust at dark pigeon meat clinging to the small bones, swimming in thick gravy, and sprinkled with carrot rings and onion strings.

Doug smiles briefly. "Tastes good, Mummy." We agree and eat.

I chase the last of my potato around with my fork, mopping my plate. Only when it's clean do I pause to drink from my glass of milk. Mummy smiles. "That's right, Ardith. Remember, there are starving children in Europe."

I wonder how the starving children can see my clean plate. Perhaps they can rise up out of their bodies and fly across the sky to peek into our kitchen. I roll my eyes upward, but see nothing except the solid wooden boards of the ceiling.

"Now look here, Ardith," says Mummy. "Don't you go rolling up your eyes when I speak to you of the starving children in Europe. It's the truth. And you are being disrespectful to your elders. Never be disrespectful. You must always do as they say. Without question. And without making faces. I want you to be a good girl."

"Yes, Mummy. Sorry, Mummy," I murmur and lower my eyelids, ashamed.

"Do we have dessert, Mummy?" asks Doug hopefully. He has neatly turned Mummy's attention and I'm glad.

"Bread pudding with raspberries and cream," she announces.

"I'll serve it," offers Ruby. "Finish your food before it gets cold." She divides the dessert onto plates for us.

It's dim in the house now, but Mummy doesn't light the kerosene lamp just yet. It's nice to sit in the gloom, to listen to the fire crackling and to rest a bit after a busy day.

Next day, as I approach the house, I hear strange voices coming from the open kitchen door—company! I creep closer to listen.

"Ardith is really plastered, ain't she?" a clear voice asks. Sounds like Mrs. Thomas, I think. I'm horrified to hear Mummy's response, "Yes, she certainly is, all over her face, arms and legs."

Plastered? I turn away. I know very well the meaning of the word "plastered." Only last week, when our family returned from town late in the evening, we came upon Mr. Patrick, lying by the side of the road, vomiting. After we were well past him and out of earshot, Mummy explained, "Mr. Patrick has taken too much to drink. He is plastered." It was an awful sight.

Now I realize I must be an unpleasant sight too—plastered! I creep into my secret tansy patch. Check over myself carefully. What am I so covered with that I make people up-chuck when they look at me? Freckles? Ah-h-h! That's the reason! My freckles make me plastered.

What shall I do? Everyone who sees me feels sick. I'm plastered. Ugly. I feel wretched.

THREE

Our Old House

*The Ray's old home
which burned down in 1939.*

Winter winds moderate, and huge drifts form caves beside the range line. What fun! When we are cold, Noël and I scramble to the house, pull off our moccasins and socks, and step out of our snowsuits. We sit on the leather davenport near the box heater in our front room. Noël mounts Ol' Dobbin, the rocking horse that Doug has outgrown. After all, Doug's nearly seven. Dobbin looks tatty; his mane and tail are sparse, but his eyes still sparkle.

I play with my dollies, singing a lullaby in time to the creaking of Ol' Dobbin's rockers. I glance around our living room, a large bright room, pretty along the west window sills where Mummy's geraniums bloom. Mummy says her secret for keeping the plants blooming into February is to water them with cold tea left over from meals.

A large bookcase and shiny black piano fill the south wall, with space for the back door that leads to the sun deck. Hardly anyone ever uses that door; everyone comes through the kitchen door and we usually stay in the kitchen. Most entertainment happens in the kitchen, which we consider to be the front of the house. So the kitchen door is the only door in use.

Now Mummy prepares a meal there because the kids will soon be home from school. She works in the long narrow kitchen beside the wood-burning cookstove. There's a table, chairs, a cabinet for foods and a cream separator. A big wooden box holds firewood for both stoves, and tucked along the west wall is a narrow cot that serves as a spare bed.

The front room has a double-wide door to the bedroom. It's crowded in there with an iron-framed double bed, a large crib, dresser, sewing machine and wardrobe; lots of our out-of-season clothes have to be stored in boxes and set out on the veranda.

Our house is old and creaky with wide floorboards. In the living room there's a trapdoor opening to the cellar, where our root vegetables and jars of home-canned foods stand in rows on rough shelves. Mummy is proud of her canning: quart jars filled with raspberries, blueberries, strawberries, saskatoons mixed with rhubarb, jelly jars of various shapes and sizes full of raspberry jam or jelly, chokecherry syrup, blueberry jam and cranberry jelly. And large two-quart sealers full of canned peas, beans, beet pickles, cucumber dill pickles, coleslaw and marrow garnished with raisins.

Under the shelves are piles of potatoes, turnips, cabbages and pumpkins making knobby mountains from the earthen floor, while braids of onions and strings of pearly garlic hang from the rafters.

The cellar smells musty, and it is spooky if I'm down there when Daddy shuts the trapdoor. Then I cry and beg to be freed. Doug always lifts the trapdoor to let me out while Daddy laughs.

Our house is made of wood, with a brick chimney going from the living room through the attic. From the outside, the house looks old; it has brown curling shingles on the walls, and a low roof.

One early morning in March, our house catches on fire! Daddy, outside starting chores, is the first to see smoke seeping through the shingles. Soon the boards are burning and crackling on the roof. Mummy shakes the davenport where Ruby, Douglas and I are still asleep. "Get up! Our house is on fire. Get dressed. Put on your snowsuits. We have to save as much as we can."

As she shouts, she takes Noël from the crib and wraps her into a tight cocoon using the quilt, tying the corners so it won't loosen and allow Noël to run back into the house. Mummy rushes outside and places Noël on the woodpile, a safe distance from the fire and high enough to see what's happening. The heat flushes my face when I come to the kitchen door, but Mummy won't let me back in. She thrusts a dishpan loaded with cutlery and towels into my arms.

"Dump it on the woodpile. Hurry back with the pan. Run. Run!"

I wallow through deep snow, stagger to the woodpile where Noël sits crying, "Get the dolls! Get the dolls!"

I dump my load and rush back to the burning house, exchanging my empty pan for a full one. I run with it to the woodpile and dump the cups, plates and little jars of jelly. Then I rush back to the house for more. Doug is carrying panfuls too.

"Don't come in," warns Mummy. "The roof might cave. Here's another load."

Sparks float like fireflies in the updraft. Bottles explode in the crackling flames. My eyes smart from the smoke. Ruby is everywhere. She helps Daddy haul the crib and sewing machine out the bedroom window, rescues blankets and clothing, and comforts Noël at the woodpile. Faster and faster we work as fire eats our home. I can't breathe for the sickly stench of scorching rubber, and my face is streaked with soot. My heart hammers in fear.

Our neighbours see the billowing smoke and arrive in time to heave our precious piano out into the snow. It takes only three men to run that piano away from the flames. They carry out our gramophone too. I see our tall cactus clawing at the windowpane as though begging for rescue. It collapses against the glass, as its flesh bubbles away to slime. Poor Ol' Dobbin, our hobby horse, dies. I begin to cry. We couldn't save him.

We watch the roof fall. Mummy holds Noël while Ruby passes a dolly up to her. I'm crying and Doug squeezes my hand. We stand on a snowbank among a few pieces of furniture, some scorched blankets and a heap of pots and dishes. Sealers full of raspberries and blueberries lie like coloured beads against the snow. When Daddy glances around our yard, his eyes light on a granary standing on skids. "We'll fix that up," he speaks in a husky voice. "It'll do temporarily. We'll build next year."

All the neighbours help. We must be settled by nightfall. They set up our cabinet and cookstove. Its pipe turns outdoors through a sheet of tin nailed over a crude hole in the wall. They build a strong door and nail a bunk across the entire back wall. Mummy sews sheets together into huge bags. "I'm making ticks," she explains. The women stuff the ticks with straw.

She tells Noël and me, "Up on the bunk."

"How can I get up? I can't even reach that high."

When I turn imploring eyes to her, she takes my cold hand. "Step on the chair. Now stand on the table. Then hop up onto the bunk."

I shrink back. Did she say "stand on the table"? I'm not allowed to put even my elbows on the table. How can I put my feet on it? I just stand there, not sure what to do.

"Hurry," Mummy urges. "It's warmer up there."

It is true. We huddle on the straw tick under the quilts, catching a bit of heat from the freshly lit cookstove.

"Push the sewing machine and crib under the bunk," Daddy says. "I'll make a storage cupboard of orange crates for that home canning. We'll save one orange crate for a wash-stand. This apple crate will hold firewood." We have several wooden crates on hand. They originally held apples or oranges.

Our good friend, the blacksmith, offers to keep our piano and gramophone until we have a new house. Only glowing embers remain of our old place as six men struggle to hoist our piano onto a sleigh. By nightfall our friends have gone and we are settled in our temporary shelter.

"Let's call this place 'the cabin,' so it sounds cosy," Mummy smiles. But I see her eyes are bleak.

We have fresh milk with bread sops for supper and settle for the night. We three girls sleep at one end of the bunk, with Mummy and Daddy at the other end. Doug curls up in the crib, which is under the bunk.

Late that night I feel my parents moving at the far end of the bunk. And Daddy whispers, "Maybe we should take the dole, you know, relief, government welfare."

"Never," Mummy hisses as she stiffens her body until the straw rustles in the tick. "This Great Depression brought us tough times, but we'll pull through. I don't want anyone to find out we haven't any money."

There is silence, and I think they've fallen asleep until I hear Daddy whisper, "I know how to earn a fast buck. I'll join up. With war starting, they need guys like me. And I'll send you money every payday."

"Oh Willie, don't even think of it. What would we do without you?"

"Just raise the kids, Edith. And save up my wages. When you get ahead, you can have a new house built."

"But what about the land?"

"Our dads will pitch in," Daddy says. "Lucky we settled right between their farms. You'll be fine."

"How can you be so happy-go-lucky?" Mummy wails.

I wonder what will happen to us. Within the week, Daddy joins the air force; his brother Lawrence joins the army. They leave from the CN train station, and Daddy promises, "I'll send home as much money as I can for a new house." He kisses us while the steam hisses from the locomotive. Then he swings to the open door as the train pulls away from the station. Daddy waves and waves until I see him no more. The train is gone, and Daddy is gone. We are alone and my heart feels like a stone. Why is Daddy leaving us? And will he come back soon? Will he still play mean tricks on me? I'm kind of glad he's going away for a while. But I better not tell anyone about my relief. It's a secret. The telegraph machine clicks its tongue with sympathy as Mummy turns to go home. Our whole world has humpty-dumptied. Nothing is ever the same again.

FOUR

Our Hero

*Ardith, Douglas, Ruby and Noël
make a wagonload. 1938.*

While Mummy makes us bloomers and pyjamas from Granny's clothes, Noël and I share the scissors to cut paper dolls from an outdated Eaton's catalogue. We play with them while Ruby and Doug are at school. Or we sit on the bunk and press egg cups into the ice on the windowpane, making faces of fairy tale people, Snow White, the wicked witch, Hansel and Gretel or Beauty and the Beast, while Mummy tells their stories. We're careful not to move about too much on the bunk, because it makes chaff sift from the ticks onto the sewing machine, which upsets Mummy.

Then she says, "I'm tired of your chatter. Off you go to play in the barn."

We bundle up and run to the barn. We open the door and a smell of sweet cured clover rises from the manger, softening the sharp reek of fresh manure. "I love the smell of these sweaty old leather harnesses hanging here on hooks," I tell Noël, "and I like the smell of that new hemp rope coiled near the sliding door." The pigs grunt and snuffle in their straw bed and the calves thrust their faces over the rails to be petted. A few chickens scratch at the gutter and the barred-rock rooster crows with authority. It is soothing to hear the familiar munch of the cattle, and their warmth protects us from a chill.

"It's nice out here," Noël declares. "There are no bedbugs in the barn."

It is true. I tell my little sister, "Mummy despises bedbugs. She's afraid that if we squash them on the wall, people will see that we have bedbugs in the cabin. I'll bet they know anyway. They must recognize that buggy stink. Besides, we're covered with welts from their bites."

"I like to watch Mummy catch bedbugs with the lamp," Noël laughs. "The bug scrambles along until she holds the globe just under it so it loses its grip and falls into the flame. It fries and dies."

"I'd rather capture a bedbug with my fingers and climb down off the bunk to fling it on the hot stove," I mutter. "Either way, it still stinks up the cabin. But so what, if we have bedbugs? We can't help it."

Gradually the weather softens and the drifts take on a grainy texture. Noël and I walk with Mummy to visit Nan, Mummy's mother. We call her Nan to distinguish her from Daddy's mother. (Now that Granny has died, this distinction is no longer necessary, but the name sticks.) Nan is extremely lame, her right leg stiff from waist to ankle. She wears a thick extension boot to lengthen that leg, and drags it across the floor as she

*Douglas, Ardith, Ruby and Noël wear
hand-made clothes. 1938.*

shuffles her left leg forward. She is almost blind, and completely housebound, unable to negotiate the rough terrain outdoors.

"How come Ruby gets to stay so often with Nan?" Noël begins.

"Nan needs help," Mummy explains. "And Ruby is the oldest, so she can do the most. She never complains about missing the fun we have at home, so you mustn't complain about Ruby. Her help allows Grandpapa to go outside to do his chores and farm work without concern about Nan."

"Why doesn't Aunt Nancy stay inside with Nan?" I ask.

"She likes to work outdoors with Grandpapa, or to work in the garden," Mummy explains.

"When I grow bigger, may I help Nan?" I ask.

"Of course," Mummy smiles.

"Why do you put oil of old lady on your face at night?" Noël asks.

Mummy chuckles. "It's called Oil of Olay," she says, "and it keeps my skin soft."

"Why must I put pine tar on my skin?" I demand. "It smells awful and I look ugly with black smears all over my face and arms."

"You have eczema, Ardith," Mummy explains. "That salve takes away the itching. Without it, you'd scratch big red patches on your skin."

If only pine tar were a pretty pink colour, so I'd look pretty. "I wish I could use Oil of Olay," I mutter. "It would smell better."

Noël and I play soldiers with Nan's dominoes while the two ladies drink coffee, as we all listen to *The Happy Gang* on Nan's radio.

Later that spring when I wander into the cabin, Mummy waves a telegram in my face. "Daddy's coming home on this Friday night's train. He can stay until Monday morning!" She clears the table and begins to prepare our evening meal as she speaks. My heart drops into my shoes. Daddy is coming back home.

All week we anticipate Daddy's furlough. On Friday morning, Ruby changes the sheets at our parents' end of the bunk. There is only one extra set of sheets so the girls' side will be changed next week. Meanwhile, I draw up the quilt.

Doug shakes the rag rug. Dust flies in all directions, much of it blowing back into the cabin, which brings howls of protest from Ruby, who is sweeping the floor.

Noël appears at the doorway with her little fist full of marsh marigolds. She surprises us all by fetching them herself. She waded into the murky swamp with total disregard for her shoes and stockings, and now clutches her bouquet proudly. But her stockings are sodden; dirty water squelches through her toes and runs in rills across the wooden floor.

"Oh Noël," reproaches Ruby. "You're wet." She tries to dry Noël's shoes with an old rag, but has to pull them off, and she pulls off Noël's stockings too.

"Never mind, dear." Mummy sees Noël's face fall. "Here's the orange vase for your flowers. Daddy likes marigolds," as she arranges the fragile stems so yellow blossoms trail over the bowl's edge. "They look beautiful." Noël flushes with pleasure from the praise.

All is in readiness for our daddy's arrival. Noël gets clean stockings and pulls on her old rubber boots. The mournful whistle sounds as the train approaches the trestle. It's dusk and the sky turns rhubarb coloured, shot with purple streaks to the north.

Doug knows every whistle's meaning. "The train is just about to cross the bridge." He has a fascination for trains.

We scamper across the summer fallow along the shortcut to town. It's only half a mile. Mummy holds Noël's hand as she clumps along in her heavy boots. Around the muskeg and through the pasture we run and arrive out of breath at the station platform. We're swallowed in a belch of steam from the hissing locomotive.

"There he is," cries Noël. "Daddy! Daddy!" She flings herself into his arms. We cluster around him. He looks important in a serge uniform with polished brass buttons and wedge cap. He holds his duffle bag in one hand and Noël close to his broad chest with the other. Smiling and winking at us kids, he hugs Mummy briefly.

We set off for home, choosing to return by road so that we can walk abreast. Doug manfully struggles to carry the duffle bag, while I speculate about its contents, slipping my hand into Daddy's huge palm.

By the time we turn from the range line into the sloping lane, Doug is lagging, dragging the duffle bag by its strap. Daddy tousles his hair as he swings the bag over his shoulder and marches to the cabin. "Left. Left. Left, right, left." We chant escorting our hero home.

Mummy shoos us outside so she can prepare supper. An hour later, as I step into the cabin, I smell frying fish. I peek into the pan, where thick whitish-pink slabs are cooking in spitting hot grease.

"Where did you get the fish?"

"Granddad brought us two fat suckers," Mummy is slicing potatoes to bake. They're running in the river."

"Ugh!" I know only too well that the meat will be mushy, like a wad of tired chewing gum. "Gooey, gummy suckers!"

"Now, now, Ardith," reproaches Mummy. "It's kind of Granddad to bring them. You must run over after supper and tell him how much we enjoyed them. Always be good to your elders, Ardith."

"Yes, Mummy."

It is Noël's turn to recite grace. After we have washed our hands and are seated, we bow heads reverently as Noël chants

> God is great. God is good.
> Let us spank Him for our food.

"A-men," chime in all the family. I snicker secretly over Noël's grace, although Mummy never seems to catch the humour of it.

The fish are mushy all right! But Mummy has baked biscuits, fluffy and hot, with butter melting through the cracks. We eat scalloped potatoes in cream sauce, disguising the fact that the potatoes, too, are turning soft and spongy.

"Now, Ruby, Noël will wipe the plates for you while Ardith runs down to thank Granddad for the fish. Doug and I will help Daddy with the barn chores. Let's hustle. It looks as though it will rain tonight."

The sky is grey and drizzly, but it isn't raining as I hurry along the range line. In no time, I'm banging on the weathered door of Granddad's house.

Granddad has a brisk fire in the range and his kettle is boiling.

"Are you having a late supper?" I eye the kettle with interest.

"No, I et," he responds.

"Daddy has to leave tomorrow. It's a short furlough this time."

"Oh."

"Mummy says thanks for the fish," I report. "We ate it all."

Granddad smiles. "Those suckers are really pushing upstream to spawn."

"What does that mean?"

"Spawn means to lay eggs, for new baby fish to hatch."

"Granddad, why do we call Aunt Nancy our aunt? Since Mummy's an only child, and Daddy has only one brother, Uncle Lawrence, who isn't married yet, we don't have a *real* aunt, do we?"

"That's right, Honey Child. She's not your real aunt. She's your Grandpapa's friend, so you call her Aunt Nancy just to be friendly."

"Why does she live with Nan and Grandpapa?"

"She came to help your Nan in the house. But she prefers the outdoors with Grandpapa. I guess she helps them both.

Want some cocoa, Honey Child?" He fixes a mugful. I slowly drink the cocoa.

"Gonna rain, Child. Run away home. See ya soon."

I smack my bare feet flat against the packed clay of the range line. The first few raindrops fall, making the soil slick and shiny. Not a star brightens the overcast sky.

I stand in the half-filled basin, warming my feet as I wash them, and then climb up onto the bunk and whisper my prayers so that I won't disturb Noël, who is already sleeping.

The sound of raindrops pattering against the window-pane seems like fairies tapping against the glass, asking for shelter from the cold darkness outside. I'm content to watch the flickering lamp flame until I fall asleep.

FIVE

Birthday Girl

Ardith and Nan celebrate Ardith's 7th birthday. 1941

The world is very still when I waken. There's only a faint glow to the air, before light comes. It must be nearly morning because birds are rustling in the shelterbelt. A damp coolness presses around me, a freshness in the air. The rain has stopped during the night and I can hear drops plop from the eaves into the water barrel. I pull the quilt over my chest because I'm chilly and pass the time by counting the steady drops of water. Plop. Plop. Plop.

A gentle daylight brightens the cabin so the family begins to stir. Daddy gets up and goes directly outside.

By the time I'm dressed, the sky is a pearly grey and a wet breeze stirs the trees. Mummy pokes kindling into the stove, starting a brisk fire.

"Well, young lady, you're up awfully early! Why don't you slide back under the covers for a bit. I'll just get the cow milked so we can have fresh milk on our porridge."

"Can I go to the barn with you?" I beg. "I'd like to see Sampson."

"All right, dear. Come along. But slip on your jacket; it's surprisingly cool this morning, after all the hot weather we've been having."

The loamy smell of damp earth strikes me as soon as the door opens, and I cry out in delight to see the world's a cloud, as if I've fallen into the sky! Fog is so thick I can't make out the barn or shed. "Oh, Mummy! It's magic! The barn has disappeared!"

"Yes, dear, and so will you if you don't take my hand. Come on, we'll find that barn!"

Together we set out. I can feel my skin getting cold, drops of moisture form on my forehead.

What direction are we going? Mummy forges ahead with confidence until suddenly, looming high, I catch sight of the hip roof of the barn, like Noah's ark.

A sound overhead startles me—a beating, muffled by the fog. Is it the heartbeat of God? No, only a pigeon beating its wings under the eaves.

Mummy pulls the barn door open and the warm fragrance of hay and animal smells welcome us. Mummy unhooks the wooden milk stool and settles her head into Annette's flank, coaxing the cow to let down her milk, while I call Sampson. He meows, but leaves me to sit on his haunches and beg for a squirt of milk. Mummy laughs, squeezing a stream of warm milk from a well-aimed teat until the cat catches a few mouthfuls mid-air. Mummy continues to milk, singing in rhythm:

> *Cushy cow, bonny, let down thy milk,*
> *And I will give thee a gown of silk;*
> *A gown of silk and a silver tea*
> *If thou wilt let down thy milk to me.*

I tickle Sampson with a timothy straw, and laugh each time he pounces on a lure made with a piece of twine tied to a jag of paper.

By the time Mummy completes her barn chores, the fog is hanging at eye level. Through a small tear in the fog, sunlight beams on the cabin, showing up the weathered walls. Mummy marches straight to the doorway to prepare breakfast.

I can't bear to leave the magic of the mist. Fog lifts in a great swirl, revealing chunks of machinery like skeletons of dead dinosaurs standing around the yard, until it settles again, hiding them from view. I run through the yard, marvelling at the curtains of fog folding and unfolding around me, like Gulliver's cloak.

I try to locate the watering trough. Perhaps it will unveil a magical secret today. But it seems like looking at my reflection in a frozen pool because although the surface shines like glass, what is beneath is dark and black, giving up no secrets. I shiver with disappointment and seek the safety of the cabin.

Mummy is stirring up batter and I peek at it hopefully. "Pancakes?"

"No," Mummy smiles. "Don't you remember? Today is your birthday, Ardith, and I'm whipping up a cake!"

"Och, Mummy! I'd forgotten all about it! How could I?"

"Everyone forgets things. Now, I'll slide this into the oven and it'll be ready by the time these sleepyheads have eaten. Come on! Stir your stumps! Ardith and I have been up for hours!" Daddy steps into the cabin, making it seem quite crowded until we settle around the table.

After a breakfast of rolled oats and warm milk, Noël and I take a small lard tin and set off to pick wild strawberries. Mummy needs enough to garnish the cake. We head straight to the meadow where the cows' grazing has made it easy to spot the tiny red berries. The grass is moist and cool to our bare feet. Fog still hangs in pockets.

By noon we have a half pailful of delicious sticky strawberries. "Oh, Noël. You look covered in blood!" I point at the red stains on her fingers and lips.

"So do you," Noël says shortly. "Let's go. This is enough."

The darkening sky promises a storm, although sunbeams like searchlights burst out between the clouds, making an eerie shifting pattern in the meadow as we trudge home. We leave our berry bucket on the table and wander outdoors again.

"Let's go see Nan! I wonder if she remembers it's my birthday."

The sweet scent of cinnamon meets us as we open Nan's kitchen door. She stoops to pull a pan of cinnamon buns from the oven, teetering as she bends, balancing with the broomstick. She straightens with a smile. "Happy birthday, Ardith."

"Oh, Nan! I was afraid you'd forgotten."

"Tut-tut! I'd never forget your birthday. Come in. Come in. I've made buns for lunch. Who would like to lay the table?"

"I will," I say as Noël cries, "Me!"

"You may both do it. Just shake the breakfast cloth outdoors, Ardith, and it will do another turn."

By the time everything is in place, Grandpapa comes. We sink to our seats as Grandpapa bows his head.

"Our Father, we would ask Thee to bless this food to its use, and us to Thy service for Christ's sake ... "

"A-men," we add.

We devour the buns, washing them down with milk.

"Will you sing us a song, Grandpapa?" I beg. "For my birthday."

"Of course, I will. How about Little Birds' Ball?" So Grandpapa sings umpteen verses about the birdies' ball while Noël and I join him on the chorus:

> *Tra-la la-la-la*
> *la la la-la-la*
> *la la la-la-la*
> *la-la, la-la, la!*

Our faces are flushed by the end of the ballad. Grandpapa sings a serious song next: Mr. Froggie Went A-Courting, and we have only to sing "Um-hm, Um-hm," looking as solemn as two bullfrogs.

Although Nan moves like winter's molasses, she has cleared the table and lowers herself into her rocker by the time the music ends and Grandpapa reaches for his cap.

"Thank you, Grandpapa!" I call, and he chuckles as he heads out.

Nan has a delicate lavender scent. I love to burrow my nose deep into her lap to inhale that faint flower fragrance. Nan strokes my hair. "Tisk-tisk!" says Nan. "Do you feel any older today?"

I put my hand on Nan's wrist, a wrist so thin that I can feel the fine, birdlike bones through her delicate skin, and the slow beating of Nan's pulse.

"I guess so," I reply. "I'm five now."

"Och, Ardith. Such a strong, big girl you are, too."

But she didn't say pretty, I notice. No one says I'm pretty. Just Turkey Egg and now strong. Oh well …

We visit all afternoon, entertaining Nan with tales of our adventures picking berries. I tell of the fog and Nan exclaims with delight. "Your stories are life itself to someone housebound."

"We'd best go, Nan," I say at last. "Mummy baked a birthday cake, and Daddy's home so I know there'll be a party at suppertime. Thank you for a lovely visit," as I kiss Nan goodbye.

"Bye, Nan," murmurs Noël as she kisses her grandma.

It is hot. The fog has burned off and a brassy sunlight blazes overhead. We seek the shade of the shelterbelt to rest.

As the shadows lengthen, we know it must be mealtime. I'm delighted to see Granddad come strolling along—my special guest on this important day. Of course, I must say the blessing after which we all chorus, "A-men."

I admire the birthday supper table. Mummy uses a proper tablecloth and decorates with a fresh wild-rose centrepiece. "An especially good meal for our birthday girl," Mummy's face flushes, "Porcupines with salad." We cheer! A treat indeed to have red meat in summer. Mummy has walked to town and splurged on a pound of hamburger, which she mixes with onions and rice, forming balls baked in tomato sauce. The rice sticks out like little quills from each ball, so we call them porcupines. There's plenty of bread and butter to fill us up, and a dandelion–chive salad complements the meat dish.

"We must eat either rice or macaroni all this month," explains Mummy to the men, "because we've eaten the last of the potatoes."

Granddad laughs, "I'm eating lots of beans these days. My spuds are out, too."

"It's all right, Mom," says Doug. "New tatties will be a real treat by August."

I tell the tale of my frolic in the fog: "This morning I got up early and stepped into a cloud. I felt like Jack and the Beanstalk when I discovered lots of strange things in the cloud. I found a dead dinosaur with its ribs all sticking up, but when I got closer, it was only the hay rake. What a surprise!"

"That was an Ardith-saur-eyes!" says Doug, as we laugh. Then Mummy lights the candles and the family sings:

Happy birthday to you,
Happy birthday to you.
Happy birthday dear Ardith,
Happy birthday to you.

I think of a wish, which I mustn't say aloud, or it won't come true: I wish my freckles would disappear! Then, in one mighty puff I extinguish every candle.

I survey my vanilla layer cake smothered in whipped cream, and no one comments that the strawberry garnish is scant. Those tiny, tart wild strawberries are delicious, the first of the season. Mummy helps me divide the cake, and then pours coffee for the adults.

"May I have coffee, too?" I beg.

"No, it'll stunt your growth," Mummy says.

Then comes gift opening time! Mummy clears a space for a brown paper parcel tied with yellow yarn. First, *Honey Bear*, a story book written in rhyme, by Dixie Wilson. Next, a thin lawn hanky edged in lace, from Nan. A big chocolate bar from Daddy. And finally, Granddad hands me green satin ribbons for my braids.

I'm excused from helping with the dishes, because I'm the birthday girl. So I climb onto Granddad's knee and beg, "Tell us a story, Granddad, please. About Br'er Rabbit." While Ruby and Noël do the dishes and Mummy clears away, we all listen to a tale of Uncle Remus, told in Granddad's southern drawl. Doug sits on Daddy's knee.

Ruby leaves to spend the night with Nan. And Granddad goes home.

After prayers are said and I flop onto the bunk, I burst out, "Oh, Mummy! This is my best-est birthday yet!" Smiling, Mummy settles down to read us the new storybook, lying between her girls with Doug listening from his crib beneath the bunk.

SIX

Disobedience

Nan and Grandpapa Black's house. 1938.

Daddy leaves on the early train, with only Doug to see him off. Mummy and Ruby go to the garden while Noël and I sleep late. I eat my toast, leaving the best till the last. That is to say, I eat the crust all the way around, not that I love the crust. Quite the opposite, really. I hate crust! So by getting it all down first, I'm left with the soft bit in the centre, where the black currant jam oozes, making me almost drool.

The sharp smell of currants reminds me of sunshiny summer days. I love picking the fat black currants that grow along the edge of the garden, but Noël would rather sneak into the pea patch and eat the green peas right out of the pods.

The peas are really yielding in the August sunshine. Mummy and Ruby have been out since sun-up, pulling fat pods from the vines before the heat drives the women to the shade.

I survey the two five-gallon buckets full of fresh pea pods and feel my heart plunk. "That's a lot of peas."

"Yes, so you and Noël get busy shelling them right away, while they're still crisp," says Mummy. "You can sit out in the shade of the shelterbelt."

I fetch two unsplit blocks of wood for myself and Noël to sit on while she gets two flat pans from the cabin. I choose a small handful of pods, and as soon as I burst the first pod open, its delicious scent rises to my nostrils—the most wonderful aroma of the summer!

We shell peas for a long time. What was a pleasure at first soon becomes a drudgery. It gets hotter and hotter. My fingers feel sticky and my thumb hurts. I no longer eat the raw peas or listen to the dull plunk as the tiny green balls pile higher in the pans. Each time my pan fills and empties into a big pot, my heart leaps, thinking we are finished, but the pile of pods scarcely changes.

My seat hurts. The block of wood is uncomfortable. Noël and I toil on, more and more slowly.

At last I whisper, "I know a wonderful new hiding place. If I take you there, will you promise not to tell?"

Noël rolls her blue eyes in delight. "Sure. Where is it?"

We leave the pea pods and scoot along the edge of the shelterbelt, emerging momentarily at the chicken house, then disappearing behind the big willow. I climb into the icehouse, pulling Noël in behind. Oh, it's so cool and dark and musty smelling. A perfect hiding spot! Noël worries about getting dirty, but I tell her, "It's just damp sawdust. It will fall off when we go outside."

We burrow like gophers covering our legs and bodies in the cool sawdust. We toss handfuls at each other. Finally we lie back, relax and enjoy the coolness, the quiet and the secrecy.

"No one must ever know where we are," I warn Noël, "Remember, you promised not to tell."

Finally dusk shrouds the icehouse. Everything is very quiet. "I suppose we should head home," I venture. "Mummy might be wondering where we are. And then, there are those peas ... "

We step out of the icehouse and shake thoroughly. We take off our dresses and flap them sharply. We dust each other's hair and rub our arms and feet. I dread facing Mummy. There is nowhere to go but home.

We march along briskly as though we have something important in mind, but my knees are quaking.

"And where have you young ladies been?" inquires Mummy, her eyes blazing, her voice crackling like cooling bacon grease.

"We were ... that is ... we got tired .... I mean, there were so many .... It was hot and ... we stopped for a while," I lamely concluded.

"For a while!" explodes Mummy. "Do you realize you've been gone two hours? Look at those pods! All wilty. They'll be twice as hard to shell now, and if we leave them any longer, they'll be poisonous."

"But Mummy—"

"No. I don't want to hear any excuses. I gave you a job to do and you let me down. You didn't ask to be excused. Or to rest. You just left. I won't tolerate that behaviour."

"But our fingers were sore."

"There will be more than your fingers sore. Now whose idea was it to leave?"

Noël says nothing. I swallow hard. "Mine."

"That's what I expected. You always have your head in the clouds. I am going to thrash you, Ardith. Thrash you for disobedience. Go and choose your switch."

I know that I was in the wrong. I set off to choose my whip from the shelterbelt. I've learned that a poplar branch is stiffer and hurts less than a springy willow. So I yank a ropy poplar switch; it smells from being torn loose. I hand it to Mummy, whose mouth is set in a grim line.

The switch swishes through the air. One, two .... Striking my thighs.

I automatically count the lashes .... Nineteen ... twenty.

"I'm at my wits' end," Mummy scolds. "I can't keep up with all the work and you little people's disobedience."

Her face is drawn by the time Mummy flings the switch away. Noël and I creep to the loft. I'm weeping. I didn't know the peas would spoil if we left them. I know I've been bad. We leave Mummy sitting at the back step, snapping the peas as if they were bullets. She is angry at me for our sneaky laziness. I am a rotten kid.

Now, Mummy's eyes are wet and jumpy, and she is startled when Doug slides silently beside her and begins shelling peas. "I'll help, Mom," he says. "The girls didn't mean to be naughty." But Noël and I don't see this. Douglas tells me later.

That evening Mummy tries to make the cabin cheery. Her orange vase, filled with a brilliant splash of nasturtiums, is set in the centre of the wooden table. I bury my nose in velvety blossoms even though the pollen makes me sneeze. Then I nibble a petal and find it has a tangy taste. I chew up several petals, furtively checking to see if I'll be scolded, but no one notices. Oh-oh. What if these plants are poisonous? Will I die of poison like Granny did? I deserve to die, I know, for being so naughty. I lie quietly on the bunk later that evening, waiting to die. But nothing happens.

SEVEN

Playing War

"Let's hit the trenches!" challenges Doug. We hide ourselves in the ditch on Grandpapa's eroded bank. Entrenched, we shoot down millions of enemy planes with our machine guns. We successfully advance from trench to trench, right into the jaws of the enemy. But our troops are surrounded. "Quick, Douglas. The white flag!"

Doug produces his cloot, a bit of an old sheet he has as a handkerchief, and I fashion a flag by tying two corners to a stick. We signal surrender. Capture is brief. We crawl and crouch to escape the enemy guards, and make it to the shelter of the straw pile. Safe!

Whenever enemy soldiers draw near, we seek refuge in the leafy branches of the willow until Doug calmly clears the area, using his sniper rifle. He is a crack shot, never missing his mark. But when he is mortally wounded, we are finally overcome by the enemy, and fall to the ground below. Then the sturdy branches spring upright once more, leaving our lifeless little bodies below.

After a decent period of being dead, we revive and head for the slough, a short distance from the big willow tree.

Doug designs a raft by lashing several poles together and places an old wooden gate atop. We launch the raft in the shallow slough behind the icehouse. Many shipwrecks are dramatized upon these warm high seas.

"What were you three little people up to today?" asks

Mummy that evening. Her face has loosened from the tightness of last week.

"We was shipwrecked," announces Noël.

"Were shipwrecked," corrects Mummy. She is quick to correct any grammatical errors.

Every chance we get, we fight another battle on the war field. Doug leads. We girls obey. Sometimes he takes us to the river, a popular battlefield. Lots of kids are there.

Billy launches a ship by dropping a small log over the bridge upstream. We troops remain in ambush on the opposite side of the bridge, armed to the hilt with clods of earth and small stones. When the ship floats majestically into view, we bombard it. A direct hit! Hurrah! Doug shouts, "While we have the advantage, let's go under the bridge and blast it so the enemy can't cross. Bring the dynamite. Got the line?" I wire the bridge, making laborious twists with strands of binder twine we brought from the straw pile at home.

"Okay! Quickly now. You back off while I light the fuse!" Doug efficiently sends his troops to safety before the final torching. Then he scrambles out. A mighty BOOM sends him hurtling down the bank, heels over head like a tumbleweed in a high wind.

He survives! The bridge collapses! We choke from dust and debris, half suffocated; his soldiers climb the bank and survey the wreckage.

Mission accomplished. We head for home.

"See ya, Billy. 'Bye now."

Another glorious Saturday morning, and Douglas suggests, "Let's take lunch and go to the river." On our way, we meet Billy. "Hey, you guys, let's climb the trestle!"

My heart plunks like a stone thrown in a deep creek. I'm still scared of heights. But away we go. We walk the rails of the railroad track and balance like tightrope walkers. Douglas is most steady. We check pebbles along the grade and find coal chunks that glisten among the gravel.

"Billy and Ardith, you go under the trestle. Noël and I will go on top. Get right under a barrel stand. We'll bomb you with the water in the barrel. Get going now!" Doug organizes his troops. Billy and I scramble through brambles below the bridge, and then gaze upward as a blob of blue water spreads and falls a hundred feet. Whistles! Turns like a thrown cat landing on its feet. We bow forward as the swooshy blob falls faster. SPLAT! The force flattens us face down in the mud. We're water-bombed wet, with sloppy, soppy hair. But we don't care! Another bomb! BOOM! SPLAT! Flat again! Doug empties the whole barrel. Too bad if a spark from the loco-motive crossing the bridge sets the tar ablaze on the deck. No water is left to douse hot cinders that might spit from the fire-box either. Finally, the bombs cease.

Exhausted and filthy, our group heads for the river for a quick dip. Racing headlong into the water, clothes and all, we rinse and head home, drying as we run. Mummy never minds mud. It's part of farm life. She's too busy to fuss over the con-dition of our clothes.

After harvest there's a long warm spell of Indian summer. The days are hot and hazy, while the evenings are cool. The flies become sticky and the geese begin to gather. The pump-kin vines blacken and it's time to dig the "neeps and tatties."

Although we kids work diligently to gather the garden produce, we still find time to play. Doug discovers a fine new war game. It's the threshing machine! This huge machine has been moved to our farm from Grandpapa's to make a straw pile near our barn, to provide bedding for old Annette and the calves. When Noël and I clamber into the bowels of the machine and lie flat on the shakers, we can imagine we're within a torture chamber. Doug applies all his strength to turn the outside wheel by hand, which makes the sharp cutting knives above the shakers loom close and closer to the quaking bodies inside the torture chamber. Regardless of how we are threatened by these punishing knives, we never tell the secrets of war to the enemy. We throw chaff from the blower. Poison gas! Killing everyone in its wake as it drifts over the country-side. Death! Destruction! Delightful!

When cold weather makes the iron threshing machine uninviting, we build bomb shelters. This is no easy task! Fortunately, we have help from the cattle who munch under the lower edges of the straw stack. With a little more tunnel work, we have a perfect bomb shelter, cosy and protected.

"Now we must stock up on rations out here," Douglas announces. "Noël, run to the house for supplies." She returns with raw carrot sticks and a handful of raisins. These rations are instantly devoured. We children disdain canned raspberries or saskatoons, but empty sealers are perfect containers for raisins or walnuts that we snitch from the house. Mummy never mentions the thefts, perhaps undetected since no real system for baking is followed. If she discovers her sealers lying around in the pasture, she chooses not to mention it.

"At least they're not quarrelling," I hear her tell Grandpapa.

Another favourite wintertime area is Grandpapa's cosy workshop. I love to help Douglas manufacture wooden toys there: rifles, bayonets, airplanes, battleships and tanks are crafted from lumber scraps. The sounds of snapping sparks in the box heater mingle with the wood-smoke and the scent of rasped spruce lumber give a very satisfying atmosphere in which to work.

EIGHT

Preparing for Winter

*Water bombs flattened us when they were dropped 100 feet
from the longest all-wooden constructed bridge in Alberta:
Rochfort Bridge CN trestle. 1940*

Making a visor of my hand, I narrow my eyes to count Canada geese high overhead, pointing their arrowhead south. The cool breeze smells of crop dust and ruffles my bangs. I sing:

> *Wild geese in my sky today*
> *I really don't want you to stay*
> *and walk on this ground.*
> *I don't like you around—*
> *So fly, wild geese, fly, fly away.*

Now that Douglas and Ruby have returned to school, I'm often at loose ends while Noël naps. Mummy helps Grandpapa in the fields. The golden crops and orange poplar trees look bright in the slanting sunlight. I step into the cabin. There is a peculiar stuffy smell as though eggs have boiled dry in the saucepan. I move the saucepan to the back of the stove and leave the cabin door ajar, even though flies swarm in. It's warm and peaceful in the cabin. Noël rouses as I clear the table, piling dirty mugs into the dishpan.

Now fully awake, Noël laughs, "Don't be so persnickety!"

"What do you mean?"

"Look at the way you tidy things. Why? Who cares?"

"I guess I do. I like things to be orderly. But it looks fine now. Let's go outdoors."

We move into the brilliant sunlight where Noël takes a running leap, somersaulting on the grass. I twirl behind her, spinning faster and faster until I get so dizzy I fall down laughing. Noël is twisting a hank of hair around one finger, "The kids should soon be back from school."

Noël is right. Ruby and Douglas come up the lane. Douglas goes straight to the field, and Ruby prepares a casserole. Then she heads over to Nan's, calling back, "You girls keep the fire up, and do your chores."

"Might as well start with the chicken house." I carry fresh water to their pan, then feel in all the nests, finding only a couple of eggs. Noël sets these on the kitchen cabinet, while I stoke the fires, and we head to the woodpile, which is getting very small. We will soon need a huge pile of wood for the coming year. Lots of work for Grandpapa.

By now it's dusk and damp with dew. I feel moisture on my bare feet from the cool grass as we gather chips to carry to the cabin for tomorrow's fire.

There is a sudden flutter of wide wings, fanning my face. "What's that?" I cry in alarm, feeling a chill as though something is clutching at me. "What's swooping and darting through the gloom? Watch it!"

"A bat! Oh, Ardith. It's a bat!"

"Watch your hair, Noël! If it tangles in your hair, we'll have to cut it out."

We rush screeching and screaming along the path. Noël throws her skirt up over her bowed head and flings the chips to the side. I drop my load of wood. We plough straight into Mummy.

"What on earth is wrong?" she demands. "Stop that screeching! What's wrong?"

"Oh, Mummy! It's a bat! A huge bat! We're afraid it will tangle in Noël's hair. Oh Mummy! We didn't fetch any chips!" We begin to cry.

"There! Stop crying. Doug will bring a few chips in. Put your cap on, Doug, to be sure you don't need a Batman haircut," laughs Mummy. We climb gratefully onto the bunk.

The casserole of cabbage, onions and rice with bits of chicken smells delicious and is quickly eaten. Doug heads to the barn with Mummy while we wash up the dishes.

When I wake during the night, I sit up to peer out the cabin window at a full moon lighting the countryside. Farm dogs are baying under the mad moon. They answer one another from farmyard to farmyard, until the night is filled with yowls. I roll the shreddy old quilt around myself, trying to settle.

"Today let's finish the potato picking," Mummy says. "I've done all I can in the fields. Grandpapa insists on doing the stooking himself. He thinks the job's too heavy for me. Bless him; he's been at it for days."

Mummy sticks her garden fork into the soil, piling the shaws at the edge of the patch.

Noël holds up a large red potato. "Look at this knobbly nose."

"Looks like Wimpy!" I chuckle as my fingers search the soil for more potatoes.

All our crisp vegetables are being stored in Granddad's cellar, and Noël and I get to ride on the stoneboat holding the bulging potato sacks to add to our supply.

Finally our garden is harvested and Mummy turns her attention to the granaries. She sweeps them out in readiness for fresh grain, and Noël and I practise parachute jumps from the roof.

"Geronimo!" Our skirts billow briefly as we fall.

A huge harvest moon hangs low in the sky, and the warm weather holds. It's a wonderful time of year. The first few frosts have painted the leaves with glorious splashes of colour.

"Daddy is coming home tonight, girls. He has managed a furlough so he'll be able to help with the threshing and butcher a hog."

We walk to the station to meet Daddy. A small crowd gathers on the platform. "Daddy!" shrieks Noël, flinging herself into his arms. I kiss Daddy, and then hang back so that Ruby and Mummy can claim their kisses.

Doug gives him a big bear hug in welcome, and we flock around Daddy, chattering all the way home.

On Friday evening, I know it is time for a hog butchering. I know because Daddy rolls the black iron cauldron into a clearing in the barnyard. I know because Noël and I are told to pile a thick layer of chips all around the cauldron while Daddy fills it to the brim with fresh cold water. I know because Doug stacks a pile of logs nearby.

Saturday morning is torn with screams, screams that send Noël to bury her head beneath her pillow; screams that put my teeth on edge. We know that Daddy has stuck the pig with a long knife. He has a lasso on one hind leg of the pig;

when Daddy jerks the rope, the pig attempts to escape, making blood spurt from its jugular vein until it weakens. Its squeals, like those of a child in pain, change to gurgles. Then silence. Daddy quickly hoists the carcass up the tripod, suspending it over the boiling water. He plunges the carcass into the scalding water, softening the bristles. Once. Twice. Three times. He then scrapes the skin with a knife.

> *Barber, barber, shave a pig,*
> *How many hairs to make a wig?*
> *Four and twenty. That's enough.*
> *Give the barber a pinch of snuff.*

Noël and I chant as Daddy works, to avoid the horror of seeing the pig change into a carcass. We are terrified, and yet we're fascinated. Daddy cuts off the pig's head, but it lies grinning on the ground.

Daddy guts the carcass. The pig is no longer an animal. It is pork. Heart, liver, kidneys, small intestines, all are saved. We stare in wonder at these shapes, sizes and smells.

Ruby and Mummy are elbow-deep in ground meat mixed with salt, sage and seasonings, pepper and garlic. They pack it into freshly washed intestines. Then they turn to making headcheese, using trimmings from the head and body.

Mummy slices the warm liver into even pieces and fries it with a smothering of onions, our first pork meal this fall. She puts the plump heart to boil in the black cast-iron pot on the back of the range.

Daddy rubs coarse brown salt all over the large chunks of ham and slaps large flat slabs of bacon with curing salt. It looks like brown grit from the bottom of a bird cage, I decide after eyeing it with suspicion.

Hams and bacon slabs hang in the smokehouse above a

slow-burning willow fire for the next two weeks. Finally the fire is allowed to die, but the meat remains hanging, waiting for table use. I hate the smoked-meat smell, and bury my face into my dress, taking comfort from the clean, dry scent of a hot iron on starched cotton; clearing from my nose the smell of death.

We are preparing for threshers. The gang should be coming tomorrow, if the good weather holds. Mummy has gone to Granddad's for a turkey, food for the crew. She has already baked apple and pumpkin pies.

She returns with the turkey, freshly butchered and still dripping blood from the beak, head hanging, loosely swinging like a pendulum—back and forth. I shudder. Mummy hangs the bird outside on a stout nail high on the cabin wall, and brings out the square tub with a kettle of boiling water. Laying the carcass into the tub, she pours the scalding water over it, then suspends the bird again as she strips off the feathers, dropping them into the tub.

I admire the feathers. "Mummy, can we have some of those pretty tail feathers?"

"Help yourself."

I stick a glossy plume into my braid. "Me Geronimo."

Noël is bedecked with a feather. We whoop around the yard until tired. Mummy finishes plucking and drawing the bird.

I hold my nose as I watch. "Phew!"

"Now, Ardith," corrects Mummy. "Don't be coarse. If you don't like the smell, don't come near. If you do come near, don't speak of it."

"Sorry, Mummy. I just want to see the innards. They are interesting. What is that green stuff?"

"Bile. I'm cutting it off because it would make the meat bitter. Now, watch while I open this gizzard."

"Why are there stones in the gizzard?"

"Because, dear," Mummy explains, "birds have no teeth, so their food is ground in the gizzard, by stones and grit."

Mummy pops the intestines into the fire. But the feathers are taken to the trash barrel to burn, since the odour of burning feathers inside would drive us from the cabin.

By nightfall everything is ready for tomorrow's threshers. Mummy looks exhausted but proud, too, of what she has accomplished.

I wake to shouts of strange men. Daddy is parking the huge threshing machine near the empty granary and lining up the pulleys while a couple of neighbours are blocking the wheels. Soon the rig is in place. The men climb into their bundle wagons and set off to the far corners to gather the sheaves.

"Oh, Mummy. Can Noël and I ride on a bundle wagon?"

"No, you may *not*!" says Mummy emphatically. "You girls stay strictly away from those men. You'd better stay near the cabin in case I need you."

We help Mummy carry out the lunch that afternoon. It is a noisy picnic with the threshing machine never stopping. Men arrive in turn to gobble a couple of sandwiches and gulp coffee, finishing with a handful of gingersnaps. I watch each man eating: the same hurried chewing, the same bobbing Adam's apples, the wiping of hands across the lips after drinking, the half-moons of dirt under the fingernails, the whiskers like thistle bristles.

They work far into the evening, arriving for supper after dark. The harvest moon lights their road home later, their empty hay racks rattling down the road. In two days, they have come and gone.

A huge stack of fresh straw, a field cleared of stooks and a granary full of oats remain. Now Daddy's long furlough is over. He must leave until Christmas. We wave goodbye as the train takes him from sight. Christmas is a long time away.

NINE

Quarantine

*Douglas, Ardith, Noël, Ruby. Owls were chicken thieves
which Grandpapa shot. 1940.*

The weather grows sharper with stronger winds. Curled dead leaves skitter along the edge of the wood. The copper meadow grasses, dead from frost, crackle underfoot. Feeling restless, I suggest, "Let's walk down to the river." But when Noël and I reach the water, the river is murky and smells of soil and fallen leaves. I slide among the white stones that clatter under my feet. The stones under water appear to shimmer green, like slabs of jade, yet when I lift them from the cold water, they're ugly and uninteresting.

"It's too cold to play in this water," I shiver. "It's freezing. Let's go back home." Wind blasts the banks of the river; sand stings my face. Even the water sounds mean.

I shiver again, my vision suddenly blurred with tears. "I feel sick, Noël." We walk back to the cabin. Empty. Mummy must be with Nan, we decide.

I check my reflection in the wavy looking glass. My eyes look sunken and I draw down my mouth and roll my lower lip outward. I stick out my tongue and am alarmed to see a furry coat. No wonder my breath smells like a mouldy onion. I must have an upset tummy.

I lie on the bunk, rolling myself in the quilt. I feel prickly, hot and itchy. Finally I doze.

By the time Mummy returns, I'm feverish. Mummy feels my forehead and says, "You must be coming down with a cold, dear. Why don't you stay in bed? Noël can bring in the chips."

I sink back gratefully. My mouth is dry and my throat aches. There's a roaring in my ears. I can't face my supper. Mummy mixes up a cup of warm eggnog, freckled with cinnamon. I try a bit, but it won't stay down. I shake my head, "No more eggnog, Mummy," and fall back onto the bunk.

As Mummy does her bedbug rounds late that evening, she checks on me. My face is flushed, lips swollen. Mummy holds the light high. "Measles! No wonder you feel sick. You're covered with a rash!"

The next day, Mummy tries to keep me comfortable. Then Noël begins vomiting, and by nightfall she, too, has measles. We lie in misery, sullen and silent.

An icy drizzle pelts the windowpane and slides down the glass in freezing streams. Doug manfully does the chores, but he has a hacking cough. Mummy tucks him into his crib, folding his legs to fit. By morning, he's rashy and feverish too—measles!

I begin climbing the cabin walls and singing in delirium.

The noble Duke of York
He had ten thousand men.
He marched them up a hill one day
And he ... marched ... them ... down ... again.

My song flattens like a gramophone winding down, slower and lower, as I sink to my knees on the quilts. I lie quiet for a few moments. Then I begin again, "*The noble Duke of York ...* "

Mummy is making chicken soup. "Ruby, dear, can you comfort Ardith?"

Ruby struggles with me until she, too, begins to complain. "Phew, Mummy, I can't manage Ardith—I feel so wretched!"

"Ardith, dear, please don't yank down that drape. You'll ruin your eyes. Don't, I say!"

But I'm at the window fumbling at the curtain, staring with unseeing eyes out into the bleak winter brightness. Mummy finally nails the cloth all the way along both edges of the frame, taking care to hammer the nails completely down. Noël moans, dazed, her hands cold and damp. Doug has a raspy cough. Mummy is everywhere at once, serving broth to Ruby and Doug, water to Noël, and pulling me away from the wall, tucking me under the sheets.

Suddenly there's a knock at the door. "Is everything all right?" calls Granddad. "I couldn't see no light out yer window," he explains. "So I thought I'd better check. What's wrong?"

He steps in the door, looking around in bewilderment. There's a nauseating smell in the kitchen, a boiling floor-cloth odour.

Mummy begins to laugh and weep. "All the children are sick and I'm just frantic. Ardith is in a delirium and Noël has a high fever. Doug mustn't go out and Ruby is weak. I have no aspirins and the wood is running low. I haven't gathered eggs nor fed the poor hens. I've neither milked the cow nor fed the livestock. I'm low on water and the children all need a good washing. And I'm almost out of kerosene from burning the lamp all day, although I'm keeping the wick low. Look at their eyes. They're all weepy and puffed. I'm so glad you stopped by!" Mummy's voice broke.

"All right. It's all right now," says Granddad briskly. "You tend the kids. I'll do the chores. Then I'll go to town, so write a list of what you need."

Mummy unclenches her hands and wets her lips. "I'm soaked in sweat. I wish I could run out into the snow and drag fresh air into my lungs. I seem to be melting in my own body heat, heaving like a winded animal. And we need to post quarantine signs on the door, in case someone comes to visit."

She sits down, shaking, her palms sweaty as she draws up her list. Granddad helps for the next three weeks. We slowly and steadily recover. No one but Granddad ventures near.

Even when back to normal, with Doug and Ruby back to school, I'm run-down and suffer severely from the cold.

The winter weather moderates at last, and a full moon hangs in the clear sky amid a million twinkling stars. But their presence is lost to us kids; our vision is impaired due to the measles.

TEN

Christmas Preparations

Ruby, Mary (Anne) Logan, Noël, Douglas, Ardith. 1941

I skip on top of crusty slabs of snow and burst into Nan's kitchen. "Hi there!"

"Come in, dear." Nan perches on a high stool, pulling the sadiron across the dampened laundry, making hot starchy smells.

"I'll put these away for you, Nan," I offer, and stack the hankies and underwear which I take to Nan's bedroom. As I slide open the top dresser drawer, whiffs of lavender waft out. After tucking everything into its proper place, I skip to the kitchen and arrange the tea towels. Then back to the bedroom with a stack of aprons.

I study myself in Nan's dresser mirror; bevelled edges catch sunbeams, making tiny rainbows. My eyes are wide as saucers, like the second dog in "The Tinder Box" story. I sink onto the bed feeling shiny bits of satin on the quilt with my fingertips.

As I loosen my braids and shake my hair, I glance at my reflection again. "Rapunzel, Rapunzel, let down your hair!" I purse my lips and wait for the handsome prince. And I hear a sound, step, shuffle, slide, step, shuffle, slide. Nan walks into her bedroom.

"Och, now, there you are, child. I came to see if you're all right."

"Why do you drag your leg?" I ask.

"This bad leg is my cross to bear," Nan sighs. "But it's the will of God." She turns and shuffles away, leaving me to puzzle this out. I picture Nan's leg nailed to a cross that she carries. But how can she bear the cross with only one leg left? Does she mean that both her legs are nailed in a cross-like position still attached to her body? Surely God wouldn't do that to poor Nan.

"What do you mean, Nan?" I've followed her out to the living room.

"Pshaw! I just mean that my biggest job in this life is walking." I realize that I have vexed her, forcing her strongest expletive from her thin lips.

"Would you like to hear my song for the concert?" I sing Star of the East in a clear, high voice. "Do I sound like an angel?"

"Certainly, child. A lovely angel voice."

"But I don't look like an angel. I've never seen a picture of an angel with freckles."

Nan laughs. "Come to think of it, neither have I, Ardith."

"Why did Auntie Nancy take her piano away?" I ask my grandmother. "When will she be coming back? Where is she?"

"She has gone to a country school named Tipperary, near Glenevis, to teach the children there. With this war on, many schoolteachers joined the armed forces to help fight the war. So Aunt Nancy was asked to teach a classroom. She was formerly a teacher in England, you know."

"Oh. I guess she'll play songs on her piano for the kids to sing at her school. That's why she took the piano. But when will she come back?"

Nan sighs, "When the war ends, perhaps."

Grandpapa comes stamping through the back porch into the kitchen. "It's getting up a wind." He shakes off his cap. "You'd best head home, Ardith. It feels like more snow."

It's cold, all right. The wind goes right through my clothes. I shiver as I hurry home.

By the time Ruby and Doug get home, it's wild with snow pelting the windowpane. The storm lasts for three days. Noël and I sit with the Eaton's catalogue planning our list for Santa Claus. I practise my singing. Mummy gives us an outdated catalogue to cut paper dolls. Now and then, we peer out at the white-shrouded farmyard. Ice seals the cracks around the frosted windowpane, and skeleton fingers of ice from the eaves glitter brittle beauty in the sunlight.

We are careful not to sift chaff on the Christmas baking spread on the table: gingersnaps, fudge and suet pudding in a clooty bag.

"Daddy will be home this evening," Mummy tells us. "He has only a few days off for Christmas, so I'm trying to get all my baking done before he gets here."

"But Mummy, who will meet the train? Won't we all be at the concert?" I worry.

"Of course, dear. Daddy can find his way from the station to the hall. He knows today is the last day of school and tonight is the concert," laughs Mummy. "Now, let me put up your hair, Ardith, so you can have curls for a change."

I endure having my wet hair wound tightly in rags. "I look like Topsy!" I complain mildly, anxious to see how curls will change my appearance. Mummy heats the curling tongs in flames, quickly crimping Noël's hair. There's an unpleasant scorchy smell as her hair turns wavy.

Mummy arranges her own tresses, curling a sleek pompadour. "We'll eat early so we have time to dress." She prepares clapshot casserole of potatoes mashed with turnip, garnished with onion and bacon strips. She pushes a pan of bannock into the oven and smiles at us. We know she's happy because Daddy's coming home.

Noël and I sit on the floor at the front of the hall so we can see the stage. We're enthralled by the performances—glittering costumes, beaming faces, enthusiastic singing. In the midst of it all, I catch sight of a blue uniform with shiny gold buttons—Daddy! I poke Noël and we slither from our places and quietly hug Daddy, who is seated with Mummy near the back.

"Is this Ardith?" Daddy teases, pulling at my ringlets. "You look like a princess!" I glow at the praise. Noël creeps onto Daddy's knee. "I'm staying here."

I return alone and settle among other preschoolers, losing myself in the magic of Christmas. Sighs and gasps of delight sound when Ruby sings her solo; her true voice hushes the hall.

A sudden jingle of bells up the aisle announces the arrival of Santa Claus. Miss McPhillip helps distribute candy bags. Hearing "Ardith Ray," I go forward to claim my bag, catching a whiff of mothballs and whiskey as Santa whispers, "Have you been a good girl?"

"Yes, indeed," I reply firmly, knowing it to be true.

Santa chuckles, thrusting a cheesecloth bag into my hand. "Got a kish for Santy?" he persists, lowering his face, but I can't locate lips and end with a mouthful of cotton wool. I scamper to my parents, peering into my bag. A Jap orange nestles near the bottom, surrounded by a handful of peanuts and sticky hard-rock candies. I peel a candy off the bag, oblivious of the fuzz that sticks to the sweet, and suck while watching Santa treat the older children. Finally he staggers onto the stage.

"Guesh I can shing one shong." He begins a very droll tune, but is ushered offstage and on his way amid a jingle of sleigh-bells. The adults chuckle and shake their heads.

"What's wrong with Santa?" I ask as Daddy laughs.

"Nothing. He's just feeling good."

Daddy won't go to the Sunday school concert on Sunday afternoon. It isn't surprising; Daddy never goes to church.

"Hurry now!" calls Mummy. "We have to hustle to get you all in costume before two o'clock. Are you ready?"

We scurry to town, glad to find a fire crackling and the hall warm. It smells of wood-smoke and spruce. The huge

Christmas tree still stands in the corner since the school concert. United Church folk have no real church building, and
rent the hall every Sunday for service.

"Noël first," offers Mummy. "I'll roll Grandpapa's sheep-
skin rug over you and bind it around your tummy. Now for
ears! Nan had quite a chuckle knitting these!" Noël keeps
shaking her head so her long ears flop in her face, making me
laugh.

Doug wraps himself in Nan's housecoat and stands
twirling his crook while he waits for his headgear. "How do I
fold this tea towel?" he asks. Mummy pins it round his head
and adds his furry beard.

"You look forty years older," I tell him.

"Come, Ardith," Ruby peels me down to my shift, while
I hold up my arms so she can drop a delicate cheesecloth gown
over me. "Stand still now, or you'll tear your cellophane," she
warns, as she twists wings around my shoulders. I wish I could
see myself. These gossamer wings feel like fairy wings. I'll bet
I can fly!

"Stand still," Ruby says, "or I'll never get your halo fixed.
This popsicle stick slips through your hair and the tinsel's sliding. Now don't sit down or you'll crush your wings!"

Mummy helps Ruby slip into her gauzy gown with trans-
parent wings and tinsel halo, and I gaze in awe at my big sister.

"The program was a huge success," Mummy reports to Nan
later that afternoon. "All my children performed perfectly.
Ardith was especially entertaining, holding her tinsel star
smack dab against her nose all the time she was singing. We
could see one eye peering out from either side. Everyone
howled! She was the star of the show!"

But I cower under the table, hidden by the cloth, and
remember how everyone had laughed at me. I must be really

ugly! They kept laughing even though I hid my freckles with the star—I was the ugly angel! I begin to cry. I cry all the way home, climb onto the bunk and cry myself to sleep.

"Time to hang up your stockings," Mummy calls, waking me. "Come, dear, you've missed your supper. Here, I warmed some milk with bread sops and honey. Eat up and hang your stocking. It's bedtime."

Noël is first to waken. "He came! Santa was here!" We find a Jap orange and a handful of peanuts in our socks. This is breakfast, eaten on the bunk.

"Get dressed," says Mummy, "so you can go to the barn with Daddy."

We scramble into our clothes, open the cabin door and step outdoors.

What a surprise! A little Christmas tree, bright with decorations and laden with gifts! Tinsel flutters and glitters in a gentle breeze.

"Look what Santa did for us!" I laugh. "And we thought we'd have no tree this year since there's no room in the cabin."

"Presents! I see presents!" Noël tugs at a parcel.

"Just a minute, Noël," cautions Mummy. "There are names—look at the tags."

Doug steps forward. "I'll read them and you can pass them," he tells our little sister.

Ruby gets a Fuller brush for her long blond hair. "I've been needing a brush." She smiles into Mummy's eyes.

"A kewpie doll!" cries Noël. "Just like the one in the catalogue! This is 'xactly what I want!"

"A mouth organ!" I smile with satisfaction, sucking out sounds while Doug unrolls a very long, thin package.

"Ah-ha," he laughs. "An archer set! Look how long this bow is, Noël. Let's go to the loft to try it! I'll be Robin Hood!"

As we scamper away, Mummy turns to Ruby. "Run over to tell Nan how much the children enjoy their gifts and help her make brunch. We'll be along after I slide the turkey into the oven and Daddy does the chores."

Nine for brunch, we look like a Norman Rockwell family at our meal. Grandpapa offers the blessing and we chime "Amen."

A pyramid of white soft-boiled eggs, a rasher of fried bacon, towers of toast, cups of milk and steaming coffee cups fill the table. Nan's precious egg cups for us—mine is a broody red hen with wings spread wide, my egg on end inside.

"Off with his head!" cries Daddy, King of Hearts, as he chops. Mummy slices toast fingers for Noël and me to dip our yolks.

"Too bad Lawrence isn't home," says Grandpapa to Granddad. "Where is he stationed now, Walter?"

Granddad shakes his head. "In England some place. He gits moved around."

"I hope that's where I end up," says Daddy. "I've always fancied England." Mummy tightens her lips.

"More coffee, anyone?" asks Nan quickly. "Ruby, can you bring the oranges and nuts, please?"

Ruby sets a large stack of Jap oranges onto the table, adding a platter of mixed nuts, nutcracker and six silver nut picks. Grandpapa cracks a nut for each of us and we pick at the meat.

Ruby and Mummy clear the table and wash dishes while Daddy talks to the grandfathers; Nan and we kids listen with interest.

"Let's catch the news before we leave." Mummy sits quietly as the CBC broadcast fills the room. I don't pay attention to the news.

The cabin holds delicious smells—roast turkey, scorched orange and spice. The clooty dumpling steams on the back of the range, and the pile of orange peelings on the back burner has scorched brown.

"Would you three little people please disappear to the barn while I prepare our feast?" Mummy asks.

"Let's play Robin Hood!" Douglas robs the rich and feeds the poor, shooting anyone who opposes him while Noël sits on old Annette and I blow my bugle to announce Robin's victories. Then I provide a lively mouth organ noise for the merry men to dance in Sherwood Forest. The cow, old Annette, rolls her eyes in astonishment at the commotion in the barn. Suddenly the barn door swings open and Friar Tuck arrives.

"If you please, my merry men, dinner is served," he announces, bowing and smiling. And bearing Maid Marian on his arm, Daddy leads the procession to the cabin. Granddad has come and all is ready. Doug recites grace. Mummy immediately begins to serve each plate from the pots on the stove.

"Everything for this meal has been home-grown," she proudly claims. "The turkey is from Granddad," and here she smiles appreciatively at him. "The cranberries were picked from his muskeg. The potatoes, peas and corn are from our garden. Oh, yes, and the rhubarb relish. Old Annette provides our milk, cream and butter. But of course, I bought the raisins, currants and peel for the suet pudding."

"But the suet is from the butchering," Ruby puts in.

"True," says Mummy. "So almost everything here is home-grown."

The feast is much quieter than our brunch. We're scrunched on three sides of a square table, with no room to pull the fourth side from under the bunk. As it is, Mummy is almost on the oven and becomes very flushed. All at once she rushes outdoors to stand in the snow for a few minutes.

No one comments, since she often has to cool herself suddenly. Daddy helps Ruby clear the table and Granddad ambles home. There's enough space to wash up the dishes while Noël and I make butterflies of twisted toffee wrappers and toss them high above our heads so they flutter and twist to the bunk. My thoughts twist like the butterflies. Did Aunt Nancy spend Christmas all alone?

Mummy makes the rounds with the lamp collecting bedbugs and the familiar scorching smell makes me bury my nose in the quilt. Before I know it, I fall fast asleep; my Christmas Day is over.

Daddy leaves next morning. "He's stationed at Fort Mcleod now," Mummy explains. "So he won't be home often—that's a long way from Rochfort Bridge."

"But Mummy," argues Douglas. "Our river flows right into McLeod."

"That's McLeod River, dear," Mummy corrects him. "Daddy is at the town of Fort Mcleod. Look here," she unfolds a road map of Alberta, pointing to a dot on the paper—almost at the bottom of the map. "Here is Fort Mcleod. And here is Rochfort Bridge."

I study the map. "We live very near where Alberta's broken," I observe.

"Broken? What do you mean?" asks Mummy.

"See, Alberta is straight on all the edges except that broken corner," I explain. "We're near the broken bit." Everyone laughs.

ELEVEN

Keeping in Good Health

Ardith goes to Edmonton for eye examination. 1942.

Nineteen forty begins with a world of no shadows. Fog. The washing hangs from the clothesline in ghostly shapes "like enemy artillery," I think, as I grope my way to the woodpile. My nose drips an icicle; dense fog presses heavy as slush against my face. It flattens the landscape, but a faint aurora marks a sun far overhead.

I'm fetching huge armloads of wood for heating bath water. I hear Doug's shovel on the metal bucket as he gathers snow, but sounds muffle and distort in the fog. I make up a little verse, and after I step indoors, I sing,

> *The travelling clinic comes to town.*
> *And all us kids are going down*

So don't forget to wash you neck
The doctor will closely inspect!

"How true!" agrees Mummy. "So climb into the tub, Noël, and I'll scrub your neck. We sure don't want the doctor to find any dirt on us!"

Noël settles into the square galvanized washtub on the cabin floor; Mummy vigorously scrubs my sister's hair and rinses it by pouring warm water over her head. "Come, Ardith," she calls. "Your turn. Climb in. You start your hair while I dry Noël's."

Mummy gives her smallest daughter a brisk rub and tosses her up onto the bunk. "That's right, Ardith. Close your eyes now. Here comes more warm water." Mummy pours it over my long hair.

"Hurry, Ruby, before this cools off. Jump in." As she speaks, she towel-dries me. "I'll braid that hair in a jiffy, Ardith. You girls wait on the bunk until I help Ruby. Oh dear, we're almost out of snow water. Good thing there's only Doug left. Up to the bunk, Ruby. Give the guy a little privacy."

Doug's waiting patiently in the crib and quietly sinks into the tub. "I'll braid your hair now, Ardith," Mummy says, "while Ruby gets the rags ready for Noël and herself. Ringlets tomorrow, you blondies."

"Doug, when you're done I must trim your hair or else I'll have to buy you a dog licence. Come sit on the stool," adds Mummy, flourishing her sewing shears.

"Let's say prayers and off to sleep, all of you. It will be a big day tomorrow."

Mummy makes a quick scan for bedbugs with the lamp, and then begins to lay out clean handmade clothing. We girls have fleece-lined bloomers over waist-shirts, with pleated flannel skirts attached to cotton vests, designed from castoffs. We have long hand-knit woollen stockings and sweaters lovingly made by Nan. She spends hours knitting toques, scarves and mittens of colourful yarn scraps to contrast our drab melton-cloth coats and snowsuits.

Mummy has bartered for buckskin moccasins with a native Indian family. We gladly wear moccasins decorated with colourful beading, and the native children are just as happy to get handsome toques and mittens with matching scarves that Nan has made.

Mummy examines Doug's old underwear. "I must make Doug a new set." She wheels out her Singer foot-treadle sewing machine, fashions a pair and sews white bias tape along the raw edges. She breathes a sigh. "I hope the drop-seat isn't too bulky under his breeks." Doug's matching pullover sweater and knee-socks are designed by Nan.

"I want you children to look presentable," Mummy explains as she runs her fingers along the edges of the knitting, checking for ravels. She tugs each button to be sure it's securely sewn. "I guess your clothes are fine," she decides at last. "I probably won't sleep a wink on these steel curlers. I'll check for bedbugs before I bank the fire. Ah! Good to be in bed." Mummy settles down at last.

Next morning brings a flurry of preparation. "Eat your porridge in your pyjamas," Mummy urges, "so nothing spills on your clean clothes. Just stack the bowls in the dishpan. As soon as you're dressed, I'll do your hair. Grandpapa has offered to do the chores this morning, so we won't be late. Ready? Let's go."

It is still dark when we leave the warmth of the cabin and flock across the field toward town. A few twinkling lights in the village prove that other families, too, are up early, preparing to attend the clinic in the town hall.

"Now I want you little people to behave properly,"

Mummy warns. "This isn't a picnic. The government board of health is providing a free clinic so that you may be examined by a medical doctor. Think of that. It will be the first time a doctor ever lays eyes on you. I want you to stand straight and tall, and do exactly as you are told. And remember your manners."

Suddenly a square form looms ahead, blocking our path. Doug, who is breaking trail, slows to a stop. "Oh, hi, Granddad," he breathes in relief. "You look different in this fog."

"Are you taking the kids to that clinic?" Granddad demands sternly.

"Yes, I am," Mummy firmly replies. "It is a chance for a free medical examination for them. And we're very short of cash."

"Hah!" snorts Granddad. "That clinic is nothing but a butcher shop. There's not a thing wrong with the kids— they're as healthy as horses. They don't need a team of doctors to tell you that. I don't like this, Edith."

"Well, I'm taking them anyway," Mummy announces. "So we'd better hurry." And we move off through the fog.

Soon we are stripped of our outer clothing and shiver nervously in a line-up. Each child has been issued a cloth cape that covers bare shoulders and chest. We are allowed to wear our own underpants and stockings.

"So much for dressing you properly," Mummy murmurs. "You children look exactly the same as all the others in the hall."

Finally it is our turn to be examined. None of us has ever been medically inspected. Mummy had been delivered of her children at home and never have we required medical attention. Mummy hovers protectively over her brood.

The clinical team check us efficiently. The oldest three are severely myopic. Doug and I need braces for crooked teeth, and we both require a tonsillectomy.

"She snores," Mummy reports over my head, so the examiner adds "adenoids removed" on my chart.

"Your children are sturdy and well," announces the doctor, "except for dental work and eyeglasses." Mummy stares at him in dismay. How can we afford glasses or have our teeth straightened?

"Bring you son and this little redhead in tomorrow for their tonsillectomy. Here's a list of instructions. Please follow them." Mummy only nods. We are subdued as we quietly dress and trudge back home across the frozen drifts.

Douglas' medical report from Traveling Clinic. 1942.

"Ruby, dear," says Mummy. "Will you stay with the children and watch the fire while I slip over to Nan's with the news? Ever since our home burned to the ground, I've had a deathly dread of house fires, you know."

"I'll guard the fire," Ruby promises.

Mummy returns with a bundle of striped pink and blue flannelette from Nan.

"Before I begin sewing," she says, "I must warn you, Ardith and Doug, not to eat anything at all for the rest of today, and nothing tomorrow until after your surgery."

"How come?" asks Doug.

"Because you'll be given ether to make you sleep through your operation, and if there's anything in your stomach, you'll throw it up. I must give you each an enema in the morning, so your bowels are cleaned."

I roll my eyes at Doug, but we say nothing. What can we say? If Mummy has been told what to do by the doctor, she will do it.

And she does. Mummy sits up half the night preparing matching pyjama sets for us. Early next morning, a jingle of sleigh-bells sounds in the yard. There's Grandpapa, with his Winnipeg couch and mattress in the sleigh. "We thought you'd need this for the children," he calls out. "It will be warmer than a tick on the floor in the hall."

"Yes, Papa, such a good idea. Thanks. Well, we're ready."

The three of us climb into the sleigh box and set off down the lane, taking the road since the sleigh is too wide for the shortcut. Grandpapa helps set up the couch and lays out his own feather tick for us. Then he drives off, promising, "I'll pick you up in the late afternoon." Meanwhile, Ruby stays with Noël and keeps the fire up in the cabin.

Douglas and I modestly climb into our new pyjamas

65

behind a small screen and then lie down, one head at each end of the couch, our feet nearly meeting at the middle. Mummy slides a lard pail discreetly under our bed. In case we throw up.

From our vantage point, we survey the hall. It has been transformed into a hospital ward, with rows of pallets and cots up and down both walls, and one row down the middle. The beds swarm with half-clad children who wait their turn for surgery. A few bodies lie strangely silent, sound asleep.

A heavy smell of ether permeates the hall. An operating table is set up on the stage, which has the best lighting and the privacy of a curtain.

In no time, it's my turn. A nurse leads me to the stage and helps me onto the table. A strange cone is put over my nose. "Can you count?" asks the nurse.

Of course, I can. After all, I am five years old. But why … ? Before I have time to wonder why I should count one … two … three … , I am out like a light.

I waken much later. A burning throat. Nausea. Pain. I feel dizzy … miserable. Mummy nods reassuringly. "It's okay, Ardith. Go back to sleep." I doze again. I half hear the moans and groans from the pallets around me. Kids vomit into buckets. Vile odours mingle with the heavy scent of ether. A smell of perspiration and wood-smoke wafts from the heater. I feel chilly, burrow under my blanket, doze off.

Much later, I open my eyes to see the local schoolteacher, Miss McPhillip, smile at me … offer me an ice-cream cone. The cone dances as my vision blurs. I take it politely, smile … can only croak "thank you" in a froggy voice. Lick … a marble sticks in my throat. I can't swallow … pain … lick again. The marble becomes a baseball. I hold the cone loosely, weakly … watch the rich cream melt … dribble across my fingers. Sticky drips run around my wrists. I watch helplessly, too weak to care. Mummy rescues me ... by eating the cone herself. She gently wipes my fingers with a cold damp rag. Refreshed, I doze again.

Eventually Grandpapa arrives and carries us to the sleigh and home.

I no longer snore when I sleep.

Mummy keeps both Douglas and me indoors for a couple of weeks until our throats entirely heal. Granddad's warning of "butchering" the children really frightened her.

TWELVE

Mummy's Sick

The weather rapidly improves; warmth from a bright sun melts the snow until water gushes along the ditches. Slush becomes muck from wagon wheels that churn up solid clay lumps on the roads, making the range line almost impassable.

Strong sunlight makes velvet pussies burst from the willows, maple buds drip stickiness, blades of green grass appear, and dandelion blossoms finally brighten the wet loam.

I love to walk with the family through the dense woods that provide pasture for the cattle. Mummy identifies the plants, correctly naming each specimen as she takes us hiking through the bush.

"Dewberry," she announces. "See how a single berry grows at the very tip of this strong, straight stem?" I peer with interest at the shiny crimson berry that nestles like the crown jewels on a coronet of green spikes. All of us, myopic since our bout of measles, look closely.

"Now, Noël," says Mummy. "This dewberry is safe to eat. You may pick it and see how juicy and sweet it tastes. You older ones try to find your own. There should be plenty growing along the path in shady spots where it's moist." Mummy makes her nature lessons so interesting that we don't realize how much information she's instilling. We scramble in search of more dewberries.

After our hike, we scatter. Ruby goes to visit Nan while Doug cleans the henhouse. Armed with hoe and shovel, he attacks the droppings, flinging them onto a dung heap behind the building, to be spread onto the garden when the smelly manure changes to fertilizer.

Noël and I head for the cool shade of evergreens, where I spread an old blanket on which to relax. "I love springtime. No mosquitoes to plague us, no burning sun to blister my skin. And just smell the air, Noël. Nothing smells fresher than spring."

Later, I find Mummy sitting idle and listless by the wooden table. Why is she staying indoors this afternoon?

Lost in thought, I don't realize that my eyes are blankly staring straight at Mummy's face. She has a very noticeable facial twitch, which results from a bout of St. Vitus' Dance. She has no control of her facial muscles. Her right eyebrow suddenly shoots upward, then the eyeball rolls as her nose pulls down and the corner of her mouth twitches until she swallows, which seems to stop the spasm. Then the pattern repeats. This involuntary action upsets her, although we kids are so accustomed to it that we think nothing of it.

Whap!

A sharp blow to the side of my head makes my face tingle and my ear sting. I focus fearfully on Mummy's face. What have I done? What did I do?

Mummy glares at me furiously. I draw back, rubbing my tender ear. Why did Mummy swat me? Did I do something wrong?

"Don't stare! Don't stare at me! I can't help it if my face twitches."

"But I wasn't, Mummy," I protest. "I was just … thinking." I never know when she will punish me; it is unexpected, unpredictable. It makes me unsure of myself, nervous.

Sometimes I discover Mummy lying on the bunk during daylight hours. This is puzzling because she's usually busy and active.

"Are you okay, Mummy? Do you feel sick?"

"A little bit, child," Mummy says. "Never mind, dear. Run and play." But I worry.

I run to consult my magic mirror in the watering trough.

Mirror, mirror, blue as sky,
Is our Mummy going to die?

I watch for a sign from the water, but it lies quiet, smooth. What does that mean?

A strange lady arrives at the cabin. Mummy draws us around her to explain her situation. She doesn't want to frighten us, so she speaks in a fake-happy voice. "This is Mary Blake. She is going to live here to take care of you. She'll cook your meals and keep you company. But you must all be very, very good, and obedient. Do what Mary says. I have to stay in Edmonton for a few weeks so that the doctor can help me. You all know I haven't been feeling well. Now that the warm weather's here, I'm not so worried about leaving you with the stove going full blast. I'm going to be away a while—maybe quite a while. You must all be very good. I'm counting on you." And she hugs each of us fiercely.

Then she leaves on the train.

I watch Mary Blake stand by the stove turning sourdough pancakes. She makes a heaping platter of rich flapjacks with butter and Roger's Golden Syrup, but I'm not hungry.

I study Mary closely. Homely as a mud-dabbed fence. I've never before seen a grossly overweight woman; it's fascinating to see swinging breasts and sagging belly. When Mary pulls herself up to the bunk, I catch sight of thighs like chunks of blue cheese shot with a network of blue veins. Not at all like our thin, tidy mother.

But Mary has a kindly face and a hearty laugh, and she's good to us kids; she directs us pleasantly, settles arguments firmly, and cooks wonderful foods with rich cream sauces.

Mary herself loves food. She spends most of her day lying on the bunk, reading *True Story* magazines, where heroines are thin, while Mary herself munches continuously on snacks washed down with homemade lemonade.

We're quiet, well-behaved and obedient, each missing Mummy in a different way.

Mary bakes a wonderful layer cake with coloured icing decorations and six birthday candles for me. Her present to me is a small clothbound book, *A Child's Garden of Verses* by Robert L. Stevenson. Poetry, with large pen-and-ink sketches. I love the lilt of the language and soon memorize every verse. And I like composing my own little rhymes—they just flash into my head.

Mary holds up my cake and says, "Have another slice of birthday cake, Turkey Egg," and she smiles at me. But I can't smile back. I just can't. Because Mary called me Turkey Egg, which wounds my feelings so deeply I determine to do something about it. I steal the Eddy matchbox from the match holder hanging on the wall behind the range, careful not to let Mary see. I scamper to the biffy, and hook the door on the inside so that no one can possibly peek. Then I rub the freckles from my nose with the strip of heavy sandpaper on the box. Tears course down my cheeks as I scrub vigorously across the bridge of my nose. Being beautiful really hurts, I decide ruefully, and fling the matchbox onto the cabinet as I head for my magic mirror in the clear water of the trough to check the results of my beauty treatment.

Mirror, mirror, of the trough,
Did I rub my freckles off?

But the mirror seems to laugh, a silent ripply laugh that wrinkles the image of my tear-filled eyes and shredded flesh. And when my nose heals, I have as many freckles as ever.

THIRTEEN
Daddy Leaves

*We are terrified when Daddy takes us up on the trestle
and the train comes. 1942.*

ummy's return to our family is a happy time. Her
face is very white and she moves slowly when we
walk over to visit Nan. Mummy has a crew cut.
When she kisses Nan on each cheek, I can see Nan's and
Mummy's tears making their eyes shiny. Noël fetches the
domino set and she and I settle on the rug to play as usual, but
I keep one ear open to Mummy's conversation with Nan. "I'm
determined not to frighten the children, but I was very near
death," she says softly.

Nan murmurs, "Tut, tut."

"Now I'm flawed," Mummy speaks louder. "I'm only half a woman, since my hysterectomy. What does Will think of that?" Mummy's hands flop like a rag doll onto her lap.

Half a woman? What does Mummy mean? I remember the Bible story when Solomon held up a baby by the foot to cut it in half. And I look at Mummy. I can see she has two ears, two arms and two legs. The only thing different about her is her hair. She's almost bald. But that's the story about Samson. Is Mummy getting her stories mixed up?

"Pshaw!" scoffs Nan. "No one will mention a thing about it. We're all happy you're home again. As for children, you've had your share. You'll do well to raise the family you've got. Willie will be thankful you've recovered. As we are. Just get your strength back, Edith. That's all we ask. Thank God you're alive. The children need you, Edith."

"I had to let Mary go," Mummy tells her mother.

"Oh, why?" asks Nan. "You're scarcely on your feet yet."

"I need the money," she says. But when she returns home to the stale smell in the neglected cabin reeking and needing a good scouring, Mummy flings herself face down on the bunk and cries.

Noël and I glance at one another, not knowing what to do. We can see she's exhausted. We slip out and sit on the woodpile. "Oh, I wish Daddy were home," Noël says.

Mummy gets strong slowly. Her hair grows thick and dark, and her body fills out, but it's a long time before she's her old self.

Ruby waves a white envelope under Mummy's nose. Mail from Daddy. Mummy sits down, slits the envelope and scans the page. We watch her face pinch, as an anxious expression comes over it. She glances over the page to our faces.

Ardith, Douglas, Noël, Mummy, Daddy, Ruby
just before Daddy is sent overseas by RCAF. 1943.

"Oh-h!" she says. "Guess what! Daddy wants us all to meet him in Edmonton. Won't that be grand?"

"But why, Mom?" asks Ruby quietly.

"Your dad has been posted overseas," Mummy explains. "He wants us to meet him in Edmonton to have a photo taken. On Friday. Oh my, we'll have to get our best clothes ready. And we'll need money … " Her voice trails off, as she runs her fingers over her head. "Money," she repeats.

"Ardith, would you please run down to Granddad's and ask him to drop by for a little visit? We'll eat before you go. I'll just scramble a few eggs to help out the potatoes. Oh, I'll be glad when the garden is ready, so we can have fresh vegetables.

The lettuce should be big enough in another week. Guess what, Douglas. Chocolate pudding. Your favourite."

Mummy babbles on about the meal, but my heart sinks. Did she say Daddy is going overseas? What will happen to him? I nibble at my food and then set off with my message.

"Granddad," I call through his fly-specked screen door. "Are you in?"

"What is it, Honey Child? Something wrong?" Granddad hears shrillness in my voice. "Come in. Come in."

"Granddad, Daddy's posted overseas and Mummy wants to talk to you."

Granddad's plain face goes quite dead as he sinks back onto his chair, his mouth hanging open like the garden gate. "Overseas … ," he mutters. "When?"

"Soon, I guess. We have to meet him in Edmonton on Friday."

Granddad is lost in thought; his fleshy thighs splay to accommodate his overhanging belly. Then he gathers himself and says, "I'd better go back with you now, to speak to your mother. I'll just get my hat."

We set off along the range line, casting tall shadows across the field as the sun sinks in the summer sky. Neither speaks. There is so much to ask, but I sense that Granddad needs quiet time.

"Oh, Walter," cries Mummy, flying straight into his arms. "Will is posted overseas and we're to meet him in Edmonton on Friday, and … little pitchers have big ears."

I know what that means. I mustn't eavesdrop. I turn away, mumbling, "Guess I'll go to bed. We're sleeping in the loft while it's so hot, Granddad. 'Night." I kiss Mummy and Granddad and amble off to the barn.

Mummy and Granddad look really sad. I begin a little verse about that:

We all feel so sad
'Cause we'll miss our Dad.
He's going overseas.

Now I'll rhyme the end word with the next stanza's end word. I try to work it out.

On Friday, our excited family climbs aboard the train. I soon find that I must sit facing forward. Riding backward makes me dizzy from the rushing trees.

"Let's go back to the observation platform," whispers Douglas. He and I lurch our way down the aisle of several cars. I am quick to step from car to car, afraid I'll slip through a crack. The noise is awful. But we make it safely to the end of the train.

"Look at those sparks flying out behind us," cries Douglas. "We must be going about a hundred miles an hour."

I finally tire of the hypnotic clickety-click of wheels on rails and return to my seat. The coach sways, and the rhythmic clickety-click and steady chug of the engine lull me to sleep. I rouse every time the coach crosses a trestle because of the sudden sound change, or when that mournful whistle sounds.

Mummy looks flustered. She opens lunch but we eat very little. Too excited, too motion-sick and too bewildered. When the train draws into Edmonton, Daddy meets us on the platform. He is handsome in his blue serge uniform with wedge cap, dark tie knotted smartly and shirt collar crisp. Buttons on his tunic are shiny as stars. I can almost see my reflection in his gleaming black shoes.

He leads us down the sidewalk for a long, long walk. Finally we enter a grand building and climb a steep stairway into a photographer's studio, McDermid's.

Mummy busily arranges our hair styles, straightens her dress and fixes our stockings. We must all look our very best.

"Smile," the photographer urges. So this is why Mummy needs Granddad, I realize. She wants a perfect picture of us all together before Daddy leaves. And she needs money for the photographer. As well as the train tickets. We're all dressed up to snuff. Smile! Daddy looks handsome, sitting in the middle with us all clustered around. This might be our last family portrait. SMILE! The thought brings a lump to my throat. But I try to lift the corners of my mouth. SMILE! Nothing must spoil this moment. Mummy wants a perfect picture. Oh, when will all this fuss and bright lights end? Do all my freckles show? SMILE!

We are finally released to see the wonders of the big city. First, Edmonton City Dairy, where a huge bottle of milk perches permanently on the roof, amazing us kids. We go in.

"Chocolate milk all around," orders Daddy. I watch an assembly belt move a never-ending line of bottles as I swallow the rich milk that slides over my tongue. We leave.

"Now watch these traffic lights," Daddy explains. "Red means we mustn't cross." We wait while trucks and smelly cars flash past.

"Green," Noël cries.

The street is crowded with people. The crush squeezes me. I stand still, wait. They squash me. They crease my good dress. The group surges ahead, although I can't see. I mustn't lose Mummy, I think, grabbing her skirt. Holding firmly, I march across the street. The crowd thins and I glance up. I'm clutching the skirt of a stranger.

"Mummy," I quaver. Then I spot Mummy waiting for me. The rising heat from the cement street makes me weep. Douglas catches my hand, squeezes it, comforts me.

We marvel at the window displays and see a stone slab building with a coat of arms—the Hudson's Bay Company. It has a very cunning door going round and round like a paddle in the butter churn—four doors really, opening one after another as we push them. I'm afraid I'll be trapped, but I always manage to escape through a sudden opening before the next door closes. Douglas bravely circles three times before he makes his exit, but I'm content to hold Daddy's hand and watch my brother's antics.

"Watch this," says Daddy, and steps onto a miraculous step that whisks him smoothly upward. Smiling down at our astonished upturned faces, he calls, "Come on," and beckons us to follow. The machine shudders and clicks as it relentlessly churns out stairs. Doug is most daring. He jumps onto a step and is swiftly carried upward. Ruby ventures next. But Noël and I are afraid. Only when Mummy holds my hand firmly does our threesome mount those threatening steps. I leap off with relief just before the platform on which we stand is swallowed forever by the jaws of the second floor. Surely nothing can surpass the magical moving stairs.

Wrong! Daddy leads us to a quiet corner of the store. Right into a large closet. "Now, Noël, see that button with number one written on it? Watch." An attendant pulls a lever to shut the door and presses that button.

Trapped! I feel faintly nauseous, as though the earth is moving. The feeling passes as the door slides open unbidden and allows us to escape onto the main floor.

We stroll through the department store, and again pack into the elevator, dropping to the basement as the attendant controls the buttons. My tummy turns toward my toes and I feel relief when the door slides open. After touring the basement, we take a vote as to how to return to the main floor.

"There are three possibilities," Mummy explains. "We can climb the stairs, ride on the escalator, or go in the elevator. Which would you like?"

"The escalator! The escalator!"

I'm secretly thankful. Although it has a mean-mouth, menacing toe-grabber, it doesn't trap me while providing a tummy-turning, gut-gunning sensation.

The fresh air outdoors seems good after our adventures in the store. "This is the streetcar track," Daddy explains. Unimpressive, I decide. It looks exactly like the rails on the trestle.

But the streetcar itself is quite different from the train. Shorter. Slower. Brighter.

Daddy presses a coin into my hand. I watch. Ah! A coin box. Money jingles as it drops through the slot. Noël needs no fare. We speed down the tracks.

The car passes the most beautiful building I've ever seen. Awesome! Surely it must be a castle! Or maybe a palace.

"That is the Legislative Building," explains Mummy. "And this is the North Saskatchewan River," she adds as we approach the High Level Bridge. A wide blue expanse of water spreads out beneath us. We seem suspended in the air ... no bridge visible from where we sit ... just that greenish-blue, rippling water, far below. Then the streetcar clanks onto solid ground again. I feel sick from excitement, from bewilderment, from weariness.

I'm thankful when Daddy, Mummy and our family climb aboard the CN train. I take refuge in one corner of a plush seat, watching the world rush by. My head is in a vice of pain; I lie limp and still. A cool wet cloth covers my eyes while rhythmic clickety-clicking of wheels and continuous swaying of the seat lull me to sleep.

When I wake, lights shine from the ceiling of the coach. "Shall we walk to the toilet?" asks Mummy. It's a long and difficult distance to the end of the car. "I never know which way I'll be thrown," I laugh.

There's scarcely room for both of us in the tiny toilet. "I'm not sitting there," I say firmly, seeing the gravel and ties of the tracks rush past through the opening when Mummy flushes. "I'll slide right out and fall on the tracks like the droppings."

"Nonsense," says Mummy. But I refuse to seat myself unless Mummy holds me.

While I wash my hands in a miniature bowl, I see myself in the mirror. My freckles seem more in evidence than ever.

> *Mirror, mirror on the train*
> *When will my face become plain?*

Mummy notices my expression and asks, "Would you like a drink of water?" She shows me a long tube filled with waxy cups.

"Look, Mummy. They're like leprechauns' hats," I laugh, holding one under a tap. After a refreshing drink, I return to my seat, where, lulled by the hypnotic clickety-clicking of the rails and swaying of the car, I sleep.

Daddy steps off the train briskly. "I can stay only two days," he warns us.

"Let's make them fun days," Mummy says with forced gaiety.

I study Daddy: his twinkling blue eyes, his laughter creases, his flashing teeth, his aftershave and sweat, his soft brown hair, his arms downy with sun-bleached hair, and his measured steps.

The next morning we gather around the table in the cabin. "Look at your silly cat." Daddy points behind me. When I turn from my meal, my plate mysteriously disappears. I look everywhere, while the family laughs.

Finally Daddy returns it—he has snitched it in fun.

"Watch this," he cries, lining up two teaspoons with his cup,

*Mom, Ruby, Ardith, Douglas, Dad and Noël at picnic
behind "The Cabin." 1945.*

striking the bowl of the end spoon sharply. The middle spoon
rises, turns an arc in the air and lands in his cup. It's amazing.

"Someone at the door. Douglas, go ask them in," Daddy
calls as he raps under the table. Doug hurries to the door. No
one.

"Who's coming onto the trestle with me?" Daddy calls.

"Not I," says Mummy quietly. "It's too far for me to walk
in this heat. But I'll have supper ready when you get back."

Noël and I eye each other. Both are afraid; neither wants
to miss going with Daddy. So we go. But when we reach it, Noël
protests. "I can't walk this bridge. Carry me." Daddy thrusts her
bare feet into his tunic pockets and carries her. Doug takes my
hand and I snail along, facing my fear.

"Picnic time," Mummy announces. "Spread quilts in the shelterbelt shade and Ruby will help me carry out the food.
Daddy, will you bring the dishes?"

"I'll carry the devilled eggs," I offer.

"Mm-m. Potato salad and green salad," smiles Douglas.

"Square meat," Noël squeals in delight. Canned Spam in

81

a square tin is a real treat. By cutting it paper-thin, one tin serves the whole family.

"I can almost see through this." I hold up my slice of Spam.

"Who has room for raspberry shortcake?" Mummy asks. No one refuses. We all enjoy the good meal.

By the time our picnic ends, it's cooler. We know by the orange sunset that our time with Daddy is almost over. As I dry the dishes, I see the hands of the clock hurrying, hurrying along with my heartbeats. The cabin is tense with unspoken thoughts but everyone keeps smiling. Ruby disappears to spend the night with Nan, motioning for us kids to head for the loft, leaving Daddy and Mummy in privacy.

I remember the prayer that I've work out, and say it aloud, kneeling on the hay with Noël and Douglas:

We all feel so sad
'Cause we will miss our Dad
He's going overseas.

Mummy cries and cries
And we all have wet eyes.
Dad's hand we squeeze.

Hear our family prayer
Keep Daddy safely there
We're on our knees.

He's going far away
Oh, bring him back some day …
God—save him, please.

Then we cuddle together under our quilt. The pigeons coo mournfully in the rafters as we fall to sleep.

After a hasty breakfast next morning, the whole family troop to the station to say goodbye to Daddy. Kisses all around. He swings aboard the train. He's leaving. Maybe forever. He stands on the train steps; he waves and waves as the train picks up speed. Daddy grows smaller and smaller.

I wave and wave … until the train disappears from view. A lump forms in my throat, which I swallow before tears follow. My Daddy is gone. Relief mingles with sadness.

Mummy's eyes are red and her face is puffy as she stumbles along the path. Ruby hugs Noël tight in her arms. I slip my hand into Doug's and our subdued family trudges silently home.

There follows a hazy period of time when the days seem to sink just beneath a murky surface, never fully emerging. Nothing seems quite real; our family drifts through the routine of chores, silently suffering the same concern—where is Daddy? What is happening to him now?

A long stretch of hot weather brings harvest early; golden heads of barley droop in the blazing sun. Noël and I spread a quilt beside the thick hedge of twisted caragana trees and lie listless. We listen to the tiny pods burst and send showers of seeds in all directions.

Ruby appears around the end of the shelterbelt with a brisk walk despite the heat. "Mom," she calls as she approaches the cabin. "Mom!" She waves an envelope in the air.

Mummy scurries out the cabin door, wiping her hands on her apron. "A letter," Ruby says. "From Dad."

We spring from our quilt and rush to the cabin. Douglas arrives dusting his hands together in anticipation.

Mummy slits the envelope and scans the message; her face contorts with anxiety and thankfulness. "Brighton," she breathes. "Daddy is stationed at Brighton."

"But where is Brighton?" asks Douglas.

"In England. Daddy's in England. Same as Uncle Lawrence." A picture of quaint thatched-roof cottages and lush hedgerows flashes through my mind. I breathe a sigh of pleasure. Daddy's in that beautiful fairyland place shown on Granddad's postcards.

"Mummy," I ask in alarm. "Why are you crying? Aren't you glad Daddy is in England?"

"Oh, I'm just so happy to hear from him." Mummy wipes her eyes. "And to know that he's all right. I had pictured his ship going down as they crossed the ocean, and everyone drowning."

Drowning! I shudder. We're all thankful he made it across.

A sudden small downpour gives instant relief from the heat—with enough moisture to settle the dust. The land turns green-gold, alive, and the air becomes easy to breathe. A half-formed rainbow hangs in the sky like God's promise. He'll keep Daddy safe; I know it in my heart.

FOURTEEN

Left-Handed

Rochfort Bridge School, Grades 1-12. 1945

Mummy receives an important letter from the government with medical allowance for our family. At last we kids can have our eyes tested. This involves a trip to Edmonton.

But finally, three pairs of glasses arrive in the mail. I place my silver-rimmed spectacles astride my freckled nose. "The grass! Look at the grass! Each blade is separate. It isn't just a green mat after all." I look up. "And the trees! Look at those trees. Each leaf on the Russian poplar trees is emerald, tipped with gold. Oh, I can see! I can see." I whirl around and around. Ruby and Doug have the same excitement. It is miraculous.

That evening when the sun goes down, I gaze in awe at the stars that sprinkle the heavens. "I always thought that stars were make-believe," I marvel to Douglas. "After all, Twinkle-Twinkle Little Star is in the same book as Humpty-Dumpty."

We work all day
with time to play
at school.

The teacher's fair
I like it there
at school.

But big kids tease,
do as they please
at school.
Call "Turkey Egg"
"Stop," I beg
at school.

But I won't tell
I behave well
at school.

I sing as I skip along the range line. "How do you like my little verse?" I ask Douglas.

"Sounds like you're enjoying school."

"I love it. I just wish the big kids wouldn't pull my pigtails and call me Turkey Egg. I hate that."

"Just smile," advises my brother. "If they think you don't mind, they'll stop doing it. They just want to see you get mad or cry. So you just fool them and smile."

"All right, I'll try." I feel doubtful.

"And don't tattle-tale either. The kids will really pay you back if you get them into trouble. So don't ever tattle-tale. No matter what they do."

"I won't," I promise.

It is a gorgeous autumn morning, blue sky as far as my eye can see. Perfect harvest weather. The crows gather for their long trek south; I can hear their raucous cries in the grove near the river hill.

"If only I weren't left-handed," I sigh. "I think school would be perfect." Miss McPhillip is determined to break me of using my left hand. Every time she sees me using it, she comes storming down to my desk with the strap and slaps it around my desk and roars at me, "Ardith Ray, are you going to be right-handed or left-handed?" And of course, I always promise that I'll use my right hand. But when she's teaching, I'm doing my lessons and somehow that pencil ends back in my left hand. I've always been left-handed. It seems natural for me. I decide to ask Douglas why it upsets Miss McPhillip.

"She told Mummy that your left hand gives you a reversal problem," he explains. "That's why you write everything backwards. Miss McPhillip says she has to hold your work to the mirror to read it. She thinks you're willful and stubborn."

"But it's not my hand that's the problem," I protest. "It's my head. I can't see the difference between *p* and *q* or *b* and *d*. Every time I must print a *d*, I think 'tummy faces the *A*' and then I can print it properly."

"What do you mean, tummy faces the *A*?" asks my brother. "Whose tummy?"

"The *d*," I cry. "In my name, A-r-d-i-t-h. See? The tummy of the *d* sticks out toward the *A*. So every time I come to a *d* or *b*, I have to think of my system. But it really slows me down, so I use my left hand to catch up and Miss McPhillip catches me and the whole thing starts all over again. I even have bad dreams about being left-handed."

"I'll tell Mummy how you feel," says Doug kindly. "Maybe she'll talk to Miss McPhillip."

Mummy is alarmed by what Douglas tells her. She visits the teacher after school the following day. "Just give Ardith a very short trial period, and if she really won't change, please leave her left-handed," she advises.

Miss McPhillip points out that the teachers are expected to break the habit, but she gives up and allows me to remain left-handed. I'm relieved, and my bad dreams disappear.

My little desk is near the door against the west wall. Doug and Ruby sit with their respective grades. Really big kids take the seats beside the windows where it is so draughty that the girls sometimes wear their coats until the heater's warmth seeps through the room.

A washstand holds an enamelled basin, a bar of Lifebuoy soap and a ten-gallon crockery cooler. By pushing the cooler's spigot firmly with my thumb, I allow water to trickle out.

Ruby teaches me to fold scrap paper into a tiny hat, and hold it upside down to make a surprisingly strong cup. I'm able to slake my thirst before my cup soaks through and leaks so drastically it has to be discarded. Half the pleasure of the drink is the folding of the cup. If there isn't time to make one, I gulp a mouthful of water from my cupped hands. Then air-dry them, or wipe them on my skirt. The hand-basin is seldom used as there is never warm water. The single cooler of water is expected to hold enough drinking water for the entire day for forty pupils.

I love opening exercises of each school day. Miss McPhillip greets us warmly, leads with God Save the King, followed by a morning hymn, and a couple of patriotic songs.

Although Miss McPhillip's desk is centre front, she seldom has time to sit, as she is constantly instructing one grade or another. The rest of us pupils write assignments from the blackboard.

I listen intently to everything Miss McPhillip says, and I learn a great deal as I struggle with my printing.

A student helper, usually Lizzy, hears me read the list of words Miss McPhillip has written on the blackboard:

<u>ell</u>

bell
cell
dell
fell
hell
jell
pell
quell
sell
well
yell

I conclude triumphantly, sure of every sound (and feeling very daring when saying "hell" aloud). I long to read well enough to hold the pointer for others to read in unison. It would be fun to correct their notebooks too, if only I could print.

My grade one class is dismissed at eleven-thirty each morning so Miss McPhillip has an opportunity to do some serious instruction while we little ones go outdoors to play. "Don't go near the slough," we're warned as we troupe, unsupervised, onto the playground.

I skip around the ball diamond along the north fence, exploring the baseball field with Billy. I long to visit the ponies in the barn at the far corner of the yard, but the grade one kids are forbidden to do so.

Children who travel long distances ride ponies that are kept in the school barn. When Miss McPhillip goes to her teacherage for lunch and to stoke her fire, kids sometimes choose me to ride on their ponies to drink at the slough.

But now the playground is deserted, with only Billy and me around. He whispers, "I seen Normie and Ted smoking behind the barn this morning. Should we tell Miss McPhillip?"

I think about the pony rides, and shake my head, "Let's keep that a secret."

Discipline is seldom a problem. All the students know that if they are punished at school, they can expect further punishment when they get home.

During recess, everyone files out and spreads across the schoolyard for ball games. I'm content to skip on the worn path, where no long grasses tangle my rope. I chant at the top of my voice:

Mother, mother, I am ill.
Send for the doctor over the hill.
In came the doctor, in came the cat.
In came the bully with a baseball bat.

It's more fun when Anita and Patsy each turn an end of the rope while I skip, all three chanting:

Teddy Bear, Teddy Bear, turn around,
Teddy Bear, Teddy Bear, touch the ground.

I bend to touch the path, my pigtails flying wildly in the sunshine, and my face flushed from exertion.

"What did you bring for lunch?" asks Anita, as we carry our lard buckets out behind the school to settle on some trampled grass in the shade.

I let her peek into my pail. "Egg salad sandwiches."

"Ah-ha, they've probably gone bad by now in this heat. Doesn't your mother know that eggs get poisonous in hot weather?"

"As a matter of fact," I answer loftily, "it isn't the egg that spoils, it's the mayonnaise. And I happen to know, since I make my own lunch, that there is no mayonnaise in my sandwiches. I flavour them with chives."

Then I take a huge bite from my dry egg sandwich. All afternoon, I wonder when I'll die. But nothing happens.

Patsy listens to this interchange without comment and chews her bologna sandwich, holding it so that neither Anita nor I can spot mayonnaise oozing from the edges. Patsy's just a bit two-faced. She's usually unsmiling, solemn and grumpy. But if she needs a favour, Patsy puts on a smile like a Cheshire cat. I'm not fooled, and I like Patsy anyway.

But one day Patsy attacks. "Aw, your face looks like a turkey egg," she jeers. "And your braids hang down like dead snake tails."

I turn away, wounded to the quick. What have I done to Patsy to be hurt in this way? I wander to the slough, peek at my reflection in the pool and speak:

> *Slough mirror, near the school,*
> *Why are kids so mean and cruel?*

But the slough lies murky and silent. No answers for me … until suddenly I hear Doug's advice ring through my head. Just smile. If they think you don't mind, they'll stop doing it. Fool them, and smile.

I practise a big smile, check my reflection in the slough. I'll just chop off a big chunk of myself—the hurting chunk— like Cinderella's ugly sister amputating her toes to fit into the glass slipper, and smile at Patsy as if nothing has happened. I'll fool her. I smile to myself and march back to the playground.

"Hey, Anita and Patsy, come with me down to the slough to see the Canada geese." We watch a few huge geese coast to the water, flap their great wings, brake speed and honk loudly. They flutter as they settle on the water. A brisk breeze tears the last bronze shred of autumn from the small grove of trees.

"Aren't they magnificent?" I smile at my friends and look them in the eyes through my silver-rimmed glasses.

"They sure are." Both girls smile in return. "Oh-oh, there goes the bell." We turn and run.

It's fun to play along the slough during noon hour. Although forbidden to go into the water, the older children may raft across the shallow surface.

"Want a ride, Ardith?" calls John. "Climb on." I scramble onto his raft, logs lashed together with an uneven platform of boards laid on top. I crouch on deck as the raft glides across the water. John navigates with a long pole. I glimpse my reflection as we flit past in the riffled water:

> *Mirror, mirror in the pool*
> *Am I pretty, now at school?*

"That's dumb!" snickers Billy from a nearby raft. "There are no magic mirrors. That's baby stuff."

I glare at him. Could Billy be right? Are there *no* magic mirrors? I glance around. Some other kids are snickering too.

I hunker on deck and pull in my neck like a heron in a hailstorm.

"Oh, forget it, little turkey egg," laughs John.

"Race you to shore!" he challenges and pushes ahead so hard that I almost fall. Our raft forges ahead.

"Beat you by a mile," I toss over my shoulder as I step grandly off the winning craft. Billy crawls slug-like up the bank behind. I can't forgive him for rudely ruining my faith in magic.

The slough entertains us youngsters year-round. Now crimson and violet leaves fall from the Balm of Gilead trees that line the banks..Crusts of lacy ice form along the seams where ducks complain it is too cold for paddling. Through my new glasses I can see the wild geese practising their alphabet, with ever-changing formations from V to W to Y, high in the slate-grey sky. I count each flock, rattling numbers all the way to one hundred.

Arithmetic is easy.

Then joy of joys. As I'm studying the *Katzenjammer Kids* in the funny papers, I suddenly realize that those white balloons above their heads contain messages. They are all printed in capital letters. But they give a message. And I can read it! I can read it! I go through the whole funny paper section, and I can read everything. I'm so proud that I carry my primer home every evening to practise.

Foxtails wave their furry brushes along the lane among the coarse couch grass while Mummy harvests long hours. Douglas helps all he can.

The cabin is framed by autumn. Pigeons strut and peck up fallen grain around the yard. After the day's heat, there is a sharpness to the evening air.

Noël stays with Nan during harvest time and Ruby hurries to help as soon as school dismisses. No one is in the cabin.

I start the fire to heat the dishwater. Morning bowls and porridge pot wait. I hate to slide my hand into that slimy pot. I rim the edges, dump the grits in the slops, gather the eggs, bring in several armloads of wood and pick a pail of chips.

Where's Ruby? Time to start supper. What will we have?

Ruby arrives in time to stir up johnnycake and pop it into the oven. By this time, it's dark inside. Ruby lights the kerosene lamp while I set the bowls and spoons out. A ten-gallon pail of Roger's Golden Syrup is set onto the middle of the table. Ruby stands the long-handled pewter spoon in it, and the spoon remains upright in the thick, rich syrup. A large mound of home-churned butter and a sealer of milk complete the meal preparations. Mummy and Doug arrive and we enjoy our simple fare.

A congregation of chickadees, cardinals and blue jays bustles around the dried sunflowers in the untidy garden. I watch them through the window until an icy drizzle pelts the glass and slowly changes to sleet.

By morning a skiff of snow covers the country and transforms drabness into a shimmering white. Douglas and I plod to school, leaving black footprints along the lane. By afternoon, it's really snowing.

After freeze-up, we children play indoors during noon-hour breaks at school. Often Lizzy plays a tune on the piano while we sing. Sometimes we clear the floor by pushing all the desks to the walls so we can dance.

"Come on, Ardith. We need one more for this square," calls Nancy. I gladly join. I love to dance. The girls can swing me clear off the floor, my toes cutting an arc through the air in a four-hand swing.

"Don't let go," they warn. But I let go. I don't mean to. It just happens. One minute I'm high in the air. Ears swoosh. Pigtails fly. The next I'm in a heap on the floor, breath knocked from my chest.

I writhe and wheeze. A ring of frightened faces surrounds me. So high above me. I grasp my chest. Gasp. Lizzie advances, waggles her finger, stands over me. "Now don't you tell!" I shake my head solemnly. Another secret.

Finally the ice on the slough is strong enough to bear weight, so the boys clear a rink. Wearing skates if they have some, or sliding on moccasined feet, the big boys choose sides for fierce hockey games. They use bent willow sticks to swat a frozen horse-turd puck. Coloured toques mark goals on each end of the rink.

I sit on a fallen log far from the action. "Hurry, Ruby," I beg. "Tie my skates so I can practise." I wait impatiently. A small rink has been cleared of snow for beginners and I'm eager to try it. I can pull on my skates myself. The worn black leather bends easily at the ankles. They are second-hand boy's skates. But I don't mind.

Ruby yanks and lashes the extra length of shoelace around my ankle for support. She tightens my scarf and fixes

Rochfort Bridge CN trestle, now reinforced with steel girders, by the Paddle River banks. 1945.

my mittens before she turns me loose to wobble under her protective eye. And wobble I do! But even though I often turn my ankles, it's fun to glide swiftly across the ice.

All too soon, the bell sounds faintly over the bank, bringing us youngsters back to the classroom for the afternoon.

FIFTEEN

Follow Your Dream

Mom and Ardith in Edmonton. 1943.

Butter, sugar, gasoline, lead (as in toothpaste containers)
were rationed. Weekly rationing coupons were issued
to assure equality for every household. Each family member
was issued a yearly ration book. 1940.

Oh, you better watch out
You'd better not spy
'Cause Santa will see
You open your eye.
Then you'll get no gift
You'll just get a stick
Santa gets mad
If you play a trick....

I stop composing my Christmas rhyme. "Mummy, does Santa really get mad at us if we peek?"

"He might."

Oh, dear. Another problem. Christmas poses lots of problems.

Nan has a lovely idea. "I want to have Christmas at our house—we have plenty of room and I'll get to see the children opening gifts."

"Are you sure that's not too much for you?" asks Mummy.

"Of course not, dear," smiles Nan. "We'll have the tree and gift opening as well as the feast here. And I'll invite Walter."

"How will Santa Claus know where to leave the gifts? Who will tell him the tree is at Nan's," I wonder.

"I'll tell him, Ardith. Don't worry," Mummy promises.

"But how will you tell him?" I persist.

Mummy catches Nan's eye. "We'll hang our stockings along the bunk in the cabin, and I'll put a note on mine telling Santa Claus to take our big presents to Grandpapa's house and leave them under the tree."

"I guess that should work."

"Nan invited Granddad, too," Mummy smiles. "So we'll all be together for our big feast." But Mummy's smile is forced and her face contorts as she speaks. "I'm so proud that you designed pretty cards for Daddy—I mailed them ages ago so he'll get them in time for his Christmas.

"Now, girls, promise not to bounce and you may stay and practise your parts for the program while I make divinity fudge and Christmas pudding. Aren't you glad we used honey for our porridge so I could save the sugar ration? I have enough sugar for a good-sized batch of baking."

We quietly recite lines and review carols, not wanting to miss the delicious aroma of Christmas baking. Douglas does the chores alone, while Ruby leaves to help Nan.

Only a few children attend United Church services, so it's a small concert. Most of our neighbours belong to the Roman Catholic or Lutheran churches. Grandpapa constantly warns us to stay away from those he thinks are the two worst influences of the district—the Catholics and the "bohunks." I'm constantly on guard ever since starting school, but I haven't recognized any of the children as being either Catholic or bohunk. They all seem like ordinary kids and are in no way different. I'll just be friends with everyone, I decide.

In my school concert, Miss McPhillip teaches grades one and two a skit. Each child is a nursery rhyme character. I'm pleased to be Twinkle, Twinkle, now that I know there are stars. Wearing my last year's angel dress, I recite clearly, my wand held stiffly in my left fist.

Billy steals the show. As Little Boy Blue, he has Miss McPhillip's tonette and nervously twists it while backstage. So when he finally marches onto the platform, stands squarely on the taped X at the centre, he says loudly, "Little Boy Blue, come blow your horn."

Then he gives a mighty blow into the tonette, but no sound comes. Billy swells up with a huge breath and blows again. Still no sound. He blows until his cheeks flush, his blue eyes bulge and he's thoroughly angry. He shakes his head and holds the tonette out to the huge audience. "This damn thing doesn't work," he declares. It brings down the house.

Santa Claus seems to have aged. He hurries with the candy bag distribution, not holding any of the children on his lap. I intend to ask him to deliver gifts to Nan's but I'm herded past. Back on the bench, I suck candy and count goodies in my bag.

The womenfolk pass boxes of sandwiches and cakes. I smell coffee brewing in a copper-bottomed wash-boiler on the flat heater. The women carry huge pots of the steamy drink along the aisles, using all of the two hundred cups stored in the kitchen. The local storekeeper passes oranges from small boxes.

Then the benches are pushed to the walls and we clear the floor for dancing. A voluntary band strikes a lively polka. Noël and I swing round and round with Anita and Patsy while

Doug slides across the floor on the seat of his pants with the other boys. Mummy sits on a bench and brushes tears from her eyes. A few other mothers also cry. I know why. Their husbands are overseas, missing this Christmas celebration. The music plays past midnight. Mummy dances with some of the other women. "We'll stay until the party ends," she smiles, "since there's no school until next year."

I'm alarmed. No school until *next year*? But Douglas explains, "Don't you see, Ardith? By the time school starts again in January, it will be a new year."

Christmas Eve at last. We gather around the tree in Grandpapa's living room. He lights candles that are in little tin candle holders clipped to the branches. As each new light appears, we make a wish aloud.

"I wish I could have singing lessons," begins Ruby.

"I wish I had muscles like Charles Atlas," adds Doug.

"I wish my freckles would disappear," I murmur.

"I wish Daddy camed home," Noël whispers.

"Would come home," automatically corrects Mummy as tears well in her eyes. "Oh, Noël, we all wish Daddy were here."

The coal oil lamp is carried out to the kitchen so we have the full effect of lighted candles. We're spellbound as the flames sputter and the CBC broadcast gives the seven o'clock news. The grownups listen earnestly for the latest war news, but my thoughts stray. Maybe the war will be over soon. That's what Mummy says. So when Daddy comes home, he'll take care of us.

After the broadcast, the radio is switched off to save batteries. Candles are blown out and we wrap for the brisk walk home.

"Merry Christmas," we chorus and leave the cosy house to trudge to our tiny cabin.

"I'll hang my biggest stocking from the edge of the bunk," I announce, sure I'll never get to sleep.

Before I know it, I hear Noël exclaim over her stocking next morning. There's a suspicious bulge in the toe of each stocking. I reach down. Sure enough, a Jap orange is in the toe. What a treat. We get oranges only at Christmastime.

This fruit serves as breakfast and each section is savoured singly. As we eat, we get dressed. When we troop over to Grandpapa's, he meets us with great excitement, motioning for us to follow him. I stare, mystified by a confusion of tracks behind the evergreens.

"See," Grandpapa points to the ground. "Here's where Santa's sleigh landed. Look at the reindeer tracks." Sure enough, their cloven hoofs make distinct indentations in the snow. We burst into the house to share the news.

"Nan! Nan! Santa left tracks behind the shelterbelt." Nan chuckles as she shakes her head in wonderment.

"Come in, come in. Take off your coats. Come right in." We stare in dismay at a bare tree. Not a present in sight. Santa Claus has not received our message. There are no presents under the tree. Noël and I swell up to cry but Douglas makes a closer inspection of the tree. He calls, "Wait a minute. Here's a tag with my name on it."

Sure enough, his name is printed on a tag attached with a blue yarn which leads away from the tree, under the dining room table, behind the Winnipeg couch, under Nan's bed, behind Nan's dresser, around Nan's wash table, behind the sewing machine, until the yarn disappears into the depths of Nan's closet. "Well, well," exclaims Nan. "Santa must be playing a trick on you."

Noël and I clasp each other in anticipation as Douglas gropes for his parcel in the dark closet. What a clever Santa.

Doug unwraps an armoured tank on rubber treads, realistic in camouflage colours of green and brown. When he winds it, the treads carry it along. It is so menacing that Noël's careful to avoid the gun on the top. We all admire Doug's gift.

"Now it's Noël's turn." Grandpapa helps find her tag with pink yarn attached. Noël rolls the yarn onto her tag, patiently following it around the table legs, under Nan's rocker, behind the kitchen range, through the cream separator legs and finally into the wood box. There lies a beautiful Raggedy Ann stuffed doll with orange hair and a bright red smile.

"Oh, look," breathes Noël and hugs her new doll. "She's as big as I am." I stop wringing my hands.

"Now Ardith's turn," says Mummy. My tag has green yarn that I wrap around it, advancing to Nan's rocker, the Winnipeg couch, then doubling back past the heater to the kitchen table, looping around two legs and going behind the cabinet, finally disappearing into Nan's washing machine. I pull out a rubber wet-um's dolly that wets her nappy every time I offer her a drink of water from a miniature baby bottle with a nipple. I smile at Noël—both of us get the dolly we want.

"Ruby now," says Mummy. "Come, dear. Follow your string." Ruby's yarn is red. She carefully winds it onto her name tag, following it past Nan's rocker, behind the wood box, past the washstand, through Grandpapa's gun rack, under Grandpapa's bed, behind his dresser, and finally to the top shelf of the pantry, finding a long box. Noël and I shiver in the cool pantry. "I'll take this box to the living room before I open it." Ruby is thoughtful. "So Nan can watch."

Ruby lifts the lid and a beautiful doll smiles up at her. "Oh-h! An Eaton's Beauty! Oh, look at her real hair. And two pearly little teeth. See how she wakes up when she stands. And falls asleep when she rests. Oh, she is so regal. I will take really,

really good care of this perfect doll, Nan. I'll keep her forever." Nan and Mummy smile to one another.

We play quietly while the elders open gifts—practical, necessary items, handmade with love.

We listen to the King's message on the radio, and to the news. As the womenfolk prepare the feast, Granddad arrives. "I'm gaunt as a goat," he announces. "But I brung good news. Lawrence got hitched to an English girl from London. Her name is Martha. So you kids have an aunt, at last."

Aunt Martha, I say to myself. I like that name. I wonder if she's like the Martha in the Bible.

The family spend a merry afternoon. "It's well worth the scrimping," Mummy says with satisfaction, "to see the pleasure those toys give to the children. But now," she declares, "we must really save our pennies toward a new house."

SIXTEEN

Strange Spring

*Ardith, Noël, Ruby, Douglas display wasp-nest
in front of "The Cabin." 1940*

Wind shakes the sash of the cabin's window frame
and streaks of moisture dry on the glass leaving
faint paths. It's too cold to play outdoors, but we're
tired of playing on the bunk. I gaze listlessly at the world
through the single windowpane. "I spy, with my little eye … ,"
I begin halfheartedly. "Oh, Noël, I wish it would warm up."

Very gradually, the weather grows milder. Sunbeams ric-
ochet from the drifts and make shadows on the snow that
mirror the trees and extend their length. Everything seems dif-

ferent. The air feels moist and heavy. The landscape changes from bridal white to dingy grey.

At last temperatures soar. I wade through slush along the path where snow supported my weight only days before. Long silver icicles hang from the eaves of the cabin.

The barnyard is a quagmire. The pasture resembles a huge white handkerchief, undisturbed by animal feet. Soggy drifts along the roadside expose tufts of withered grasses.

Gradually the puddles become small, the weather warms and the landscape changes to a delicate fresh green. Buds form and pussy willows burst from the branches of the old tree, a fairyland in the front yard.

"Look at the pussy willows. Let's pick some." We pull the soft, furry knobs until we have half a pailful.

We show our treasure to Mummy. "Don't they feel like real baby pussy-cats?"

Mummy's eyes soften. "Would you like to make fur coats for paper dolls with those?"

"Oh, yes."

"I'll just mix paste for you." Mummy whips up flour and water. "Here's the old catalogue. You can put fur coats on your paper people."

As the days grow warmer, we spend less time indoors. We love to explore the woodland. Dogwood bushes glisten blood red among the coarse leaves of last fall's slough grass that fold in clumps above the brown water.

"Sh-sh, I see a rabbit," points Noël. We watch for a long time, both standing tree-still so we don't frighten it. Later we stop to tell Nan about the rabbit and step from our high-topped boots at her door, making damp footprints with our sodden socks.

"Sorry, Nan," I say. "I'll mop our tracks so you don't slip.

First I'll take off my wet stockings and hang them over the oven railing. I'll be so glad to wear ankle socks again, 'cause my legs have a hot burn from these elastic garters.

"N'er cast a cloot till May is oot," quotes Nan with a laugh.

"What does that really mean?" asks Noël.

"It means we must not throw off our winter clothes until the end of May," Nan explains.

"But that's almost another month," I protest.

"Och now! A month will pass quickly and there's still a nip to the air."

"Well, it's hot today, Nan. But our feet are cold from the slough water. Mummy won't let us go near the river. It's in flood. It's as wide as the Red Sea, but the colour of coffee."

"Then stay away, girls. It's dangerous," warns Nan. "Come have a drink of hot cocoa and a cookie while your stockings dry out. What did you see today?"

"We saw a brown patchy rabbit, all scruffy with white hair shedding so it must be spring," I tell her.

"I saw eleven eggs in a duck nest on the edge of the slough," Noël adds. "We didn't touch the eggs."

"I saw some fresh soil clumps along the road where the bank was cut," I say, "and some tiny green brushes among the dead grass. Guess what they are, Nan?"

"I can't imagine." The old lady throws her hands help-lessly into the air.

"Baby spruce trees," I announce. "They're growing from Grandpapa's shelterbelt trees. And I notice the willow tips are red—like witches' brooms."

Nan chuckles at my description while I, in turn, try to make my observations very colourful, knowing that Nan is housebound.

"We were walking along through the dry grass when we saw a huge hump of bright green by the roadside. When we got near, we found an ant hill covered by greener and longer grasses than anywhere else," I say. "Why, Nan?"

"My goodness." Nan is thoughtful. "Well, they say ants know where to place their hills, with an underground water source. Also, I suppose the soil on top of the hill is loose and easy for grass to push through."

"Well, it has the greenest grass of all," Noël says.

"But the slough has green grass growing too," I add.

"See how important moisture is?" says Nan.

"The pussy willows aren't as pretty now," complains Noël. "They have yellow fuzz on them."

"Pollen," explains Nan. "It will attract the bees."

"The frogs sound like old men with sore throats, trying to sing," I say, making Nan laugh. "Now I guess we should go. Our socks are fairly dry. Thanks for the little lunch, Nan. See you soon."

We kiss Nan and hurry home, hating to roll up our woollen stockings. We leave them as knee-highs, to prevent chaffing from our flapping rubber boots.

Warm spring weather continues. Solid blue clouds streak out at the bottom into thin straight lines that reach clear to the ground and bleed like cheap blue jeans in their first wash.

Noël and I go into the bushes again.

"Look!" I cry. "What's this?" I point to a small tent of web wrapped around a curled leaf. Tiny black caterpillars wiggle inside. "Aren't they cute? Let's ask Mummy what they are."

Picking it carefully, we carry it home. Mummy is dismayed. "Tent caterpillars! Oh, dear! I do hope we're not going to be overrun with those. They can strip the trees. These caterpillars are harmful, girls. So I'm going to show you how to kill them."

Mummy gets an old coffee tin and fills it half full of kerosene. She thrusts the leaf into the tin. The caterpillars stop moving. "They're dead," she announces. "You girls must pick every nest you can reach and bring them home in a sack. Douglas will help you drown the caterpillars in kerosene."

This is a new game. Noël and I scour the trees and find dozens of clusters. Douglas helps us drown them. But thousands more hang out of reach and out of sight in the trees.

We search a rustling tapestry of leaves overhead.

The weather continues to warm and the river waters recede; it changes from coffee colour to a shade of weak tea. Green leaves appear on the Balm of Gilead trees along the banks.

The hordes of hatching caterpillars find plenty to eat; they strip the trees bare. As I skip along the lane and down the range line, I look around in bewilderment. I dance up Granddad's path and call out, "Granddad, something strange is happening—it sounds like it's raining all around, but it's not wet, there's not a cloud in the sky and the sun is shining. Why?"

"That's the dropping from thousands of those hungry caterpillars," says Granddad. "It sure do sound like rain pattering. Soon every leaf will be stripped from these trees if it don't rain, for sure. But come in away from those pesky caterpillars."

I bang the screen door sharply before opening it. A score of wriggling green caterpillars falls off the screen. I step over them on their side and the screen slams shut behind me.

In just a few days, every leaf is stripped from the bluff north of the cabin. The caterpillars begin to march. The grass becomes a moving current of caterpillars, all heading in a southeasterly direction. They crawl over every obstacle, never veering from their direction. When they reach the cabin, they climb straight up the north wall, across the roof and down the south wall, disappearing into the lawn as the wave continues. A few climb up the stovepipe and fall into the firebox during the night when the fire has gone out.

"My goodness," cries Mummy one morning. "When I took off the stove lid to start a fire, some black furry caterpillars marched out of the firebox. They are tent caterpillars that have crawled down the stovepipe—as black as Toby's hat, from rolling in the soot, but they are still searching for food. And there are too many to drown in kerosene. I can't afford to buy so much."

"Phew," we tell her. "There must still be some in the chimney and firebox. Don't burn them in the stove, Mummy."

The caterpillars have sticky feet and cling to our clothing and hair. They drop on me from long sticky strands whenever I venture outdoors. No place is free of caterpillars. They can be found everywhere—on clothing, on the floor, on the bunk, on the walls and even on the plates at the table.

"Yuck," says Doug. "Everywhere I step is slimy, with slippery caterpillars bursting underfoot. The grass is just waving with them. The cow won't stand still for me to milk her. She is frantic from the caterpillars crawling up her legs and across her udders."

"I think every leaf on our farm is eaten," I declare. "They're heading for the river. I'll bet the water stops the plague, and they'll all drown, just like the rats in 'The Pied Piper of Hamelin.' Let's go down to the river and watch."

Doug, Noël and I go to the river, but the caterpillars aren't drowning. "Look, girls," says Doug. "They spin webs and sail across to the other shore. I guess that's why they're called tent caterpillars."

The caterpillars relentlessly strip and devour leaves on the far shore. "If only it would rain," murmurs Mummy. But the weather remains hot and dry.

Even the classroom is invaded as caterpillars creep in through the open windows. I find it difficult to concentrate on my lessons with all the distractions. I admire Miss McPhillip for being so understanding.

I sit looking around at all the students. The boys have summer haircuts, I notice. Billy's hair looks as though someone turned a soup bowl over the crown of his head and trimmed around it. John's soft hair is clipped like a toothbrush, while Normie's looks more like a flat, black, shining Fuller brush. All the boys have a ring of freshly shaved neck shining white, making them look somehow vulnerable, like freshly shorn sheep.

Friday evening Ruby walks to town for the mail and returns with a real tale. "You should have all been to meet the train," she cries. "There was great excitement. After the freight and mailbags were dropped, the train couldn't get going. There were so many caterpillars on the track that it was greasy. Everyone helped the brakemen scatter sand on the tracks to provide traction. They even got some dry manure from the stockyards and scattered that. The track was green slime for miles—halfway to Mayerthorpe. No one has ever seen such a plague. The brakemen told us the countryside is stripped and barren all the way to Calahoo."

"If only it would rain," wails Mummy. "The caterpillars would drown." But it doesn't rain. Hot, dry days encourage the creatures to devour more juicy leaves. By now the caterpillars are enormous; many measure two and a half inches in length.

Will the minister tell us about the plagues sent to the pharaoh of Egypt? I wonder, as I dress for church on Sunday morning. Surely our plague is almost as bad. Did we do something wrong and God has sent caterpillars to punish us? I sit outdoors on the step to wait for the family.

"Are we all ready?" calls Mummy. "Hurry, girls, or we'll be late for church."

Noël steps out of the cabin wearing her red plaid dress and bright red ankle socks. I eye my little sister enviously. I feel very drab in my brown dress and white socks. "I wish I could wear bright colours," I mutter.

"Nonsense," laughs Mummy. "It would clash with your hair. Your crowning glory is bright enough. Let everyone admire your hair, Ardith."

Just then Ruby arrives from Nan's.

"Well, girls, you all look very presentable. Just button up that second blouse button, Ruby. Your bosom must never be on display," says Mummy, as we set off across the field to church. Doug has walked ahead with Grandpapa, who is responsible for unlocking the hall and arranging the pews. He leaves Jippy, his collie, at home to keep Nan company.

Flocks of sea gulls bank overhead. They have come to eat caterpillars, but there are just too many. Even if the gulls turn green, they can't eat enough to affect this plague.

By the end of that week, I notice a change in the caterpillars' behaviour. I watch one. It stands jerking its head to and fro. I peer closely. A thin strand oozes from the caterpillar's head. It's weaving a web, winding itself inside a strong silken cocoon. Within a few hours, the cocoon is completed and sticks securely under an eave of the outhouse.

Within a few days, every nook and cranny is full of fuzzy white cocoons. The caterpillars disappear.

The poor poplar trees struggle to produce a fresh batch of leaves. And now the rains come. The long-awaited moisture helps the trees regrow their leaves. Soon the world looks fresh and green again. The plague of caterpillars has ended.

SEVENTEEN

Gaining My Place

Douglas harrowing (bare feet). 1945.

I love school. The worn splintery floor smells of raw linseed oil and the chalk dust seems to promise fresh knowledge. Best of all, I like singing at the opening exercises. I long to be chosen as Little Sir Echo. Every day I shoot up my hand, offering myself. Every time, someone else is chosen.

Then one morning, "Ardith, will you please be Sir Echo?" asks Miss McPhillip. I plant my feet and lean against the back wall as the class sings, "Little Sir Echo, How do you do? Hello … "

And Sir Echo sings clear and strong: "Hello."
The class sings again, "Hello."
And Sir Echo answers "Hello."
The class sings: "Little Sir Echo will answer you. Hello."
"Hello."
Class: "Won't you come over and play?"
Sir Echo: "Play?"
Class: "You're a nice little fellow, we know by your voice,
But you're always so far away."
Sir Echo: "Away."

When Sir Echo marches to my seat, I feel special. I love Miss McPhillip. She makes school such fun. I throw myself wholeheartedly into action songs: Snow Is Falling, My Pigeon House, and Little Maids of Holland.

Then Miss McPhillip divides our classroom for rounds. One half starts the round and the second half begins when they are half-through: Row, Row, Row Your Boat, Are You Sleeping? and Little Owls Look Wise. When the children begin White Choral Bells, they get mixed up and stop in confusion. I'm impatient. I can hold my part through a hurricane.

It is Friday. Drama time. Miss McPhillip promises to let the grade one class act a new story. "Ardith, will you please be Rapunzel?"

I know why I'm chosen. I have the longest hair. I carefully climb up atop Miss McPhillip's chair, which is perched on the teacher's wide walnut desk. It's easy for me to imagine I'm in a high tower, and when I hear handsome Prince Billy call, "Rapunzel, Rapunzel, let down your hair," I fling my braids down my back, certain they reach almost to the floor.

So radiant am I in my role that a few of the older students begin calling me Rapunzel, which I greatly prefer to Turkey Egg. So I gain a little confidence and self-esteem with my dramatic ways.

And so the winter months pass while Miss McPhillip provides suitable indoor activities as entertainment.

Finally the weather becomes milder. The windowpane, crusted with trapped icy patches, begins to clear. I slosh along the path in my high-topped rubber boots. There are monsters lurking beneath the surface of the slush, sucking, gurgling, grabbing my boots and holding them fast.

As soon as it's warm enough, we eat our lunches outdoors at noon, down by the slough. The schoolgirls love to sit on the dock to eat their sandwiches. I dangle my legs off the dock, chew my jam sandwiches and fling my crusts to the blackbirds that perch on the willows. Ruby reproves me sharply. "Ardith, you know there are starving children in Europe who would love to have your crusts to eat."

"Yes, Mother," is my cheeky reply.

I am a big girl now, a sturdy seven-year-old, as spotted with freckles as the orange tiger lilies that thrive on the new breaking. Miss McPhillip says in despair, "Will you please tell your mother I want to talk to her?"

I rush home with the news and Mummy agrees to visit the teacher the next afternoon. "Ardith prints everything backwards and her printing resembles ancient hieroglyphics," Miss McPhillip reports. "She has an excellent command of the English language, Mrs. Ray, thanks to your fine example. And she understands sophisticated vocabulary."

"Thank you," murmurs Mummy.

"She is familiar with all the fairy tales, nursery rhymes and folklore. What a wealth of information your children have."

The teacher smiles at Mummy who nods, "I read to them and tell them stories while I sew or do needlework," she explains.

Miss McPhillip says, "I notice she watches and copies whatever she sees as successful by other students in her extreme effort to please me. I wish she'd just relax so we could all enjoy her sunny disposition."

"Do you hear that, Ardith?" Mummy asks. "Your teacher wants you to smile more." I nod.

Miss McPhillip continues, "She has a quick mind and loves to compose poems and stories where she can use her vivid imagination."

"She certainly has a vivid imagination. She's always composing something. And she idolizes Douglas, who's very protective."

"You're doing well with your children," Miss McPhillip says. "They are all top students and very well behaved. I'm sure Ardith's printing will improve. I'd swear she sees everything in a pool of water—totally backwards. But I find that if I hold it to a mirror, it is perfectly correct. I've never seen anything like it. I won't be harsh, since she's beginning to sort it out herself."

"Thank you," says Mummy, shaking my teacher's hand. "Good day."

I feel light-hearted as we head home. Miss McPhillip has praised me. "I won't be too hard on you children either," Mummy tells me. "You're really all obedient. And you all work well. I know. I'll give you little people the day off tomorrow. How's that?"

EIGHTEEN

Winter Chores

Douglas, Ruby, Mummy, Noël and Ardith. 1940.

Autumn is here, with cool winds and a riot of coloured leaves. The sky is clear.

I love to visit Nan. "We need some porridge," I tell her.

"I'll ask Grandpapa to grind some wheat. You'll all enjoy fresh porridge now it's cooler," says Nan as I settle to read by her rocker. "And he might butcher as soon as it snows."

"Fresh meat!' I burst out. "We haven't had any since the meat man was here with his wagon last month. Does he bring fresh meat all winter, Nan?"

"No need," explains my patient grandmother. "When it freezes, farmers butcher and freeze the meat in their meat-house. They all have their own fresh frozen meat all winter, like Grandpapa does. He'll cure bacon and we'll make sausage, too. That hog should last all winter, with hams till spring. Bones for Jippy. Then we'll have to settle for chicken or pigeon until the meat man comes. But guess what meat we're having today?"

I think for a second. "Wild goose?" I've seen V-shaped flocks heading south today.

"No, grouse," says Nan. "Won't that be a treat? Jip flushed a covey and Grandpapa shot five. Two for us and the rest for your Mummy. Would you like a pretty tail feather for your bookmark?"

"Thanks, Nan." I notice Nan has brown spots all over the backs of her hand, the same colour as this grouse feather. Mummy says you can tell Nan's age by her liver spots. I'll count them. One, two, three, four, five … But I can't do it. I get mixed up. I wonder if Nan's freckles count as liver spots. If so, she must be a hundred years old. Maybe even a thousand. Is that what Mummy means by saying she can tell Nan's age by her liver spots?

Freeze-up! The river freezes over, making a smooth track of ice. Still no snow, so it's ideal for skating.

"Hurry with your chores and you may skate tonight while Noël and I visit Nan." Mummy announces. "I have a treat for each of you."

We complete chores in record time, dress warmly and sling our skates over our shoulders by their long laces. Mummy tucks a hot baked potato into each of our skates. What a surprise.

"These will keep your skates nice and toasty until you put your feet into them," she smiles. "Now, Ardith, have you got double mitts?"

I have to hustle to keep up to Doug and Ruby as we walk down the river hill.

Some of the town kids are already there, building a bonfire on a tiny island just upstream from the bridge. Normie brought his hatchet to chop at young willow trees that have curved ends, suitable for hockey sticks. Other boys gather dead spruce boughs and brush for the fire. As the flames blaze, we watch the bigger boys gather around. A few lace up their skates. Those who have none are content to slide on moccasined feet.

"Did anyone bring a puck?" Normie calls.

"Right here," laughs John. "I gathered several frozen horse turds from the road. Here's one for starters." He tosses a turd onto the ice, placing the rest carefully on the bank, in case the first one disintegrates.

"Great. Here's a few good sticks."

Normie hands out bent willows, perfect for clubbing the puck. "I'll be goalie," offers Douglas, and drops his toque to mark his goal. John throws his toque down for the other marker. Billy and Normie are captains. They choose their teams and the game is on.

Meanwhile, I settle on a fallen log and yank off my moccasins. I shake out my baked potatoes and thrust my toes into deliciously warm skates, and while I wait impatiently for Ruby to lash my laces, I munch my potatoes. Ready at last. I emerge from the shadow of the bridge and glide upstream on ice that shines like glass. The stately Balm of Gilead trees throw shadows on the ice. Lots of kids are sliding along the silver ribbon of ice; laughter and shouts echo through the valley.

"Beat you to the beaver dam." A challenge I never accept. The big girls pump furiously upstream, with whoops and shouts, while I circle near the bridge. I have enough challenge keeping on my feet. I'm really not a strong skater.

I certainly won't play hockey. Those boys are too rough, slashing their sticks at the puck, always aiming in the direction of their opponents' goal. Back and forth run the defencemen on swift moccasined feet. The forwards wear skates, and zoom about wildly.

I gingerly slide past the game to get warm at the fire. I'm freezing. I stand as close to the flames as I dare, and feel heat penetrate my mittens. Ruby stands guard nearby in case I topple onto the fire.

My toes and fingers tingle and my cheeks are like frozen apples when we climb the river hill. I go straight up on the bunk.

Mummy kisses us and makes her rounds with the kerosene lamp to scorch bedbugs before she settles on her end of the bunk.

The cabin grows quiet except for the sounds of straw rustling whenever someone shifts on the tick. The fire sputters and flares as a log smoulders in the stove. Heat from the range is really unable to conquer the blades of cold air that seep through the cracks and creep around the edges of the old wooden frame on the makeshift window. I cuddle Noël for warmth.

I feel bone-weary next morning. The skating party last night leaves me stiff and sore, and I have chilblains from the cold.

"Run and fill the washtub with snow," Mummy says. "I'm going to wash clothes tomorrow. Be sure to use a clean drift," she calls as Noël and I bundle up and go out with our buckets and snow shovel.

During the cold winter, the square galvanized tub remains on the back of the kitchen range. We're responsible for keeping that tub full of snow. If we use snow water for washing, Douglas and I have less water carrying from

Grandpapa's well, to bring drinking water. But gathering fresh snow constantly is a big task because when the snow melts, it makes very little water. It takes lots of snow to make a tubful of water.

Douglas and I carry ten-pound Roger's Golden Syrup pails full of water from Grandpapa's well house. By the time we reach home, our fingers are indented like accordion pleats because the wire handles cut into our fingers. It takes several minutes to restore circulation to my tingling fingers. But I enjoy the walks because I can have my brother's attention all to myself.

Throughout the summer months, we catch rainwater from the eaves and save it in a rain barrel to provide soft wash water. But the fresh water from Grandpapa's well is still needed for drinking and cooking.

"I'm an angel." I fling myself backward off the edge of the path into unbroken new snow.

"Me, too." Noël flops beside me. We raise and lower our arms to make wings; at the same time we open and close our legs to form skirts.

"Boost us up, please, Douglas," we beg. "We don't want to ruin our snow angels." We wait patiently; the world looks different from the entirely new perspective.

"Look at my breath." Noël blows a steamy veil.

Douglas pulls us to our feet and we race to the cabin.

Next morning Douglas and I walk to school through falling flakes of snow that drift straight down from sullen grey clouds.

I become secretive in my behaviour. I instinctively behave as perfectly as possible around my mother, trying to escape notice and seldom draw attention to myself, but then feel ignored, unimportant. "I'm either too small to do what Ruby is allowed to do," I think, as the middle child, "or else I'm too big to do the cute things Noël gets away with. I'm just plain old Miss In-Between."

I wander to the cabin, where Mummy arranges the cabinet. "The Watkins man called in today and sold me a new kind of tapioca. It's crushed, so it won't take so long to cook. Isn't that marvelous? We'll try some soon. I also bought some more pine tar salve for your eczema. You've finished all your salve."

I find a small ledge under the table top where the leg is screwed at the corner, so I begin secretly stashing my mealtime crusts there. I remember to sneak these out to the kittens while I'm doing dishes. But after a few days, I become careless. I forget to empty my hoard. When Mummy slams the table against the wall to wash the floor underneath, a shower of dried crusts hits the wet floor.

"Don't you realize there are starving children in Europe who would love to eat the crusts you waste?" she asks.

"Yes, Mummy," I agree meekly.

Winter seems never-ending, but finally the air begins to soften.

Noël declares, "I wish spring would come."

"It will," I tell her. "I hear crows scolding one another and partridges drum too. Spring's just around the corner."

"I'm tired of snow. And I'm tired of salt pork and canned vegetables. Nothing tastes fresh. I'm tired of winter!" Noël complains.

"I know how you feel," I agree. "I crave something fresh too. Oh, Mummy, can we have a slice of raw potato?" I beg. It's a real treat to bite into a crisp raw vegetable with a light sprinkling of salt on it. The starchy juice puckers my lips.

"Enjoy these potatoes while they're still firm," says Mummy. "The turnips in Grandpapa's root cellar are all pithy.

William Ray (Daddy) in RCAF uniform. 1942.

I threw them to his pigs. The carrots are woody, too, but we still have plenty of onions. Perhaps I'll make scalloped potatoes with scrambled eggs for supper, and saskatoons with rhubarb for dessert. We won't be able to spare milk for pudding until Annette has her calf this spring."

I love to watch the ripple of movement on Annette's side as her unborn calf moves within the cow's tightly stretched skin. The old cow looks sleek and fat as she rubs her restless neck on the wooden stanchion bars.

I still enjoy the wave of warmth that rolls out to greet me when I enter the barn. I enjoy the sounds of different rhythms of breathing, the grunts of drowsy pigs, the stamp of hoofs on the manure-plastered planks and the jostle of the rambunctious yearling steers.

NINETEEN

The New House

Grandpapa Black entertains on his fiddle. 1943.

> *We're building a house on the hill*
> *Though living in our cabin still*
> *The house is so tall*
> *With a very high wall*
> *But we can't move in it until ... it's finished.*

"Mummy! I can't write a limerick. Miss McPhillip showed the grade five kids how to do them, and it sounds like fun. But mine doesn't work out right."

I read it aloud. "See, There's no room for my ending. What should I do?"

"Try again, dear," says Mummy reasonably.

I struggle with another limerick:

> *A new house for us is the plan.*
> *We're saving as much as we can*
> *So we can afford*
> *A window or board*
> *And hire a carpenter man.*

"Do you like this one better?"

"I love it," declares Mummy. "It's a splendid limerick."

Two neighbours, the Brown brothers, are hired to trench out a basement for our new home. Tom handles a team of heavy horses, while Fred manoeuvres the fresno, which is a large scoop that bites chunks of earth and carries them from an ever-deepening hole. Fred tips the fresno on a pile of clay that gets higher with each load. On and on. Then the workers build a frame and fill it with hand-mixed cement from sand and cement mix. Round and round, like a giant's churn. Slosh. They leave openings in the concrete for windows, two on each side of the foundation. "I'll not have my children trapped in a burning house," declares Mummy. "I'm fire-conscious after losing our first home." She worries over the safety of us kids.

During coffee breaks with the men, she insists that Noël and I remain in the cabin, which surprises me. We're usually banished to the barn when guests arrive. Now Mummy instructs us to sit on the bunk like sparrows learning to fly and munch our snacks.

Fred is very friendly and winks at Mummy like a chicken with pinkeye. She ignores him and talks to Tom. She hurries through coffee and scoots them out.

Noël stays behind. "Why do we call them brown broth-ers? They're black."

Mummy laughs. "It's just their name, sweetheart."

Fred is the darker of the two. He is muscular and lonely, too, ever since his wife left him. He longs for some-one to cook his meals, and he watches Mummy hopefully.

Tom is more shy. His belly hangs over his belt, and his pants are suspended from narrow hips, giving him a top-heavy appearance.

Mummy clears the table, thankful the men are back at work. Phew. The cabin reeks of sweat.

I hear the men talking as they hitch up the team. "A good woman. Good little mother," Tom says. "Works too hard though. Never seen anything like it. Farms like a man." He shakes his head in admiration.

"Training her kids good, too. Mannerly. Proper. Real pleasure to work for a lady like Mrs. Ray."

Such comments spread through the neighbourhood. Rays are getting a new house at last; they've been in that shack for three years now.

Mummy hoards the service allowance, and later that spring invites a local carpenter to the cabin for an interview. He arrives early one morning, before Noël and I are up. We lie quietly on the bunk, listening as she outlines her contract plan with Mr. Williams.

"I'd like a large frame house built on our basement foun-dation, with upstairs bedrooms. Would you be willing to build in instalments? I don't want to go into debt. So you would build only what I can afford. Then there will be a delay until I save more allowance from my husband. The work will be interrupted, although the contract is a huge undertaking. Would you be will-ing to build under these conditions?"

While Mr. Williams rolls himself a cigarette, deep in

thought, I glance at the cabin wall near my head where a large bedbug marches along. I remember Mummy's instructions. Capturing the bedbug alive between my thumb and finger, I make not a single smear on the wall. I grasp it, scramble down off the bunk and stand on the table top beside Mr. Williams' half-filled coffee cup. Much to his astonishment, I step over his ashtray onto the empty chair, and then down to the floor. I fling the bedbug directly onto the hot stove and watch with satisfaction as it sizzles and scorches.

Whap! A blow to the side of my head makes me fear it will roll across the floor. I shield my ear and turn questioning eyes toward my mother. She's furious, eyes blazing.

"Get to bed!" She grabs me, flings me onto the bunk so hard that I hit the back wall and lie stunned. Why did Mummy hit me? I followed instructions exactly. Yet Mummy is angry with me. It seems to me that rules change unexpectedly.

Later, after Mr. Williams has agreed to build the new house and gone, Mummy lectures me. "When company is present, you must never carry a bedbug on display, because then *everyone will know* that we have bugs."

Now I understand and realize that she'd feel mortified by everyone's knowing.

We love to play Concert in the henhouse. "Let's pull out the roosts to make a stage since this raised floor can be our platform. I'll operate the curtain," Douglas organizes. He refers to a canvas roll above the roosting stall to protect the fowl from fierce cold.

"Me first." Noël scrambles up and stands amid droppings on the platform, singing:

> *I'm a little teapot, short and stout.*
> *Here is my handle. Here is my spout.*

When I start to steam up, hear me shout.
Tip me over. And pour me out.

She acts it out, bends dangerously to one side, then bows to her audience. Douglas lowers the curtain with a flourish, showering lime-dust and chicken feathers that choke us. It's a glorious concert.

"Guess what," exclaims Mummy as we return to the cabin. "Another Jacqui Box. Grandpapa brought it home in the wagon. Hurry with chores so we can open it together." We tear into our tasks, all the while thinking of the cardboard carton from Jacqui, a distant relative who has shipped it from Edmonton. What an assortment of second-hand clothing for Mummy to convert into useful garments for us. She sorts them; one pile for redesigning and one for useless or outlandish items.

"I can't imagine a single thing I'd make from these." She flings some into the empty box, saying, "Douglas, take this box to the junk granary, please. You little people may use them for dress-up."

What wonderful fashion parades. Noël and I enjoy carefree hours dressing in fancy clothes while dust moats float above our heads. The junk granary is so named because the building is stuffed with supplies that won't fit in the crowded cabin.

"Girls," calls Mummy from the cabin door. "I see the lamb's quarters are ready. Each take a big bucket and pick a pailful. Shake the dirt off the roots and don't pick any with blossoms. We'll have a real feast tonight."

"Ugh!" I say. "We have to pick pigweed. Only Mummy calls it lamb's quarters. Let's look along the south line fence in the old pigpen. It's about four inches tall there." We yank handfuls of the leafy weeds, mindful to shake off the soil. In no time, our buckets are full. Ruby rinses each plant and boils a mess in the largest canning kettle. It shrinks as it cooks. Salted and served with a dash of vinegar these first fresh greens replenish the iron we lack from our diet of dried staples—prunes, figs and beans.

"Guess what?" Douglas comes from morning chores. "The cow calved. A black heifer. Nice and strong. Annette has lots of milk, too.

"Oh, great," exclaims Mummy. "You can pop in after school to tell Granddad. He'll be happy to get milk from us again."

Mummy and I visit Nan. I sit with them and drink my milk while they have tea. "Ardith seems serious and withdrawn," says Nan. "I wonder why?"

"Oh, I'm not surprised," Mummy says. "It's the war. Everyone is anxious these days. She hears about our neighbours getting those dreaded telegrams that start off 'regret to inform you' or 'missing in action.' She takes it all to heart and gets anxious. I'm anxious too … anxious to get my family out of that cabin."

The two women sit in silence, slowly draining their cups.

"Will heard from Lawrence. It's a girl. They named her Aster Mary. Poor wee tyke was born during a raid. Apparently that baby sleeps in the bureau drawer, so it can be shut if there's another raid. That's no life for a child. I'm so thankful our children are safe from harm."

Nan nods agreement.

"Well, I must fly. Mr. Williams will be back tomorrow to work on the house. Thanks for the tea, Mama."

As we hurry home, she says, "Imagine my new niece sleeping in a drawer for safety. Poor little tyke."

Mummy talks with Mr. Williams, careful to keep Noël and me always with her. "I have to get these children into a proper home. They're too cramped in here. Douglas is still sleeping in a crib at nine years of age. The girls need privacy. And I'm afraid Will may never come back from that war. I seldom hear from him."

Mr. Williams scratches his hair, pushing his cap above one ear. It sounds like a rasp against pine wood. He is lank and lean; he smokes constantly and coughs continuously. But he's a careful and exacting carpenter.

"Yes, I know," he says. "I'll hurry all I can."

Mr. Williams builds a large framework with a high gable roof. He completely encloses the building like a shell with no windows or doors. It looks rather peculiar to the neighbours, but Mummy has her savings plan in mind. As money trickles in, Mr. Williams frames in a door and hangs the door in place. Later he returns to cut a window space, frame it and place a shiny glass window into the opening. Gradually, the structure transforms into a house. Our neighbours nod in approval. "Edith Ray is pretty smart. By building a shell with no openings, no moisture gets in to warp the lumber. That house is nice and straight. And *big*."

Mummy warns, "Now don't you little people bother Mr. Williams while he's building. He's here to work, not to chat with you. You keep strictly away."

She has our safety in mind—can't be too careful. "All these strange men," she tells Granddad. "I must watch my children."

We're obedient. We wait until Mr. Williams leaves before we collect small bits of discarded boards. We pile fine, dry wood for kindling. Doug claims any pieces he can use to design into rifles, pistols, tanks, airplanes and battleships. These ingenious inventions he scales to size. Toiling in Grandpapa's shop, he and I use the vice, rasps and saws. I'm most impressed with the battleships that have layers of swivel turrets and nails slanted as guns along each side. "Come, Doug," I cry. "Let's try them in the cistern." They float majestically, towed by twine nailed to the prow. They fire from the murky water whenever I fling enemy aircraft overhead. The doomed airplanes make satisfying splashes as they're shot down (and later retrieved) from the cistern.

Doug makes long wooden rifles with tiny nail sights and sharp bayonets. I braid binder-twine shoulder straps. Thus armed, we three set off to skirmish in the straw stack.

"This is my war zone," I announce and dramatically swing my bayonet in a wide arc around me. Unfortunately, Noël's legs are within the radius, and to my horror, I slash them both. Noël runs screeching to the cabin, blood streaming down her legs. We follow fearfully. What will Mummy say?

Mummy is too busy doctoring Noël to speak. I suffer in silence until she's put to bed. Then Mummy says, "Go fetch a willow switch."

I know what that means. I'm to be whipped with the switch of my choice. In vain I protest, "I didn't mean to hurt Noël. I didn't even know the gun would reach that far. I was just swinging it."

"You were cruel to your baby sister," retorts Mummy. "I'm going to show you how it feels when someone bigger than yourself hurts you. Now go get a willow switch."

I select a small willow twig and return to the cabin, but Mummy glances scornfully at the switch.

"Too small," she sneers. "Go and get a bigger one." I set off again. I'll choose a big club. I don't care if Mummy beats me to death. She never believes me anyhow.

Mummy grabs the switch and thrashes me. "I'll teach you to be more careful with sticks." Five. Six. "Don't do that again."

I cuddle Noël on the bunk, weeping. Douglas sympathizes. "I know you didn't mean to hurt Noël," he whispers. "I'm so sorry, Ardith."

I find comfort from his words. Douglas cares about me. No one else does.

That night, I have horrendous technicolour dreams of being beaten to death. I wet the bed. My screams waken everyone.

"I'm sorry," I wail. "I didn't mean to be bad to Noël. Now I'm really bad. I wet the bed." I burst into a frenzy of grief and guilt. Mummy tries to comfort me.

Since there's no radio in the cabin, Mummy takes time from her field work next morning to visit Nan, taking me along. Over coffee, we listen to *The Happy Gang* and Mummy tells the events of the previous evening, and of our interrupted sleep.

"I just don't seem to be able to handle the children," Mummy says. "What do you think I should do, Mama?" Nan sits quietly thoughtful.

"Sing," she says suddenly.

"What?" asks Mummy. "This isn't the solution I expect. I remember you and I often sang hymns together, in harmony, but how does that apply to my present problem?"

"Yes, sing," repeats Nan. "If the children sing together, they won't quarrel. Try to have them sing as they work, as well as at church and in the evening. We'll have sing-songs here, too. I'll have Papa tune up his fiddle and teach them the old ballads. We've been entirely too serious lately. Just because we're worried over the war is no reason to take the joy of life from the children. Let's all sing more."

Mummy leads me home. "Nan has a good idea. We'll sing." And sing we do. Inspired by a meadow alive with flowers, we sing as we fetch the cows:

Who'll buy my lavender?
Fresh gathered lavender.
Lavender. Three bunches.
A penny. Come buy.

We sing as we wash dishes:

Faintly as tolls the evening chime
Our voices keep tune and our oars keep time.

It seems to hurry the chore, although we hate doing dishes.
We sing as we walk to town to check the mail for a letter
from Daddy,

Pack up your troubles in your old kit bag
And smile, smile, smile,

marching in time to our own voices along the wooded trail.
We sing as we pick berries:

And as she passed along the road
The weather hot and dry.
She rested on a grassy slope
And her true love came riding by.

I secretly hope a handsome prince will pass along the
road where we're picking.

We sing as we do chores around the yard:

Jimmy crack corn and I don't care.
Jimmy crack corn and I don't care.
Jimmy crack corn and I don't care ...
My master's gone away.

133

We're thinking of Daddy gone away to war.

Soon we learn to sing in harmony. I follow Mummy's rich alto voice; the others sing melody.

Grandpapa does his part. He rosins up the old bow every Friday evening after the six o'clock CBC news. To lively fiddle music, we sing until hoarse. Grandpapa plays jigs and reels, highland fling, schottische, hornpipe, sword dance, waltz, polka. We dance them all. Lively times. Nan's eyes are soft and warm as cinnamon on a fresh bun. Mummy puffs like a turkey with heatstroke. Grandpapa's mouth is stern, but his eyes twinkle with wrinkled creases at the corners. Jip yowls in protest because the high notes hurt her ears, but that adds to the merriment.

The musical training is good for us. At musical festivals, where competitions are held between schools in the municipality, we kids excel in solo, duets, drama and dance. I hold the alto part in the school choir.

"Oh, Mama," exclaims Mummy. "Things are going more smoothly now. Singing is a wonderful idea. The children seldom quarrel; they are so busy learning new tunes. It will be grand when the house is finished and we can get my piano back from the blacksmith. So kind of him to store it after our fire. But I miss it so. Then my children can take music lessons. Things are working out splendidly."

TWENTY

One Shot Too Many

Grandpapa and Jip on stoneboat. 1945.

Douglas is constantly practising his shooting skills. He aims his homemade lumber rifle and bull's-eyes his targets with skill. Every evening after chores he spends a while with that gun.

"Mummy, Grandpapa is going to teach me how to shoot," cries Douglas. "He says to come over on Saturday and he'll have Jip flush some rabbits." My brother practises even more, determined to show Grandpapa what a fine shot he is.

"Good luck, son," calls Mummy, as he leaves that Saturday. "Rabbit stew will certainly be a welcome change from salt pork." I wait impatiently for Doug's return.

Much later, a dejected boy drags in to the cabin and sits heavily on a chair. Red-rimmed eyes are magnified through his thick glasses lenses. He looks awful.

"Douglas, dear, what happened?" demands Mummy.

"I shot Jip." Doug puts his head on the table and sobs.

"Oh, no. How?" Quiet in the cabin.

"I had the gun. We sent Jip around the bluff to flush the rabbits. I held the gun to my eye … all ready, and I saw a blur of brown, aimed … shot at it. Grandpapa shouted. But it was too late. Jip … was coming out of the bushes. I killed her. Aw, Mummy … I killed poor Jip."

I grip Noël. Mummy hugs her heartbroken son. What could she say?

"Aw, Grandpapa cried. I didn't know that big men cry." Doug goes over and over the whole thing, punishing himself.

"I killed poor Jip," he repeats, "the best little collie Grandpapa ever had. And I loved her, too. I just wanted to prove what a great shot I am. And Grandpapa trusted me with his rifle. But I didn't wait—I couldn't wait. I was so cocksure I could hit those rabbits. I didn't even look carefully. Just a sudden brown blur and BLAM! I shot her! When Grandpapa gathered her in his arms and cried, I felt sick—hopeless. I wish I'd never gone shooting. Killing something feels terrible! Awful! I'll never kill anything again!"

I hug him. He's disconsolate. I understand how he feels. Boys have deep feelings; even Grandpapa cried. Words wouldn't console poor Douglas.

We insist on a funeral for Jip. Grandpapa wisely asks Douglas to dig the grave, understanding his need to work it out physically. We gather solemnly in the pet cemetery, where wooden crosses mark graves of former pets.

Ruby reads a prayer. My throat is swollen, like stones choking me, so that I can scarcely say my limerick made in Jippy's memory:

There once was a collie named Jip
She was brown with white spots on her hip.
She was Grandpapa's friend
But she met a sad end
And Doug never will get over it.

Granddad stays to help Grandpapa and Douglas cover the little body, shrouded in a sugar sack. Granddad's dog, Sandy, watches sorrowfully. We girls leave to tell Nan and Mummy about the funeral. Lunch is ready at Nan's for everyone.

But my brother doesn't eat anything; he disappears. I find him at work in Grandpapa's shop. His wooden rifle is in the vice, and he's nailing my rifle across it.

"What is it?" I whisper.

"A cross for Jippy's grave," he says bitterly. "I'll never play war again! Killing something gives a terrible feeling. An awful feeling!" I walk with my brother to the pet cemetery. He pounds the rifle butt, driving the barrel deep into the freshly dug clay. "Sorry, Jippy," he murmurs. "I'll never kill again!"

Doug viciously attacks the manure pile behind the henhouse. Hauling it on the stoneboat, he spreads it on the garden by dragging the stoneboat upside down, to crosshatch the patch like a dingy quilt. Grandpapa cultivates it, ready for planting. When the leaves of the Balm of Gilead are the size of a squirrel's ear, it will be planting time.

TWENTY-ONE

Spring on the Farm

"Run and pull the rhubarb, girls," says Mummy. "We'll have fresh fruit at last." We walk through the moist garden to a large clump of heavy leaves, grasp each firmly, pull the juicy red stalks and break off the leaves.

"These leaves are poisonous. Isn't that strange? We can eat the stem but not the leaves." I munch on a stalk as tart juice stains my chin.

"Sour!" Noël giggles at my wry face. We gather an arm load and take it to the cabin.

Our evening meal is simple. Mummy saves the last few potatoes for seed, but luckily the hens are laying again, so the cast-iron frying pan is full of scrambled eggs. I make toast by placing two slices of bread into a folding wire rack shut by a loop over the long handles. Laying the rack on the range, I keep the handles over the edge so I can turn the toaster when the down side browns. There's rich butter to slather on cornmeal bread and, for dessert, blancmange pudding with warm rhubarb sauce.

The hens are laying so well now that we have eggs for sale. Mummy warns me not to break them as she packs two pails full.

I deliver the fresh eggs to town in the syrup pails, which I carry carefully from door to door. One dozen for Mrs. Ross and one dozen for Mrs. Blake. I bring the coins home and stash them in the cracked teapot.

Granddad gets a postcard from Aunt Martha, from London, England. I stare at the beautiful card—a fairyland with thatched-roof cottages, rolling fields and twisting hedgerows. "Uncle Lawrence is so far away."

Our whole family becomes very patriotic. War news is extremely important in our lives. Nan knits "for the troops." Her skilful fingers turn out a staggering quantity of socks and mittens, which she feels are contributions to "the cause." The garments are sent to the Red Cross.

Nan is totally housebound, her balance so poor that she can no longer trust herself on the doorstep, nor to the privy. She keeps a high chamber pot in her bedroom. Mummy tries to have one of us kids stay with Nan continuously, and take turns entertaining her. We read while she knits, and Nan listens so attentively that I don't realize she has heard the stories before, first from Ruby and then from Douglas. If I falter in my story, I spell out the word and Nan pronounces it. Such extra practice in oral reading helps all of us become fluent, expressive readers. When Noël and I go home, Ruby comes to spend the evenings. She's Nan's constant companion.

School gets even more interesting to me when Mrs. Shaw, a patriotic neighbour with three sons in the service, visits our classroom and offers one war savings stamp for each poem a student composes.

Wonderful incentive for me! I make up verses until I earn a whole book of stamps. Enough to buy a war bond. Nan quietly and patiently advises and encourages my poetic efforts.

Although we live on a farm, we are never allowed to say "bull" or "boar." We're taught to say "the animal." To save confusion, each animal is named. Grandpapa's bull is Bunty, while the boar is known as Buffy. We have no knowledge of each animal's use for breeding.

Whenever a neighbour lady comes puffing up the lane, half dragged by a wild-eyed cow, Grandpapa hastily takes the cow to the barn "for a rest," while Nan puts the kettle on to serve the unexpected guest a refreshing cup of tea. I'm sometimes invited to this tea party. If Nan has no cake, she serves baking powder biscuits quickly stirred up as she raises the oven temperature by feeding the fire dry kindling. Or if the day is stifling hot, Nan serves soda crackers with jelly.

"Grandpapa," I ask after he leads a visiting cow to the owner and they are quietly leaving, "Why do those ladies always bring a cow when they come to tea with Nan?"

Grandpapa just chuckles as he stashes the coins the lady has given him into his worn leather pouch. "Oh," he says evasively, "I guess her cow gets lonely for company just like your Mummy gets lonely with Daddy away in the war. And the ladies enjoy a visit with your Nan."

The sky turns murky and dim as though it were under water, and great gusts of wind blow the grass flat.

"Oh dear! It looks like rain!" Mummy worries. "You girls scurry out and pick the green beans before they get wet or they'll mould. I did the yellow beans yesterday. Take the big pail and run, now."

"I don't mind pulling beans when it's so cool," I announce as Noël and I work our way along the row.

"I like the heat better than this wind," Noël says. "Wind gives me a headache."

"Let's get these beans done before it gets any worse." I pick faster.

We have our bucket more than half full when the first few drops begin to fall. "That's all," Noël calls. "Let's run in."

"Oh, dear," says Mummy. "Is it raining already? I wanted you to run down to Granddad's to get a small bucket of honey, Ardith. I still have a few raspberries to can, and I'm completely out of sugar. I've used our total sugar ration."

"I can fetch the honey. A little rain won't hurt me."

"That's my good girl," smiles Mummy. "Hurry back so I

can do up the berries. They're getting soft."

It is raining harder but no moisture is as yet dripping through the thick evergreens along the path. Even the trees seem to stand closer together to shelter me. So I scurry along, comfortable and dry. But when I reach the range line, the rain pelts down and the wind is stronger.

I run up Granddad's walk and call, "Are you home, Granddad? Mummy needs a bucket of honey right away. She's canning raspberries."

"Cain't you stay, Child, for a while?"

"Not today, Granddad. I've got to get straight home."

"Honey for my honey, then." He hands me a heavy bucket.

By the time I reach our lane, I'm sodden and the skyline has completely disappeared. I feel bedraggled. I begin punching my left hand into my right, like a pestle and mortar, to relieve the pain of the heavy pail which I had to put down to stretch my fingers.

I grab it again and hurry home. "Oh, Ardith, you're drenched. Slip off your clothes and slide into bed."

I'm lulled to sleep by the patter of raindrops on the roof and the bubbling sounds from the canner.

By morning, there is a lull in the rain and the wind drops. The morning light glows and birds begin a deafening clamour. I feel eager to get outdoors. The cabin, which had seemed so cosy last night, now feels stuffy. I scramble into my clothing and find my high-topped boots. I tug open the rain-swollen door and step into a freshly washed world.

I notice that the flowers beside the walk are battered into the mud by the force of the storm. But the soil has the earthy smell of newly washed loam. Long pink earthworms stretch across the flagstones and by noon the sun has dried the mud.

"Would you girls please find some tender dandelion leaves for salad?" Mummy asks. "I'm going to cream them with onions. We have only a few left. Might as well use them up. The chives are coming, and winter onions too, so we'll have more onions soon."

The steaming slough hums with mosquitoes. I can hear the argumentative babble of the pair of mallard ducks who choose to nest on that small mound of grass in the middle of the dark murky water.

"I'm catching polliwogs." I dip my old jam tin into the slough. "Look at these treasures, Noël."

We can scarcely see the tadpoles in the tin. "Mummy, can we have a big clean jar for our pets? Please?"

Many interesting creatures show through the clear glass jar. "I'll change this water every day. Guess what those tadpoles will change into—frogs. Isn't that wonderful, Noël?"

I love the wildflowers in the meadow. First comes a profusion of dandelions. We braid crowns and necklaces from their milky stems. Next I pick the delicate buttercups, which look elegant in Mummy's orange vase. White daisies change the meadow into a field of snow, and give me a chance to check if "he loves me" as I pluck the petals. But the wildflower I admire the most is the regal Scotch thistle with its crimson-purple blossoms—much too thorny to pick, but beautiful to behold.

I lie in the tansy patch, inhaling the pungent odour. Rows of blueberry cream-puff clouds float on a clear cellophane sky high above my head.

School is almost over and Sunday school is finished for the summer. I have plenty of free time to dream, time to pretend and time to grow.

TWENTY-TWO

School's Out

June has ended. School is out.
And I passed into Grade 3.
I'm as happy as can be.
I just want to laugh and shout.
I won best attendance prize,
Didn't miss a single day.
Excellent, my teacher says
Won't my mother be surprised?

I go skipping home with *Rebecca of Sunnybrook Farm*, my attendance prize, under my arm, and my report card swinging—it's good, too, except for printing. Mummy will be proud.

"All three children have wonderful report cards," Mummy reports to Nan. Proud as a broody hen with her hatch of chickies. "And this fall Noël starts school. All my children in school. That will seem strange," she smiles. "I must get a letter off to the broadcasting studio."

A wonderful children's program on the radio provides relief from frightening war broadcasts. *The Farmer* advertises Sunny Boy Cereal, which he claims is the best. I hate our homemade Sunny Boy, which Grandpapa grinds from crushed wheat, fistfuls of flaxseed, buckwheat and bindweed, and stores in a sugar sack. Served with honey, it sticks in my craw till noon, like glue in my belly. Thick enough to stop a bullet.

But I forgive *The Farmer* since he has supernatural knowledge about when birthdays are and where birthday presents are hidden, announcing it to the world. He blares out of the radio the names of those important children who have a birthday.

My birthday has come at last. We'll celebrate at Nan's where there's more space, and Nan can join in. Best of all, there's a radio there. *The Farmer* might know about my gift, Mummy hints. I'm feverish with anticipation. I skip ahead to Nan's, neat pigtails flying, and my pleated skirt billowing. My family follow; the hot dry grass crackles underfoot. Ruby has made a layer cake, stuck together with lemon pudding with slathers of rich brown icing. A squiggly 8 in green is surrounded by candles like posts along a fence line. "One, two, three, four, five, six, seven, eight," I check. Nan's camera catches me making my silent wish. I wish my freckles would disappear. Won't come true if anyone hears. Puff! The smoke chokes Nan. I neatly lay the slices onto matching china plates, mindful of the good linen tea cloth. Ladies first: Nan, Mummy. Oh, adults first: Grandpapa. Now children: Ruby, Noël, Douglas, me last. I flourish my knife, knowing I have the correct order. Mummy nods approval. Everyone nibbles while we listen intently to *The Farmer*. "Happy eighth birthday, Ardith Ray. You will find your presents in Nan's wood box."

I rush to the kitchen. Sure enough. Neatly wrapped packages in brown paper are tied with yellow yarn. The biggest first. A warm, soft green sweater from Nan.

"Thank you, so much." As I kiss the wrinkled cheeks, I'm careful not to bump Nan's boot, which sticks stiffly from folds of her long lavender dress.

A book from Mummy, *Anne of Green Gables*. "Oh, thank you, Mummy. I'll read this to Nan."

It's a perfect day for me. I feel lavished with love.

July brings hot, hazy days, perfect haying weather. Grandpapa cuts the hay, and swaths like serpents in the sunlight wait to be coiled with his pitchfork into loose haycocks, and then forked onto the hay rack as Doug drives the team. Ruby flattens, levels and packs the load while Noël and I stay in the loft.

The sun burns my skin and Noël is too small to work in the field. It's cool for us in the loft. Our job is to move hay back, away from the door. More arriving! Mounds of sweet, dry hay. The sharp ends poke my buttocks. My face gets red as turkey wattles from the exertion.

"Come with me," urges Granddad. "I'll show you a big patch of saskatoons. Then you kin bring the girls to help pick them. Surprise for yer Mom."

I love to walk with Granddad. He strolls, rolls from side to side on heavy legs. Then he halts, puts his thumb against his nose, leans over and blows. *Honk.* Sounds like a wild grey goose flushed from a pond, and makes an arc of shiny mucus like a silvery rainbow. Next, the other nostril. Commences walking, as though nothing has happened. I marvel at how far he shoots his snot. I secretly practise, but never master the knack.

Later, I lead the girls to the patch, armed with berry pails, straw hats, water bottle and long sleeves. We pick saskatoons until our pails are full. Mummy cans the fruit with rhubarb.

"That's wonderful, Ardith. Ask Granddad if he knows of any pin-cherry patches. And keep your eyes out for chokecherries ripening," instructs Mummy. "We'll try and keep up with our raspberries. You girls must help pick. We have so many that Ardith can peddle a few pails in town."

TWENTY-THREE

Stormy Adventures

*Ardith and Noël run away from home
riding Nipper. 1945.*

One morning we have a wonderful surprise. Grandpapa arrives in our yard with a pony. She's half the height of his workhorses, round and sleek. She's bay with black legs, mane and tail, white socks and markings on her forehead.

"She has very intelligent eyes," reports Grandpapa. "But she nips if you don't get on her back quickly."

"Let's call her Nipper," cries Noël. We all laugh, but the name sticks.

We love that little horse, and she thrives on our attention. She's so gentle that she waits whenever we fall off her back. At first we fall a lot.

Mummy worries about our safety. "No saddle, please, Papa. I don't want my children dragged by a stirrup. They can ride bareback. The worst that can happen is a fall. And Nipper's not tall. Now, listen, you little people. Don't ever, *ever*, tie yourself to the pony. Hold the reins loosely in your hand. *Never, ever*, tie yourself to an animal. Do you understand?" Of course, we do. I'd hate to be dragged.

I enjoy berry picking. Granddad gives me a quarter for a pailful of fresh saskatoons. I show Noël. "Let's sneak downtown and buy ice-cream cones," I say daringly. "No one will see us."

The cones seem more delicious because we're being sneaky. We head straight home from town, but Grandpapa, noticing us crossing the field, mentions it to Mummy.

"Girls, were you in town today?"

"Yes, Mummy," we answer meekly.

"Did you ask permission?"

"No, Mummy."

"Go fetch a switch each."

I eye Noël, knowing it's my fault that we're disobedient. She wouldn't have gone alone. It was my money and my fault.

I watch my little sister get thrashed and feel sorry. Sorry for myself as well. I'm always bad. I must be flawed.

Mummy thrashes me soundly. "Never go to a strange place without permission. Terrible things can happen to you."

Noël and I cry and huddle on the bunk. Finally we fall asleep, but a daring plan forms in my mind after a scary night with bad dreams.

"Noël, let's run away from home," I say sadly. "Mummy doesn't love us. We'll take Nipper and ride far, far away. To a better land."

"All right," agrees Noël. "What shall we take?"

"I'm going to pack my dolly, teddy bear and all my books." I stuff my treasures into a gunny sack and hold the neck open for Noël's. "What are you taking?"

"I guess I'll take my dolly. And my kitty. I don't need much," says Noël carelessly, and adds her stuffed dolly to the pile. "Here, kitty, kitty, kitty." She captures Joseph, who winks at us with conspiring yellow eyes.

I bridle Nipper, boost Noël on, hand her the cat and the sack and climb in front to hold the reins. It's difficult to balance the sack across Nipper's sleek neck. But the ride is quite enjoyable. Jogging along, we feel defiant, daring. Several miles later, the pleasure pales. The bulges and bumps in the bag annoy the pony. Constant motion makes the bag slide first to one side, then the other. I haul it straight and hold both reins while I entertain Noël, who's having her own problems. Her cat has never ridden horseback and begins to protest. The squalls spook the pony. She bolts down the road. Books drop. To control the horse, I have to drop the bag, which spooks Nipper more. We have a rough ride as the frantic cat claws along our legs and Nipper's back. Finally I manage to stop the pony on the hill at Four-Mile Corner.

"I guess we'll have to go back for the sack," I say.

"I think so," agrees Noël. We silently return. Thinking deep thoughts.

"Looks like rain," Noël remarks hopefully.

I glance at the sky. "Yes, doesn't it?"

In fact, it does look like it'll rain. Sullen grey clouds scud along the horizon. The humidity is high, and grasshoppers rasp like out-of-tune fiddlers. The leaves of the quivering aspen hang point down, twist, shiver and rustle.

The sack lies where we dropped it, a pile of hemp like a huge ant hill. I slide off the pony and pass Noël the sack. I walk and lead Nipper, as I gather books at intervals along the road.

"I guess that's everything," I announce. "Shall we go?"

"Oh, let's go home," begs Noël. "Running away is no fun."

"Well," I say practically, "if we hurry, we'll get back before Mummy comes in for supper and no one will notice. It could be just our secret. Okay, Noël?"

By the time we turn Nipper into the pasture, the sky is leaden. By evening a steady drizzle develops, and during the night, it begins to pour. I lie on the bunk and listen to the drumming on the roof like wagon wheels that rumble across a bridge. Thankful to escape the downpour. Glad to be home, safe, warm and dry. Slashes of lightning tear the night with brilliant light. Sudden bursts of thunder threaten to deafen me. I burrow into the old quilt, feeling damp and chilly.

It rains for three days and nights. The soil around our step is sodden; the barnyard sloppy. The drooping hens stop laying and stand bedraggled on their roosts to dodge leaks in the roof. The pigs are in their glory, up to their haunches in muck. Douglas stumps through the yard in high-topped rubber boots to do chores. We little girls play with paper dolls on the bunk. Mummy allows us to use her sewing shears and gives us an outdated Eaton's catalogue to cut out figures for our pretend families. Ruby uses a length of heavy grey building paper from the new house to make folders for each of us girls. The folder has separate pockets for each character. We trim a new outfit and slide it into that character's file. This job entertains us for hours.

Mummy sews below us, though the light is dim in the cabin. The wet wood burns poorly, making puffs of black smoke that choke us on the bunk. The fire won't draw well since the stovepipe is damp. Smelly sodden socks and underwear dry above the stove on a short clothesline.

Doug, drenched from the driving rain, wrings his toque over the basin; discoloured drops spatter a pattern on the enamel pan. His pant legs are spattered with mud. He rests on his hunkers to avoid soiling a chair while he warms his hands. I'm thankful to him for doing my chores too.

The rain continues all week. Gullies of water gush along the roadside. The wooden culvert can't contain the torrent; overflows form bog holes at the sides of the road. The bullocks stand with rears toward the storm, waiting for better weather.

Finally the sun reappears as grey clouds curl and die. Mummy longs to fetch the mail, to get a letter from Daddy. "I just have to get out of this cabin, away from you children, away from the noises and the smells," she says. "It's wonderfully fresh outdoors after the drenching rain."

Shaking a bucket of oats, she coaxes Nipper from the sodden pasture. The pony comes willingly to munch her treat as Mummy slips on the bridle. She sets off to town splashing through puddles.

We watch Mummy leave on the pony. We understand that she is desperate to get away by herself for a while.

When they come splashing back up the lane, we can see that Mummy is vexed with Nipper. She yanks off the bridle and turns the pony to pasture. Still angry, she whips up pancakes for supper. Too muddy to dig vegetables today. She slaps the batter onto the hot cast-iron pan. I watch Mummy sideways as I set out the plates. Everyone eats in silence, afraid to talk. Mummy's face twitches faster than usual. Finally Doug ventures, "What happened, Mom?"

"Oh, that stubborn Nipper," she bursts out. "I whipped her with the reins but she absolutely refused to go into the water at this end of the bridge. Wouldn't budge at all. Stubborn mule!" Mummy sputters and slaps more hot cakes onto our plates. "You little people are spoiling that pony. She's good for nothing!"

We finish our hot cakes and hurry through the dishes, then sidle out the door. It's good to be in the fresh air, away from Mummy's wrath. We plod around the yard, poking long sticks into puddles to measure their depth. When we figure Mummy has cooled off, we return to the cabin.

"Come, sit down," Mummy says. "I must explain to you what happened this afternoon so you'll understand why I was so cross."

As we settled ourselves, Mummy begins her story: "I noticed the damage to bushes along the path. The broken limbs and bent trunks told of the force of the storm. Nipper plodded on. But when we neared the river, she refused to wade into a huge pool that overflowed the road along the end of the bridge. I urged her by kicking her fat sides but Nipper just went around in circles. She absolutely refused to enter that water. That made me furious. I glanced at the river. What a torrent! Swirling murky water carrying debris of all descriptions downstream, fallen trees with huge roots turning slowly in the torrent, fence posts, chunks of boards, logs and even drowned and bloated animals were floating downstream. I felt defeated and headed Nipper home. But I was mad."

A couple of days later, Grandpapa arrives with news. "The river floodwater has receded, but the road has been totally washed out at this end of the bridge. The current washed the whole grade away. It's impossible to get to town except by walking the river bank all the way to the trestle and crossing the river there. Men are hard at it. So you see," he finishes kindly, looking at our mother, "that pony saved your life, Edith. If you had forced her into that wash-out, you'd have both been swept away in the floodwaters."

"Oh, Papa!" murmurs Mummy. "To think that I whipped that faithful little beast." She rushes out of the cabin. We start to follow.

"Stay," says Grandpapa. "Only Ardith may go along." Mummy is with Nipper. She hugs the pony and talks earnestly to her. "Thank you, Nipper, for being so wise. And thank God for providing our family with such a beast." Mummy sees me standing there and explains, "Nipper's sixth sense saved my life."

More news of the flood trickles in. The McDonald family had to flee the floodwaters, which rose two feet in depth in their home. Water had poured in their west windows and out the east.

Now the family is home again, scraping the silt from the walls and floor with hoes. Their dugout basement is filled with water, and sealers of canned food float around. When I visit Lizzy, Mrs. McDonald serves a potluck supper. She kneels on the floor at the open trapdoor, stirs the water gently with her broom, and as the sealers float past, she captures one.

"Potluck," she laughs. I'm amazed that Mrs. McDonald can joke despite their calamity.

TWENTY-FOUR

Growing Things

Granddad checks his bee supers. 1944

The summer grows humid, the air hot and gluey. Heat waves rise in wavy lines. My dress clings to my sweaty back.

Weeding the garden is tedious. Mummy has a rule—one row every day. Those rows seem never-ending. I try every excuse to avoid the job. Yet I enjoy the look of our garden: green lettuce; round, red radishes that mark the carrot rows; ferny, delicate carrot tops that will be lost in weeds if not for the radishes. It's important to weed the carrots before we pull the radishes—painstaking work. Usually Ruby gets stuck with that job.

Leafy Swiss chard is an early vegetable. String beans, peas and beets grow more slowly. We love to sneak into the garden and eat the juicy raw peas. Mummy turns a blind eye; she knows peas are good for us, cooked or raw.

Douglas searches for tatties. He feels under each plant, carefully pulling the largest potatoes without disturbing the roots. The plant will grow more potatoes. Mummy cooks delicious mealy spuds in a cream sauce. No more macaroni. The potatoes are ready.

"Girls, the currants are ripe. Can you pick the black ones first? They're starting to drop. You'll have to get the red ones tomorrow. I'm afraid the white ones are too wormy to bother with," Mummy says. Thank goodness for worms! I breathe a sigh of relief. I know it will be gooseberries next.

It's more fun to pick in the woods than in the garden. A few days later, Noël and I set off for high-bush cranberries. There are plenty in the woods, and Granddad has pointed out a patch to me. With buckets tied on our belts, and wearing wide-brimmed straw hats to prevent heat stroke, we go to Granddad's woods.

"I hate picking here," Noël complains. "The rose bushes are scratching me."

"Just keep me company, then," I tell my little sister. "Look at those clusters. I can pull handfuls at a time. I'll fill both pails easily. But stay with me, Noël."

"Oh, I'll pick, too."

We work quietly. After a while, we hear the bushes crash behind us. Here comes old Sandy, I think. He must have heard us and is coming to see me. But no dog arrives.

The crashing grows louder, with grunts and licking sounds. Whatever can it be? We stop picking. Our runners seem rooted to the ground. The noise gets louder. Suddenly we glimpse a shiny snout, beady brown eyes and little pointed ears, high above our heads. An old black bear stands on her hind legs, wrapping clusters of berries with her tongue and swallowing greedily. The bear seems unconcerned about us.

"Noël," I instruct softly. "Walk backward slowly."

Noël does. I cautiously step back too. Back more. We turn and walk away, until we reach the path. Then, our running shoes pound down the trail. Terrified. What a tale to tell!

Later, when I explain to Granddad about our brush with a bear, he isn't surprised. "An old bear was at my hives," he chuckles. "Knocked two supers off a hive. Bet the bees really went after him."

I laugh too. "I didn't check our bear for stings," I tell him. "We were too scared."

I wander to the garden where sunflowers bow their flat heads and hunch their backs in the heat. I ease my body down among them, pulling my knees up to my chest and stretch my skirt over them while I listen to the drone of busy bees. Suddenly I hear a call.

"Ardith, dear. Please help me carry berries for sale."

I hold the berry buckets high above the tall yellow sweet clover, which edges the path. Mummy and I cross a patch of pale blue flax that looks like a piece of sky fallen to the ground in the shimmering heat. We walk across the meadow, the air alive with humming black hornets until, at last, we deliver the raspberries to our delighted customers.

Mummy stashes the coins in our old cracked teapot.

TWENTY-FIVE

The Telegram

I walk to town with Mummy. The range line is purple with fall asters.

"I'll just check the mail," Mummy says.

"Mrs. Ray! Telegram for Walter. Will you be passing that way?"

"Of course." Mummy accepts the white envelope. "Thank you." She holds the letter like it's poison. We walk briskly along the aster-lined roadway and rattle Granddad's screen door sharply.

"Come in," calls Granddad; his eyes widen as we march in, and Mummy hugs and kisses him tenderly before she hands him the telegram.

He slits it open with his pocket knife and scans the message. Then he flips the card to Mummy. Swinging me around, he twirls me off my feet. Crazy! Laughing! Mummy begins to cry.

"What does it say?" I demand. "What's happening?"

"Uncle Lawrence is coming home!" Mummy laughs as tears run down her cheeks. "He is discharged from the army! With battle fatigue!"

"What is that? I ask. "Will we catch it, too?"

Mummy laughs again. "No, sweetheart! It means that Uncle Lawrence worked hard in the army and got all nervous, so he has to stop fighting and come home. Here, everyone will be good to him and he won't have any more bad things happen. If we all treat him nicely, he'll get better again. He's sick, Ardith. Do you understand?"

"Yes, Mummy. And will his wife and the little girls be coming, too?" I'm anxious to meet my new aunt, the British war bride, and their two tiny daughters.

"No, dear. Your new auntie can't come until the war ends; it wouldn't be safe for her to cross the ocean right now. She has to stay where she lives in London. But Uncle Lawrence is already in Canada. He'll be home in a couple of days."

Granddad does a flurry of housework for his son's arrival. Of course, Uncle Lawrence will live with Granddad. Everyone is excited to see him, to hear news from across the ocean and to see pictures of our little cousins, Aster and Pansy. We all want to hear about our new Auntie Martha.

Uncle Lawrence arrives a few days later. I stare at this tall strong man with broad shoulders and muscles like a boxer. His stiff black hair has a short army cut. Heavy lidded eyes look slyly at me. Thin lips line his large mouth and he squints as he sucks on his cigarette. Smokes a lot, I can tell, judging by his stained fingers, which look like jaundiced paws on a raccoon!

"So this is little Ardith," he booms. Hugging me, he grips my hips with long strong fingers that pinch me and flattens my face against a tunic that smells of sweat, tobacco and shaving cream. Rough buttons scrape my face.

"What a big girl! You're a real lady. What's that on your face?" Looks like you got a direct hit with bombed shit." He laughs at his own joke. Right then I decide I don't like my uncle.

But he likes me. Sidling behind me, he hugs me, lunges at me, plunges his arms around my shoulders, pulls my pigtails. I try to smile while I squirm away. "Be good to Uncle Lawrence," Mummy says.

Goldenrods line the lane as Noël and I skip home from school. It's grand to have Noël grown up. She's delighted to be going to school; her smile is like a half tractor-wheel with a few spokes missing. Her hair is the same pretty shade as the faded goldenrod flowers.

Noël and I pinch stinkweed pods, releasing the ripe, trapped seeds. Then I check with a late dandelion blossom held under Noël's chin to see if she loves butter.

She does! We finally reach the cabin.

"Well, here you are at last!" Ruby greets us. "Noël, run straight over to keep Nan company. Ardith, change into your old dress and take this lunch out to the field. Everyone's ready for coffee. They'll work till dark. So I'm going to start supper. Hurry now."

Horizon hazy with harvest dust. Blueberry-coloured clouds float on a cream-pie sky. I see Uncle Lawrence and Douglas stooking sheaves into teepees, building shelters for field mice on chilly nights, while Grandpapa and Mummy work with the binder. Dust rises as the machine cuts the wheat in long, straight lines and flings bound bundles aside. I walk around the white alkali crusts that border the coulee. The wind blows dust like bitter baking powder, blistering my lips. I serve Mummy first, and then Grandpapa. Between gulps of fresh coffee, he instructs, "Send Doug back to my shop for more twine. We're almost out. Tell him to hurry!" I rush to the edge of the field where Uncle Lawrence and Douglas are stooking.

Douglas takes only one swallow of coffee and sets off for home to get the twine, leaving Uncle Lawrence with his mug full, rolling a cigarette. I run after Douglas through the coarse stubble.

The next afternoon the stooking is finished and stooks dot the field, waiting for the travelling threshers. A gang of boisterous men arrive at our place one fine warm day. Hay racks, teams, and threshing machinery. The men gobble tons of food and hurry back to their task, and I hear them shout back and forth between hay wagons.

"Nice lady, Edith Ray. Wouldn't say 'shit' if her mouth is full of it!"

"Too bad Lawrence can't do nothing!"

"Acts like cock of the walk. What's he done?"

"Strutting around here like he won the war."

"Shell shock. Does that mean 'can't work'?"

"You'd think he'd grab a fork and lend a hand!"

"Big guy like him. Useless as tits on a boar!"

"Poor Walter Ray. Saddled with Lawrence again!"

But I hear no more. I have to help Mummy in the cabin.

I attack mountains of dirty dishes. Using the old oval dishpan with the chipped enamel rim set on the back of the kitchen range to keep warm, Ruby washes dishes, draining them in the square galvanized washtub, because Mummy needs the flat draining pan to bake buns. I dry the dishes. Mummy arranges rolls of dough into cinnamon buns at the table while Noël lies motionless on the bunk, munching a handful of raisins. She mustn't let chaff shower the bun pans.

"When the threshers leave, you girls can pull the ticks outdoors. We'll dump out the chaff and straw and I'll wash those ticks before we refill them with fresh clean straw from the new stack. Won't that be grand?"

None of us girls feels enthusiastic although we smile at our mother. Does she really like that fresh pokey straw? Or is Mummy just being cheerful because this will be our last winter in the cabin? The framework of our new home looms like a palace on the skyline. It is huge. But cold. No heater has been installed. The house still needs insulation and floors.

I realize that if this wheat brings a decent price when sold at the elevator, a share of the money will be used to buy gyprock lining for walls in the new house.

"Cars are in!" Uncle Lawrence surprises us by offering to haul a load of grain to the elevator. The CN Rail cars are here, ready to be loaded. Uncle Lawrence puts on the big grain box high over the wheels of Granddad's wagon, and adds the wide extended top. He fills it to the brim and disappears down the hill toward town. Driving slowly, Uncle Lawrence steers Ol' Tom and Charlie, mindful of the load.

Granddad watches for him, waiting and waiting, straining his eyes as dusk comes and the light dims. Still Uncle doesn't show.

Gritting his teeth, Granddad walks more briskly as he finishes his chores with my help. "Don't worry, Granddad. Charlie and Ol' Tom won't run. Uncle Lawrence won't get hurt!"

"Hush up, Honey. That's not what I'm worrying over." He brushes my cheeks with rough thumbs and tugs up the corners of my mouth.

"Sometimes your uncle gets real wild. You know what I mean?"

I nod solemnly. I know what he means. I head back home to bed.

Granddad arrives next morning before Noël and I are up. We hear him tell Mummy, "Lawrence whipped my old horses and drove the wagon so fast that the wheels almost shook off. He rattled to a stop. He cashed the grain cheque and spent the money. Beer for all. Nothing small about Lawrence. He left the rig in the middle of the yard for me to put away, and hit the hay. Out like a light. For the night."

Mummy's face falls when Granddad tells what happened to the money. "How could Lawrence do that?" she demands, her face convulsing.

The skin on Granddad's face is wrinkled as a brown paper sack. "I'm sorry, Edith."

Mummy tightens her lips and says no more; her eyes stare bleakly across to the huge half-finished house. "My plans will just have to wait."

I catch Noël's sad expression. I feel awful too. Mummy had it all figured out and now her plans are dashed. I wish Uncle Lawrence hadn't returned from the war.

When Noël and I draw near Granddad's house after school that day, we hear him shouting. We creep closer. "Get out! Go earn your living somewhere else. Go!"

"But I'm sick!" our uncle answers. "You can't put me out."

"I can and I will," roars Granddad. "I'll not have my son boozing it up here. I'm a clean-living man! I never touch the stuff. And I won't support your drinking habit."

Granddad is hurling hurtful words like sharpened spears. "You have a wife and kids to bring over. So quit your foolishness and buckle down. Now get out of here and don't come back until you've got a job."

Uncle Lawrence finds a job driving taxi in Edmonton.

Granddad doesn't tell us much about him, but I suspect my Granddad is angry with Uncle Lawrence because he always gets mad on weekends if Uncle shows up.

The following week, the sky pebbles with puffy clouds as Noël and I return from school. Our entire countryside turns into huge crazy quilts of yellow and brown with borders of crimson saskatoon bushes. Thin dun-coloured stems of wild brome offer meagre meals to the few songbirds that perch on the bare branches along the lane, and burrs cling to my woollen stockings as I walk through the grasses. We can hear ducks clanning in pot holes, planning with muted voices their long trek south.

TWENTY-SIX

Winter Routines

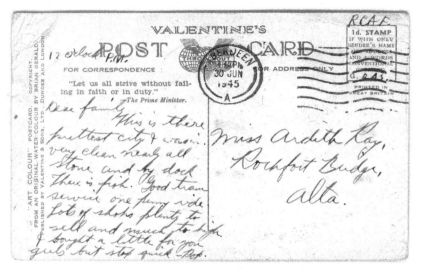

Daddy sends postcards to each child in turn. 1945.

It is a cold dark morning, and the snow lies deep and crackles underfoot. Cattle stand contentedly on a sheltered knoll as though they know this will be their last soak of sunlight. I admire their shaggy, rough coats as Douglas and I trudge to school.

A sudden snort startles me. I glance around in alarm. Just ahead of us, two huge elk leap from the ditch and cross the road. Sleek, hairy bodies, long strong legs, with magnificent racks of antlers, they roll sorrowful eyes toward us. With another snort, they disappear; only a tangle of tracks and twang of barbed wire remind us of the beautiful animals we've just seen.

"Poor things," Douglas says. "It's hunting season and they don't know where to turn. How could anyone shoot beautiful animals like that?"

As we trudge on to school, I remember about Douglas shooting poor Jippy. Does he ever think about that?

I'm horrified to learn from listening to Miss McPhillip, who is instructing the grade five class, that a mummy is a dead body preserved from rotting by binding it in bonds of cloth. Mummy in bondage! This idea is so repulsive to me that I vow then and there, I'll never call my mother Mummy again. It's as though I'm afraid the name alone might somehow endanger Mother.

School is a pleasure for me. Miss McPhillip is enthusiastic and pleasant. She offers encouragement for my improvement. Finally, I overcome my reversal problem when I graduate from printing to cursive writing. I no longer have to think "the tummy faces the A" each time I encounter the letter *d* to make identification, using my own name's appearance. This method has served me well, but is painstakingly slow. Now I can write rapidly.

I thrive on my teacher's praise, and maintain a perfect attendance record.

Now round clouds lie like scorched scones on a dark blue platter of sky. It feels like snow. My teeth chatter as the cold seeps into the classroom.

By mid-afternoon, large white flakes sift from an overcast sky, which Miss McPhillip keeps checking. Knowing that we aren't dressed for a snowstorm, she dismisses us from school early.

Noël and I love to hitch a ride home from school with neighbours who have been to town with their team and sleigh. We stand in the shallow sleigh box that glides over the crusted snow, with sleigh-bells jingling pleasantly and the bracing smell of horse sweat and old leather. Usually, there's a treat, shared from a brown paper sack newly purchased at the store. Horehound candy! Or jelly beans! But never chocolates or gum. These items are rationed.

When our neighbours drop us off at our gate, Noël says, "Let's run down to the spruce trees in the grove. Maybe the squirrels have marked the trees, so there's sap. We'll chew spruce gum." We scurry to the spruce grove and search for lumps of amber sap oozing from wounds on the trunk.

"I found some," I announce with satisfaction. "Here, Noël." I snap off globs of sap to share. We chew for hours, until our jaws ache and the sap disintegrates.

Mummy tells us the legend of Qu'Appelle, the Indian maiden who calls for her lost lover and may still be heard calling in the valley named Qu'Appelle. I find this story so romantic that I spend hours calling names, and listening intently to the echoes. But this attraction pales as the weather grows colder.

Wisps of clouds scatter across the grey sky. Granddad's two workhorses lean heads on each other as though exhausted from all the fall work.

Wind sweeps around the cabin; drifts pile high. It's bitterly cold. Mom intends to work inside the new house, to plaster cracks where the gyprock joins, but it is far too cold in that huge unheated area. The paste thickens before it can be spread, and Mom's fingers freeze. She has to give up her carpentry plans.

There are plenty of things to keep her busy in the cabin. We are growing rapidly and need more garments. She spends daylight hours bent over the treadle sewing machine, fashioning clothing from castoffs.

She is making Douglas a new windbreaker when we burst into the cabin. She sews it from an old overcoat from

Grandpapa, and is also making him a matching helmet with rabbit-skin flaps. "I've spent all day fashioning this helmet," she says proudly, her face twitching extra rapidly in her excitement.

"Look at your new cap, Douglas," cries Noël. "Grandpapa must have cured that rabbit pelt and given it to Mom for your new helmet. How do you like it?"

Douglas studies it solemnly. He tries it on, and kisses Mom. "It fits perfectly," he murmurs. "Thanks."

Later, I find Douglas in the barn, savagely shovelling manure. He heaves it far out the door onto the dung pile.

"I hate that hat," he declares through clenched teeth. "It reminds me of poor Jippy. But don't say anything, Ardith, please. Because Mom is so proud of it."

I nod in sympathy. "It'll be our secret."

The wind drops and snow falls steadily all night. It blankets the cabin in an eiderdown of insulation and transforms the countryside from dun brown to glistening white. Hoarfrost hangs all the next day. The pale winter sun refuses to ruin the shimmering beauty of bushes sparkling along the lane.

I love the brisk walk from school. Every fence post wears a marshmallow cap. Fresh snow scrunches underfoot.

Ol' Tom and Charlie warm their withers in the pasture by absorbing the weak heat of a winter sun. They breathe the brisk air and gaze at us before pawing the deep snow, uncovering scant mouthfuls of straw. Our string of cows comes hurrying along the trail to the promise of a familiar stall and the warmth of the barn. There they stand, placidly chewing their cuds, waiting for Douglas to fork down their evening feed from the loft. Noël and I help him or play with the kittens. It's roomy and interesting in the barn. The kerosene lantern provides shafts of light making patterns on the walls as Douglas completes the chores. Steam rises from the cattle's nostrils, and there is an earthy scent of warm manure mingled with the sweet incense of hay. A blur of wings from an errant moth flickers around the lantern. I sit on Nipper's back and watch spiders drop on silken strands from the broad beams supporting the loft. Deer mice on delicate feet scamper along the edge of the wall, their huge liquid eyes wary. The gentle-eyed cows continue their placid munching, undisturbed by these events. The coo of pigeons overhead is soothing and comforting. I love our barn.

But on Friday evening, I forget about the barn and go to town with Ruby for the mail. All the kids gather in the little lobby of the post office. After the train drops a bulging mail sack on the station platform, it is gathered by an arthritic postmaster. Strong young hands help him cart the bag to his office. Then the wait begins. First a rhythmic pounding, as each letter is stamped. Then fragile blue envelopes begin to appear in the glass-fronted mailboxes.

"There's one for you, Ronnie."

"A letter for you, Ned."

"Looks like your Dad wrote, Annie."

"Did you get news from your Dad, Ruby?"

We feel lucky when there is a postcard or letter from Dad. It's always addressed to one of us kids. Each, in turn, receives a beautiful picture card from that faraway land called England. Whenever mail lands in our mailbox, we clutch it and rush home.

"A letter from Dad!" we announce. Oh, it's wonderful to hear from Daddy!

I often compose a short poem to him. I carefully write it on the thin blue airmail forms, and Mom helps me with the long address. I love the shape and strangeness of these English words. I love mouthing the address and sounding each syllable separately. Mom nudges me toward more poetry writing, encouraging me the way animals nudge their young in the right direction.

TWENTY-SEVEN

By the Moon

Ardith and Noël on Paddle River Bridge. 1945.

A delicate blue glitter hangs over the drifted fields and ice crystals shine in the weak sunlight. Drifts of snow crawl across the yard and up the step. Blizzard follows blizzard, and it turns bitterly cold.

Mother keeps us in the cabin. She constantly feeds the fire with wooden sticks, but the cold creeps up from the floorboards and seeps in around the edges of the poorly fitted door and window.

I love looking at the frost blossoms on the glass. Flowers, ferns and snow castles appear. I erase the image by warming the glass with the heel of my hand. Through this clear space, I glimpse the outside world; the arms of the willow bend under a heavy white cape, the biffy is half-buried in drifts. Then the scene mists as a new scene forms on the frosted glass.

"A winter full moon is the time for long cold snaps," Mom warns. Winter seems never-ending. But Nan and Grandpapa have lively entertainment with sing-songs and dances for us every weekend. Ruby makes popcorn in the old cast-iron frying pan for these parties, and serves hot cocoa and cakes.

MORE SUPPORT NEEDED
FOR THE COMFORT OF THE TROOPS

Headlines in the newspapers appeal for knitted goods, while the Red Cross provides yarn. Nan increases her knitting efforts. She can complete a beautifully warm pair of knitted socks in one day and she determines to finish six pairs every week. Her fingers fly. I'm proud of my grandmother, and cheerfully read to her while she knits. We play a game, she and I. I listen to her softly clicking needles and read in time to the clicks. When she speeds, I speed. If she slows, I slow my voice, and we laugh together.

School is very interesting. My reading and penmanship improve but another problem presents itself. It begins with Miss McPhillip's announcement: "Grade three students have all mastered cursive writing, so you may begin using pen and ink. Billy, please pass each student a bottle of ink. Ardith, hand out the straight pens and blotting paper. You must immediately absorb all blots with this paper. No ink on the floor or on your desks, please. I am trusting you to be very careful with the ink. It stains badly."

I'm thrilled to be considered mature enough to use a pen. But my joy is dashed when I actually begin. All because I'm left-handed. The heel of my hand drags in the fresh ink before it has time to dry, so I smudge or blot out each word I write. Horrors!

Miss McPhillip is equally confounded. She asks my mother, "Will this awkward child ever learn to do handwork?"

Mother shakes her head in bewilderment. "My Ardith is truly a problem child."

Again I solve my own difficulties. I discover that by grasping my straight pen firmly and looping my arm high above the line on which I'm writing, while resting the heel of my hand on dry lines, I can write legibly and quickly. But the hook I develop with my left arm makes my writing position look even more awkward.

"Well, I declare," says Miss McPhillip. "You can certainly write quickly, Ardith. And neater, too. Whenever you finish early, you may compose a few verses or make up a little story." So I keep myself pleasantly and quietly entertained at school:

> *Tiny little footprints*
> *Lead across the snow.*
> *I wonder where they come from?*
> *I wonder where they go?*

A line runs through the markings,
Makes a single trail,
Telling me this creature
Has a dragging tail.

The tracks meander onward
Back behind the house.
Now I know who made them!
It was a tiny mouse.

Suddenly the footprints stop.
Drops of blood are found
Spattering the snowbank,
And the frozen ground.

A single feather lies here
Resting on the snow
Explains poor mouse's ending—
An owl has fed, I know.

I show Miss McPhillip and then copy my new poem in a special scribbler, to save. Whenever I have spare time, I turn to this scribbler and read my little verses.

When we reach home, Noël and I know immediately that Ruby has started refreshments for tonight's sing-along. The smell of chocolate wafts around the cabin. Sure enough, she has made a layer cake and stuck it together with lemon pudding. Ruby is a budding cook, and we admire her masterpiece waiting on the table for this evening.

But when we arrive at Nan's house, we're disappointed to find Grandpapa isn't there.

"He went to a meeting," Nan explains. "But I'm happy you came."

"How are we going to have a musical evening without Grandpapa?" I ask.

"Oh, I have a plan," laughs Nan. "Come and sit down. Here you are. A comb for each of you. And here's some cellophane. Careful not to rip it." Nan gives each of us a square of clear, crisp cellophane.

Mother's eyes begin to twinkle. She picks up a comb and puts cellophane over it. Placing it against her lips, she presses firmly with the comb, and a beautiful tune issues from the tissue.

We stare in astonishment as Mother does an eerie rendition of Marching Through Georgia.

"How'd you do that?" We all want to know. She demonstrates, sucking her cheeks into two valleys, then blowing. It looks easy.

Sure enough, after a few attempts, everyone can hum You Are My Sunshine, vibrating the tissue, making it sound like a strange instrument.

Mother fetches four spoons, two for herself and two for Douglas and shows him how to hold them against his knee, so that they crack together when he bounces his leg in time to the music. Soon Douglas can play the spoons as well as Mother. The hilarity is contagious! Everyone is giggling.

"Oh, Nan," says Noël as she stuffs the last of her chocolate cake into her mouth. "This is as much fun as when Grandpapa plays."

"Sh-sh-sh!" Nan rolls her eyes mischievously. "Better not let Grandpapa hear! He'll feel left out."

TWENTY-EIGHT

Saving Annette

Grandpapa pets Ol' Annette. 1945.

"Mom! Come quick! Something's wrong with Annette!" Doug cries from the doorway. "Oh, hurry, Mom!"

Mom grabs her mackinaw and dashes straight to the barn. Noël and I are behind her, clutching each other in terror as we stare at our old cow.

"Poor Annette!" Mom falls on her knees beside the cow. The beast sprawls in her stall with all four legs held stiffly in the air.

"Is she dead?" quavers Noël. The cow looks so unnatural. A low moan from Annette proves this is not the case.

I'm frightened by the sight of the milk bag swollen to bursting with teats rock-hard and red.

"Oh, Douglas, did you try to milk her?" demands Mom. "Just look at this swelling!"

"I tried. But the milk won't come out. What should we do?"

"She must have milk fever! Ardith, run to Granddad's to ask him to come quickly. Noël, run to Grandpapa's and ask him and Ruby to come. We'll all have to work to save her. Poor old girl! Douglas, you massage her bag, but don't try to force the milk out. I'll get some hot water and cloths. We'll use them for hot compresses on her bag. Hurry, now. Poor Annette's suffering!" The animal moans as though in agreement and involuntarily shudders a flank muscle.

Everyone arrives quickly. Noël and I hover in the background to watch the family work over the cow. Grandpapa brings his tire pump. The men force air up into the cow's udders to create pressure and loosen the caked and curdled milk. The cow bellows in pain, but the men slave over her for hours. Oh, that must hurt, I think.

Mom continues with hot compresses on the milk bag after the men have done all they can and go home. She sits on the milk stool and tears brim her eyes, as Mom's face convulses in grief, her mouth stiff and lips shrivelled like frozen rose hips. "We mustn't lose Annette." Mom prays aloud desperately, "Dear God, please save our old cow. We need her terribly. She keeps us in milk and butter. Dear God, please spare Annette."

Steam rises in the warm barn but the beams pop from the cold. It's a strange night, keeping vigil with the family in the barn. Mom applies fresh hot packs—old clothes soaked in boiling water that Ruby heats in the cabin. Douglas scurries back and forth with pails of fresh hot water and gathers more

Nan and Grandpapa. 1946.

snow for Ruby to heat. Noël and I curl under an old quilt on a mound of straw, warm from heat from the animals and lulled by the crunch of Nipper munching hay. The pony rolls her eyes to see what's causing this unexpected company in the barn. The kittens keep mewing and begging for a drink of milk, but Annette's not obliging them tonight.

Steam rises like smoke and fogs the air above the feverish cow. Monstrous sounds come from the beast, so I burrow beneath the quilt, frightened and sad. I doze fitfully.

Mom strokes the engorged udders, willing milk to stream forth. Annette bellows in agony, until finally a bluish liquid begins to drool from the teats. Annette stops her desperate bawling as clots of foul curds drop onto the straw while Mom continues to pull the teats and massage the grotesque bag.

By morning, Annette regains her feet and stands munching a choice morsel of hay offered by Douglas. Mother strokes her black back and gently strips the udders. Although Annette shudders from pain, the old cow recovers.

Dawn is breaking as we stumble to the cabin. Luckily, it's Saturday morning. No school. We all smell of the barn. Ruby has heated snow water in the square galvanized tub. Noël has a quick bath and brisk hair scrub. Me next. As Douglas prepares for his bath, Ruby disappears to help Nan, and Noël and I tumble onto the bunk and pull the quilt over our heads. Soon we're fast asleep.

TWENTY-NINE

River Antics

Gradually the weather warms, snow changes to slush, and the air softens. I curl on the bunk like bacon rind after a late breakfast. A strange noise fills the skies. I raise myself on one elbow; the sounds grow louder.

"Sandhill cranes! Oh, Mom. I hear the cranes going over. Spring is here at last!" I scramble from the bunk and rush outside. Puffs of powdery clouds scatter across a clear blue sky. A straight line of determined cranes fly northward; their strange honking brings a longing into my heart. Oh, to be free as those birds, not earthbound in this mess of mud. I survey the yard despairingly.

"Let's go fishing," Douglas suggests a few days later. "The suckers are running in the Paddle, now that the floodwater is down. Want to try snaring some, Ardith? The best days for fishing are between the new moon and the full moon. That means today."

Holding my slim pole, I squelch across the field toward the river. Douglas leads, carrying his own pole.

We slither down the bank to a sand bar beside the water, and search for suckers swimming to the headwaters of the river to spawn in the shallow riffles.

"I can see one." I point out a long fish, with a stupid flat expression like a carp on a wind kite. It lies in the rapids to rest before moving upstream, as several more slide by.

Douglas fashions a wire snare on the end of my pole and one on his own. "Wade right into the rapids," he instructs.

"We can see them best in the shallows."

I watch patiently. My toes begin to tingle from the cold water pressing against my feet through my rubber boots, but I don't budge.

"I see a couple now," reports Doug in a quiet voice. "Lower your snare slowly. Try not to wiggle it."

I manoeuvre the long pole and balance it on one knee. The snare disappears into the water. I watch, careful not to wiggle. Wait. Watch. I know suckers have to be snared, since they can't bite a hook. Finally, I'm sure I see the wire just behind the gills of a large fish. With a mighty heave, I flip the slippery sucker high onto the bank.

"I got one, Doug!" I drop my pole, and run to my catch, to guard it from flopping back into the water.

Suddenly Doug lands a sucker, too. "Here comes mine!" he warns, and rushes upon it, but only halfheartedly keeps it ashore. A few flops and his fish regains the water and swims away. I laugh.

"That's okay, Douglas, I'll snare another one!" I understand his reluctance to kill.

While I snare a second sucker, Douglas fashions a stick with a hooked branch, slides it through the gills and out the ugly, gaping mouth. "I can carry home both fish on this stick."

"Here, Nan," we cry proudly. "A fish for your frying pan." Nan dutifully admires our catch. We rush on home.

"Look Mom! We caught a big one!" Doug scales the fish at the step. He cuts off the head for Noël's cat.

"One fish fry is enough," Mom announces after supper, as she sees the leftover scraps on each plate. "Those suckers taste musky and flat."

"I don't like the feel of that fish in my mouth," I complain. "But it's exciting to snare them."

I love to listen to the honk of wild Canada geese as they

fly north high overhead, forming ever-changing patterns in the sky.

The frogs begin to chorus in the slough, and the night hawks forecast dusk with their strange cries. A pair of loons nest on the lake near the beaver dams, adding their eerie cries to the twilight hours.

Douglas builds a smudge near the cabin door to discourage millions of mosquitoes freshly hatched from the bogs. Each day the new leaves unfold more, and soon a delicate green replaces the drab brown of the landscape.

Mom is fixing a lunch of bread and jelly for us. "Noël, dear, scramble under the bunk and find us a jar of fresh jelly. They're in the apple box cupboard."

Noël chooses a sealer of clear raspberry jelly. "Is this one okay?" It looks like a jewel in the jar as Mom holds it to the light. She snaps off the lid and pries the wax seal loose.

"Oh, Mom, can Noël and I share the wax for gum?" I beg. "Please."

"I guess so. But I usually wash the wax and reuse it, you know."

"Don't wash ours, so we can have jelly-wax gum. Please, Mom." We chew this treat for hours.

I sit on an overturned bucket and sort potatoes. The cultivated garden has a rich loam smell, and the weather is perfect for planting. "Now be careful, Ardith. Don't break off these delicate white sprouts," warns Mom. "Choose only the best potatoes of uniform size for seedlings. Put them in this bucket. Throw the misshapen ones into this bucket and be sure to sprout them—we'll eat them at the table. The culls go into this slop pail for the pigs. We don't want to waste any potatoes after all our hard work growing them. I'll help Douglas line up the garden rows with twine. I see he has the stakes ready."

It feels good to wiggle my bare toes in the moist soil. No need for boots today.

"I'll sort the seed packets." Noël leans over the old bushel basket. "Mom says she wants the whole garden planted today because Mr. Williams is coming tomorrow to start building the house again. Won't it be wonderful when we can move into it?"

"I can hardly wait! Mom says we can each have our own room. Can you imagine that, Noël?" A whole room to yourself?" We smile with anticipation.

Mom is excited. Her face contorts rapidly as she instructs us. "We'll plant lettuce and onions along the grass verge," she explains. "So that even if it's wet, we can reach the salad ingredients without stepping onto the muddy garden. Next go the beans. Then peas. We'll plant marigolds among the cauliflower to discourage those awful green caterpillars. The corn must go along the northern edge where it won't shade the shorter plants. Turnips can be planted along the draw, since they don't mind a little frost. Now, have we left room for the beets?"

We work steadily, and long before twilight, the patch is planted and looks like a black blanket staked to the earth, waiting for rain.

"The seeds will germinate better," Mother explains, "because it is just before the full moon. That's the best time for planting. And there was a halo around the moon too, so that means wet weather is coming. So all in all, I'm glad to get that garden planted."

"You kids sure have grown!" Mr. Williams greets us as we start to school the next day. "I'd better hustle and build those bedrooms," and he chuckles as he dons his apron and heads for the big house.

Mom hurries through the spring planting. Grandpapa helps her. She's anxious to work with Mr. Williams. It will be so much faster when she holds up the large slabs of gyprock used to line the house and separate the rooms. Meanwhile, Mr. Williams keeps busy, and the new house changes rapidly. He sets more windows in place, allowing light to enter the cavernous interior. Now he can see to build two staircases, partition all the rooms, and build kitchen cabinets.

A Scottish mason, Mr. McLean, builds a solid brick chimney rising three storeys above the basement floor. Mom buys a second-hand heater, which the men set up in the living room until a proper furnace can be installed. Burning small scraps of lumber in this heater takes the chill off the house so Mr. Williams works near the heater, where he sleeps at night while he is working here. It's very exciting to see the house take shape. Mr. Williams works at it all spring and Mom helps him whenever possible.

The crops and garden are crying for moisture. It's hot and dry even before school is dismissed for the summer holidays, and now the stumpy grain begins to wither and wilt under the harsh sunlight. "So much for planting by the moon," Douglas says ruefully.

Finally, the sky grows overcast, and a sultry silence hangs over all. It's dead still, not a breeze to turn a leaf.

"What we need is a good rain!" declares Granddad, when he visits us. "We'll git rain, too, because the new moon is standing on its point, spilling out moisture."

"You look mottled as a mouldy mushroom," he declares, referring to my freckles. I feel flawed. I know I'm ugly. I can't seem to do anything right. I get mixed up, and I don't remember things.

The next day a soft, gentle rain freshens the leaves and moistens the soil. The leaves glisten like glazed doughnuts in the sunlight. That evening, it rains again.

"It's most likely to be rainy in the days following the new moon," Mother says. "I'd better transplant the cabbages now. I'm sure we're in for more rain."

And she's right. When we return from school the next day, there's a slight drizzle, and Mother's bending over her cabbage plants. It rains all night. But then the weather turns extremely hot and dry.

When Mother combs my waist-length hair, it's like unleashing a torrent of fire. It sparkles and crackles with electricity until Mom's long strong fingers plait the hair into thick braids again. "It feels good to get that long hair off my neck," I say thankfully. "It's so hot! If we get our chores all done, may we go swimming? Please? We'll be very careful. I'll watch out for Noël. Now that I can swim a little, we'll be perfectly safe. We'll stay with the other kids at the main swimming hole. Oh, please, Mom! It's really hot!"

"Well … ," says Mom. "I suppose you'll be safe enough if there are other people there. All right. You and Noël may go if you get your garden rows weeded in time!"

Weeds fly in all directions as we work. Promise of cool water is great incentive. After a hurried lunch of leftover pancakes with black currant jam, we set off for the Paddle.

"Hi Billy! Hi Angie! Hi John! Well, hi everybody," I call. "Looks like the whole school is here. Sure is hot, isn't it?" We peel off our shorts and shoes and wade in. We wear our swimsuits from home knowing there is scant privacy among the willows.

The water feels delicious on our bare bodies; our feet sink into the soft sand. We splash our parched skin, refreshed by the moisture.

"Will you play here while I go upstream to the rapids and swim down all the way over the hole? It's too deep for you there. But I can do it!" I tell Noël stoutly.

She promises, "I'll be right here."

As I skirt the edge, I laugh at the antics of the group in the swimming hole. John floats in an inflated inner tube. The current runs from the rapids, across "the hole" and on toward the shallows where Noël splashes with her friends. Maggie loops her arm through the tube to hitch a ride. Just as the tube floats past me, Maggie slips off. She makes a wild grab, but disappears into the hole. A second later, I see her terrified face surface and hear "Help!" before she disappears again. John is unaware of her danger as he floats tranquilly downstream in the tube.

"Help!" cries Maggie again, surfacing briefly. Down she goes again! I plunge forward to Maggie's aid. Grasping her hand, I pull Maggie. But she's terrified. She yanks me into the hole, grasping me around my neck. She raises herself above the surface, choking me down.

I'm going to drown! I realize. I can't get her off my neck. She's in a panic! I try to break the grip on my head, but I can't. If I can bounce along the bottom, I'll get out of this hole before I have to breathe. One, two, three .... I spring as far as possible with each stride, counting automatically. Long before unlucky thirteen, I feel hands peel Maggie from my neck and help us to the bank. I lie choking and windless beside Maggie.

"Way to go, Ardith!" everyone says. "You saved Maggie! She was a goner for sure!" Maggie gives me a thankful hug.

News of my heroism spreads. Soon townsfolk are telling Mother, "I won't let my children go swimming unless Ardith is there!" I love it! I'm hero of the hour. Special at last!

But my bubble soon bursts. The next week, Noël and I go swimming, and catch up to a group of friends. "Hi, Maggie," I call. "Wait up! My shoelace is untied. Would you hold my towel a minute while I tie my shoelace, please?"

"I guess I can hold it," replies Maggie. "But I won't carry it. 'Cause I don't want anyone to think it's mine!" I stare at

Maggie in shocked surprise. Her piercing blue eyes glint like glass beads. Tossing her head, she turns away. Everyone snickers.

I bow my head in shame as I tie my runner and accept my towel. I stare at it in wonder, and as though scales fall from my eyes, I see! Tattle-tale grey. I realize with dismay that the other kids have snowy white towels. Noël's and mine are dingy. The kids think we're dirty! And we are! I slink along behind the group, my swimming pleasure spoiled. What can I do about it? Walking across the field on the way home, I discuss the problem with Noël.

"We can't tell Mom what was said," I explain. "Because then Mom would realize *everyone knows* we're dirty. We can't complain to Mom. She's working too hard already. She'll never whiten our clothes. Besides, she'll say we mustn't criticize our elders. What do you think we should do?"

"I guess you'll have to wash your own clothes if it bothers you so much!" Noël says practically.

"Right!" I agree. "That's what I'll do!" From then on, I do my own washing. Mom never guesses the true reason.

THIRTY

Summer Blizzard

We move into our new house before it is completely built.
We burn wood in a heater and in the kitchen range. 1945.

I write

> *Rain! Rain! Come again!*
> *You're needed on the hill and plain.*
> *Though every day I check the sky*
> *Only sunshine meets my eye.*

And it's true. Ever since the rains of early June made every seed germinate, promising a bountiful harvest, not a drop has fallen. It is now almost the end of July. Tiny grasshoppers hatch and attack the withered grasses, sucking their scant moisture. The ground swarms with them. Every step I take, scores of grasshoppers scatter beneath my feet. "This must be like the plague of locusts in Bible times," I tell Noël. "We sure need a good rain."

The quivering aspen stand listless, not a leaf stirring. In the dead calm, heat waves rise from the parched earth and make the horizon shimmer in undulating lines.

"Could be a bumper crop, Mrs. Ray," Mr. Williams observes as they have coffee together.

"Yes," smiles Mom. "Now, if it will only rain! The peas need to fill and the berries are hard as bullets."

I listen quietly. Berries like bullets? Is that what bullets are like? I shudder.

"I'm thankful for this good crop. We'll be able to finish up the house this fall and move in before it gets cold. I'll buy a furnace as soon as I sell the barley. Oh, Mr. Williams, I can hardly wait to get out of this cabin!"

Me too. I wish Mr. Williams would hurry with his coffee, so Noël and I can go outside. It's so stuffy in this cabin.

We sit still as Mr. Williams rolls a smoke. "Actually, I'm kinda happy with this dry spell," he drawls. "You know there's not a single shingle on that roof yet. Only one layer of tar paper covering the boards so far. I sure wish you could afford them shingles, Mrs. Ray. Be a shame to have moisture warp the floors or stairwell."

Mom nods. "I'll get them straight away."

The very next day the shingles arrive. Grandpapa delivers piles of bundles with his team and wagon. Mr. Williams is delighted.

"I'll run home tonight and get my neighbour, Lucas Lester, to help me with that roof. Takes two to heft those bundles! We'll shingle tomorrow."

Dawn ushers another clear day. A haze of heat hangs like

a blanket from heaven. Not a cloud in the sky. Mr. Williams drives his pickup into the yard with Mr. Lester. "Better get started. She's going to be hot up there!" Mr. Williams jokes. "Glad to get at that job!"

I watch them hoist heavy bundles of shingles to the peak of the roof and begin the exacting job of laying rows. Boring! Such a tedious chore! Mr. Williams is right. It's terribly hot.

I find Noël in the cabin. "What should we do today? It's too stuffy in here and in the hayloft. It's too hot to swing. What should we do?"

"Let's go down to the pig pasture," Noël suggests. "It should be cooler under the willows." We find that all of Grandpapa's pigs have the same idea. They lie half buried in black, refreshing mud, like hippopotamuses in the mire.

"Shoo! Shoo!" I cry. "Don't they look funny wallowing in that gooey muck? It sounds like a big monster is sucking them under!" Finally, all the pigs escape from us and scamper through the willows—except for Bessie! The huge sow squeals and wails, moans and grunts, but she can't hoist herself from the muck. Like quicksand, it pulls her down.

"Old Bessie is really stuck! What should we do?" asks Noël.

"Let's tell Grandpapa. Maybe he'll pull her out." We rush to his barnyard.

"Grandpapa! Come quickly. Old Bessie is stuck in the muck and can't get loose!" Grandpapa chuckles at our concern, but he goes down to the wallow with us to have a look.

"Well, old girlie!" he calls, checking the immobile sow. "You are stuck, right enough."

"I'll just haul her out by her ears," Grandpapa says. But he can't get footing in the slippery mud. Standing to catch his breath, he scratches his ear thoughtfully. "That old sow's a dead weight when she's down like that. I can't lift her. I'm going to need help. Ardith, run to my tool shed and bring the lasso. Noël, go get Douglas. We'll pull old Bessie out."

We rush away, returning very shortly. I have the lariat coiled over my shoulder. Grandpapa loops it around Bessie's neck and begins to pull, with Douglas helping. They struggle and the pig struggles, squealing loudly in protest. But it's no use. The old sow seems anchored in the mire.

"Ardith, you'd better go and ask your Granddad to come and give us a hand," says Grandpapa. "Tell him what's wrong. Douglas and I will get more ropes. Noël, come with us to tell Nan what's happening. Hustle, now."

Soon both strong men heave on the rope. The old sow screeches and squeals, moans and grunts. But they can't budge her. She appears to be rooted.

The men stand for a breather, both exhausted from such exertion in the heat. "I'll hitch up Ol' Tom," says Granddad. "He'll snake that ol' hog outa there faster than an ant can jump a red-hot griddle." Granddad ambles off for home, returning astride his heavy workhorse. Sure enough! When he hitches the single-tree onto the lasso, the powerful horse pulls until POP! like a giant cork from a bottle, the fat sow is plucked from the muck. We cheer, while Bessie stops squealing and grunts her satisfaction at being free.

We're so engrossed in the tribulations of the pig, that no one notices the dramatic changes in the sky. The clouds are startling.

Black roiling coils wind and re-form across the sky, darkening the day. A sudden clap of thunder terrifies me; the lightning tears apart the dreadful sky and galvanizes us to action. "Run for it, girls!" calls Grandpapa. We scatter in different directions. Granddad lies against Ol' Tom's neck, urging the ungainly old horse into a brisk trot. They disappear as large raindrops begin to fall.

Noël and I hesitate under the willows as more flashes tear at the tops of the trees and threaten to uproot them. We're uncertain what we should do. Suddenly there's a dead calm. The rain and wind abate.

"Let's run for home!" I grab Noël's hand and leave the sheltering trees, heading straight across open fields.

Suddenly, the heavens open. A sheet of ice pelts down. Driving wind sends it slicing through the air with cutting force. We bow our heads and run blindly; cruel hail pelts our necks and shoulders, and bruises our flesh. I'm disoriented. We must seek shelter, I know, as I pull my little sister along. Black clouds, white edged, boil and churn above us.

Slanting hailstones slice my vision, bouncing as they strike the ground. The wind increases to gale force. Ice slashes in diagonal sheets, rending the air like a cutlass; daggers stab my flesh. More lightning flashes. We're lost! Caught in a summer blizzard! I begin to cry. Suddenly I slam against something flat—the board fence of the pig pen. We clamber up the side and slide down its slippery surface. Now we know where we are. The dazed turkeys stand in the lee of the fence and raise their heads to gaze at us as we rush past. They are stupefied, unaware of or unheeding their own need for shelter. We scurry on, and almost overshoot the house. Mr. Williams runs outdoors to claim Noël, rolling her under his jacket. I grasp his coattails and he leads us to shelter in the veranda of the new house. Moments later, Mr. Williams rushes out to rescue Douglas, blinded by the storm.

As the hail continues, our drenched family stand shivering under the protective roof, gazing at the chaos of the storm.

Hailstones drift against the step; the drumming on the roof is deafening. Never have I seen such fury. Mom gently pats my face, the towel a huge cotton tongue lapping moisture from my flesh. I have welts and bruises across my neck and shoulders; my arms are welted in ridges as though I've been thrashed. Blood oozes from small wounds, and plum-coloured bruises are appearing. Noël and Douglas are in the same condition.

As suddenly as it began, the hail ceases. The silence seems more deafening than the drumming of hailstones had been. We glance dumbfounded at each other.

With a wild cry, Mom flings her jacket across her shoulders and rushes to the garden. We fumble for our high-topped rubber boots to protect our bare feet, then follow our mother.

Ice crunches beneath our boots. The air is chilled. I shiver as I look at the garden. Battered vegetables smell like a giant coleslaw! The tender cabbage heads resemble shreds of green lace. Pea vines are severed from their roots. Beans lie beaten against the earth while beets bleed crimson stains on the snow as though slaughtered. One or two stalks of corn stand naked, completely stripped of leaves. Most are mashed to pulp along the path. Tiny circles of orange flesh mark carrot and turnip rows, their tender tops sliced away, exposing the roots in ridges through the ice. The potato vines tangle in total disarray. Mom has tears in her eyes as she takes in the ruins. Her face convulses and contorts in grief.

"Oh, Douglas! After you made such fine straight rows! Look at them!" Mom bursts into tears. Noël and I are frightened. Mom never cries. We stand looking at each other uncertainly, not knowing what to do. Douglas kicks a drift of ice, spraying large chunks into the air. He wants to comfort us all, but isn't sure how.

Suddenly Mother shakes her head and straightens her shoulders, seeing our frightened faces. "Now girls!" Mom cries out. "Hurry! Get the buckets and the fire shovel! Quickly! Hurry! Hurry!"

We crunch over icy crusts to obey Mom. Mystified! Bewildered as we watch Mom scoop ice into two tall buckets.

Does she think she can shovel all this ice off the garden? Will that help the vegetables?

"Here, Douglas. You fill both buckets and bring them to the cabin," instructs Mom briskly. "Girls, come with me."

Mom hurries to the cabin and begins mixing cream, sugar and eggs into the large crockery bowl. Then she runs to the junk granary and returns with an ice-cream maker. Now we understand. Mom is making ice cream, while we still have plenty of ice to freeze it.

"Here, Noël, You turn the ice-cream maker first," awards Mom. "When you reach a hundred, pass it to Ardith." What a surprise! I forget my wounds as I work at this unexpected summer treat.

"Well, we have a great deal to be thankful for," Mom remarks as our family shares our ice cream with the two workmen. "You fellows finished the roof before the storm, so the house stayed dry even though all the exposed building paper is ripped to shreds!"

"Yes," agrees Mr. Williams. "Neither of us was struck by lightning while we tried to finish the last row with that storm whipping up. I felt pretty close to God up there, I can tell you."

"Our peas, beans and leafy vegetables are ruined," declares Mom. "But the root crops should be all right. Anyway, we'll still have potatoes. But we have no crop now! I won't be able to afford a furnace. And I was so looking forward to moving into the house before winter."

"Now, Mrs. Ray, I think you'll still be able to do that. I can finish up the main floor, and you can move in there. The heater will keep you as warm as you've been in that old granary. You'll see. We'll hustle with the main floor, Mrs. Ray. But right now, I need a big chunk of building paper to repair the hail damage on that unfinished corner of the roof. Got any more?"

Mom draws Ruby, Noël and me to one side. "Girls," she says urgently. "We have no more building paper, except … "

Ruby understands. "I guess you need our paper doll folders, don't you, Mom?" she says. "I'll move my dolls into a shoe box."

Noël looks at me. "We will too, Mom." And so the men are able to completely shingle the roof.

Grandpapa brings news of the hailstorm. Veering southeast, it has taken a wide swath through the country. The Ray farm is in the very centre. Crops are totally wiped out. Mr. Peterson lost five cows. When they didn't show up, he went searching, and found all of them lying flat on their backs with all four feet sticking straight up—struck by lightning. They must have been beside the fence when a ball of lightning rolled along the wire.

"What a loss," Grandpapa sympathizes. "All we lost was one lamb. The flock huddled together in a tightly packed group at the end of the sheepfold, but when they moved out to pasture, there was one little body lying there—must have been bashed on the head by a hail stone."

"All my turkey poults was killed," Granddad tells us. "Stupid things. Didn't have sense to take shelter. Just stood there like dummies. Turkeys are so stupid. Oh, well, saves me a lot of work this fall. No young turkeys to pluck." Granddad chuckles wryly.

"We'll have no apples," says Grandpapa. "Stripped from the trees. No wild berries either. Too bad. The berries were just ready to fill out. Quite a bit of tree damage, too. Branches broken. Even a few big trees uprooted by the wind. And guess what, girls? That old poplar tree by the pig wallow was struck by lightning. Burnt black as Toby's beard. Good thing you girls had cleared out." I catch Noël's eye in alarm.

"Children," says Mom. "Never! Never, *ever* hide under the trees during a storm."

"But Mom, where should we hide?" I protest.

"You can't hide from lightning," Mom says. "Better to lie down on the ground, out in the open. Lightning strikes the highest point. Be sure that isn't your head."

Noël and I eye each other, thinking of us huddled under that poplar tree. I shiver as I think of our close call. Struck by lightning!

"Well, girls," chuckles Grandpapa. "At least the pigs are happy. That mucky wallow is a lake right now. Old Bessie won't be into that for a few days."

"I seen lots of dead grasshoppers, too," adds Granddad. "Looks like the hail done some good."

Mr. Williams is true to his word. He completes the main floor of the house before freeze-up. There are three rooms: a kitchen, large living room and bedroom. Also there's a large screened veranda. The kitchen has a cabinet built along one wall with a sink dead centre. By building a trapdoor to temporarily block the opening to the upstairs, he keeps the heat on the main floor.

Shortly before school is due to start, we move into our new home. Grandpapa and Granddad carry in the heavy furniture: kitchen range, cabinet, wooden table, sewing machine and cream separator.

Then Grandpapa hitches up the team and drives away with Granddad beside him. They must have a surprise in store, I guess from the expressions on their faces, as smug as a cat that swallowed a canary.

Later, the grandfathers return with Mother's piano, muffled in quilts like a huge pampered baby, waiting to be welcomed to its new home.

"Oh, the piano! The piano!" she cries, tears of joy streaming down her cheeks as she rushes outdoors to meet them. Mr. Williams helps manoeuvre the monstrous piano into a corner of the living room. We hold our breaths as the bulky quilts are rolled away, and our elegant shiny black piano stands there, red velvet material peeping through ornate fretwork across the front.

"Oh, Mom! Play us something," we all beg as Mother lovingly strokes the yellowish ivory keyboard. Douglas runs to fetch the piano stool, and she sits down. After a thoughtful silence, she strikes the keys firmly. A familiar hymn fills the room:

What a friend we have in Jesus,
All our sins and grief to bear.
What a privilege to carry
Everything to God in prayer.
Have we trials or temptation?
Is there trouble anywhere?
We should never be discouraged.
Take it to the Lord in prayer.

THIRTY-ONE

Nit-Picking

Picking berries. Mom on right. 1945.

There are no saskatoons or pin cherries, but the cranberries survive the hailstorm, protected by spruce trees overhanging the muskeg. I love to prowl across its spongy surface in search of ripe berries. The trees are awash with russet and golden leaves after the first slight frost. Cranberry patches flame in brilliant clusters among the dark green spruce. I enjoy the solitude of the setting. As I strip the berries with my strong fingers, my thoughts drift like the leaves.

This muskeg must have been the site of an old fort, and here along the roadway the pioneers built a picket fence. It has fallen and is buried with earth. But I can still see the sharp pointed poles poking out all along the ditch of the muskeg road. I must show Douglas. He'll help explore. Maybe we'll find the remains of the old fort. What was it like to be a pioneer? I'm glad the Indians are no longer hostile, but it must have been exciting, living in a fort.

It's an early fall. It seems Mother Nature is hurrying to ripen whatever harvest survived the hailstorm. There are signs of autumn everywhere.

The sky is darkened and frantic with migrating geese. Coloured leaves fall steadily, swept from the poplar trees by a gentle breeze. The air is sharp and clear.

I fill my bucket and hurry home. I have a surprise for Noël. "Look what I found," I call out. "Hazelnuts. There's a fine clump of hazelnut trees along the edge of the muskeg. Let's peel these for Nan."

We nibble on the soft, meaty nuts as we strip the hulls, satisfying our craving for sweets. Chocolates and gum aren't available at Rochfort Bridge; food is rationed because a war is on, an accepted fact. So we long for treats.

"Hey, Douglas! Guess what I found on the muskeg road? A pole fence. The whole thing has fallen down and is covered with dirt, but it's a fence all right. There must've been a fort up there, long ago, because the fence poles are all pointed. Will you go with me after chores and have a look at it? Maybe we'll find the logs from the old fort, too. Wouldn't that be grand?"

"Yes," admits Douglas gravely. "It certainly would. All right, I'll hurry through chores and we'll ride over on Nipper. Will you help me?"

I willingly pitch in, and after a hasty supper, we set off, riding double on Nipper's sleek back. In no time, we reach the muskeg. "Here, Doug, over here." I slide from the pony. "The top of the fence is sticking out all along the ditch. See here?"

Doug hunkers down to examine the sharply pointed poles of tamarack, which protrude along the ditch. They lie side by side, exactly as though they have fallen together, and are covered with a layer of soil about a foot deep.

"Oh, Ardith," murmurs Douglas kindly. "Do you know what you've found? Corduroy. This is the way pioneers built roadways across muskegs. You see, the ground is so spongy that their wheels would sink out of sight, so they chopped tamarack trees and laid them side by side along the trail. They shovelled good earth on top, so oxen or horses wouldn't sink their legs between the poles. The corduroy road bore the load of their wagon easily because the weight was distributed over a wider area. This old muskeg road still has the original corduroy. That's a real discovery, you know."

But I was crestfallen. "You mean this isn't a fence? There is no fort?"

"No, but you *did* discover a road built by pioneers. You must tell Nan about this. She'll be very interested."

After boosting me back onto the pony, Douglas mounts and we go home. I'm bitterly disappointed and go straight to bed.

Now that Noël's in school, we spend all our time together. "Will you show me how to make an eight? I always get mine lopsided and Miss McPhillip says I should practise," frets Noël.

While she's labouring over printing, I push the kettle onto the range and feed the flames kindling. The water soon boils.

Noël glances up. "What are you making?"

"Tea," I tell her. Noël's eyes grow round in horror.

"You know we aren't allowed to drink tea. Mom says it will stunt our growth."

"I know that. But she's away in the far field, ploughing, and she won't be home till dark. We have plenty of time to try tea. Someday I'm going to try coffee, too. It can't be that dangerous. Lots of kids at school say they drink coffee all the time."

We sip the bitter tea. What a disappointment! Even laced with sugar, the taste is unpleasant.

"Ugh!" says Noël, rinsing out her cup. "What's all the fuss over 'a good cup of tea'? I don't like it."

"Me neither." I wash away the evidence.

"Do you think I'll grow any more?" asks Noël. I look lovingly at her.

"No, I don't," I say thoughtfully. "I think you will always be small."

Mom provides nourishing school lunches for us kids. The neighbour kids stare wistfully at my sandwiches with black currant jam oozing out the edges. I seldom have cake or fresh fruit, but compared to some other lunches, I realize mine is generous, and I feel cherished.

We walk home from school next day, savouring the sunshine and watching blackbirds beating an ever-changing pattern in the sky. The birds are joining larger flocks, preparing for fall migration. The golden elders outshine all the other bushes along the lane.

"What a perfect day to go horseback riding," I say. "I'm going to ask if I may ride with Anita. She wants to go along the cut banks to the old ford. That sounds like fun."

I hurry chores and start supper. The potatoes are boiling by the time Mom comes home.

"Anita wants me to ride with her this evening, Mom. May I?"

"I'll do the dishes by myself," offers Noël.

"If you promise to be back before sundown, you may go. And please be very careful."

Nipper trots along willingly. Anita waits at her gate

astride Jack, a rangy work horse. We head westward, skirting the tops of cut banks bordering the river. Spruce trees cling to crusts of soil along the steep cut bank, and defy gravity by not losing their grip and sliding to the bottom. The horses pick their way around huge brush piles of half-burned logs, lying in tangled windrows on the breaking.

"Grandpapa is waiting for snowfall, so he can set these afire again. It's too dry to burn them right now," I tell Anita. "A fire would really spread in this dry grass."

We ride through the old slough, where long brown cat-tails stand like bottle brushes amid bent reeds. They burst and explode into puffs of powdery clouds, and Ol' Jack begins to sneeze. We giggle, light-hearted and silly.

I feel a sense of freedom, swishing through the grasses, which reach my pony's belly, cutting a track through the wilderness. I see the river, a glittering ribbon of blue through the centre of the valley.

An old trail winds down the steep bank. Nipper scoots her hind legs, dragging her front and scuttles down making me bounce.

"You sure look funny," calls Anita, her horse sedately descending. The horses wade through the shallows at the old ford, pausing to drink some cool water.

We ride home through the valley. Dogwood bushes stand blood-red in the dappled shadows, sheltered by stately Balm of Gilead trees.

"Look," calls Anita. "See that grey ball up there—on the tree." She rides closer to inspect it.

"Careful, Anita," I warn. "It's a wasp nest. They sting like anything. Let's get out of here." And I nudge Nipper into a trot.

"Race you to the bridge," challenges Anita, and off she goes loping loosely on Ol' Jack. I urge Nipper into a full gallop, and bounce like a rubber ball. Nipper stretches out, but she's no match for the bigger horse.

"Beat you by a mile," laughs Anita. "Let's trade ponies for the rest of the way."

I soon realize why Anita wants to trade. Jack has a peculiar gait, throwing the rider backward and forward in the tall saddle. I have never used a saddle and find that the stirrups irritate my ankles. I'm pleased to claim Nipper and wave goodbye to Anita.

I return the pony to the pasture. Trees trace soft shadows against the still luminous sky, and the cobalt hills blend into the horizon.

Noël and I march home from school the next week. "I hate taking this note to Mom," declares Noël. "She'll be really upset. Remember how she shook everything and washed all our bedding and towels before she moved things into the new house? She was so proud to get rid of all those bedbugs. There aren't any in our new house. And now this! I'm sure Mom will think we're the only kids that have head lice. But really, half the kids have nits, and everyone's been exposed. So we all have notes to bring home."

Noël is right. Mom is downright upset. She fetches the square galvanized washtub immediately, half filling it with rainwater. Then she pokes small sticks into the firebox to quickly heat the water in the tub.

Mom stands Noël on the back step in the bright sunshine, and combs her hair carefully. She uses a fine-toothed comb repeatedly dipped into a tomato can of kerosene, soaking every inch of hair. Then she washes Noël's hair.

"Keep your eyes closed," Mom warns. "And don't go near the fire."

I'm next. Mom unleashes my hair and examines each section closely, separating strands of hair with two toothpicks.

Sure enough! As she checks the halo region between the nape of neck and ears, Mom discovers infinitesimally tiny egg cases sticking to my hair.

"Look, Ruby," cries Mom in alarm. "These might be nits. They look like tiny, dark seeds. But I thought nits were always white. I'm going to try sliding these things along her hair. No. They won't budge. Well, Ardith dear, you have nits. We'll have to really soak you with kerosene. Hold still."

Mom slathers the smelly coal oil generously along each shaft of hair, scolding all the time. "Who were you playing with, Ardith?" Mom demands in disgust. "It must have been someone dirty."

"But I play with everyone," I wail. "I like everyone. And they all like me. None of them are dirty, Mom."

"That's true, Mom," Ruby defends me. "Miss McPhillip says anyone or everyone can catch head lice. She says the insects actually prefer the cleanest heads. And she says head lice enjoy going back to school even more than we kids do."

"Nonsense," says Mom, yanking my hair sharply. "Ardith was playing with someone who is dirty." She's annoyed that her daughter has brought home such disgrace. Head lice!

"There!" She says finally, braiding the long tresses so tightly that the veins stand out on my forehead. "Now don't announce about those nits. I don't want *everyone to know!*"

"Now I know what nit-picking means," I mutter to Noël as we wander outdoors. We have been sent out to air, so the fumes will evaporate.

Douglas and Ruby are given a louse treatment also. Last of all, Ruby checks Mom's hair.

Granddad chuckles as I whisper my shameful secret. "Bet your Mom is mad as a wet coon in a paper sack," he says.

Other families give their children checkups too, and there are no more notes from school. Head lice are under control.

"I have a surprise," Mom tells us on Friday evening. "Since there are no wild berries around here this fall, Mr. Seaton is planning to take his truck to Blue Ridge on Sunday, if the weather stays fine. We can all go along to pick blueberries. It will be an all-day trip, with a picnic in the patch. How does that sound?"

"Oh Mom, how wonderful! I've never been to Blue Ridge," exclaims Noël.

"Me neither," I agree. "And I love picking blueberries. It's so much faster than cranberry picking."

"Riding all that way in the back of a big truck sounds like fun," Douglas says.

"Will Ruby be able to come too?" asks Noël.

"I'll ask Nan," replies Mom. "We'll have to skip church, because Mr. Seaton is leaving early. You'd better stir us up a spice cake, Ardith, so we can share at the picnic. Now, let's all get our chores finished early this Saturday, so we can have a good rest."

We do chores cheerfully, keeping an eye on the sky. I'm pleased that the fine weather holds. It's crisp and clear, with no frost to spoil the blueberries. Douglas piles all our berry pails near the door, ready for a quick start in the morning. Noël eyes them with dismay.

"Do you really expect us to fill all those?" she asks.

"Better to be safe than sorry," laughs Mom. "We'll certainly try. Now I want you young people to pick as many as you possibly can. I'll have to pay Mr. Seaton gas money. So this expedition is not just a big picnic. Do you understand?"

Of course. We know how to work. Mom doesn't want us to appear lazy—then *everyone would know* she has lazy kids. Well, she doesn't have to worry about me. I love berry picking.

It takes a long time for me to settle for the night. Mom sleeps in her own bedroom now, leaving us three kids to sleep in the huge front room. Noël and I share a wooden bunk that

Grandpapa has designed. It's really a shallow box, with two-by-four legs at each corner. An edge of wood keeps our tick from shifting off. Mom's upset that the straw ticks had to follow us into her new house, but there simply isn't enough money to buy mattresses.

Doug has a narrow cot to himself. He can finally stretch to his full length when he rests. The little crib is folded away in the junk granary. Whenever Ruby spends the night at home, she sleeps with Mom in the downstairs bedroom.

I listen to the wood snap and pop in the heater. Blue Ridge, I muse. I wonder if I can make a poem about Blue Ridge. But before I do, I fall fast asleep.

Dawn finds us scurrying to do chores. Douglas milks old Annette, while Mom makes a quick breakfast. Noël checks the chickens and I make sandwiches. We have a hurried bite to eat and are ready by six. Ruby arrives from Nan's place.

"Oh, good, Ruby's coming too," breathes Noël.

"We'd better hustle." calls Mom, gathering an armful of buckets. "Come along." Everyone carries something as we rush to town. A huge harvest moon is hugging the horizon, a perfect day for blueberry picking.

"Hi, Anita! Hi, Billy!" I call. "Hey, everybody is here." It seems all the neighbours are eager to take advantage of picking berries. They pile into the truck box, sitting flat on the floor. Mr. Seaton ties his tarpaulin overhead, cutting the wind and offering protection in case the weather changes.

The loose tarp flaps wildly in the wind. It's exhilarating at first, but as the truck toils along dusty roads, the noise makes my head ache. I stop singing Old McDonald and Ten Green Bottles and doze off. I'm suffering from motion sickness when the old truck swings into the berry patch. I leap from the truck and disappear among the bushes. I'll make Mom proud, I vow. I'll fill every pail with blueberries.

Doug, Noël, Ruby and Ardith. 1943.

"Ruby," calls Mrs. Smith. "Would you stay near the truck and keep an eye on Sally for me, please?"

"And Sam," adds another neighbour.

"And Sandy," adds a third. How can she refuse? I bring my bucket to Ruby, who sorts and cleans the berries while entertaining the toddlers. Later in the day, Noël helps Ruby keep the youngsters happy.

The noon picnic is grand. Everyone shares lunches. "I'll swap my black currant jam sandwich for your turkey sandwich, Anita," I offer.

"Look at all the pies and cakes," whispers Noël. 'I'd like to try a bit of each!"

Mr. Seaton provides a large crock of cool lemonade. He smiles and smokes his pipe with satisfaction. "Glad to help out," he says sincerely when Mom thanks him for the ride.

All too soon, shadows lengthen and it's time to pile into the truck. Everyone is tired, but thankful for the bountiful berries and friendly fellowship of neighbours.

Mom sorts blueberries every evening when it gets too dark and cold to plough. She gazes with satisfaction at the sealers of dark berries she has preserved. "Such a treat for us this winter," she breathes. Praise to us kids.

I love to read aloud to Nan as the old lady knits. "Well, have you come to entertain me, dear?" Nan chuckles, her hands constantly busy. Freckles spangle her soft arms like stars on an old American flag. I try to be very creative, and change the sound effects. Even then, Nan sometimes dozes off.

Mother works late at the ploughing. Sea gulls follow the rig around the field, finding a fresh supply of juicy worms exposed in the moist, black earth. *Mom must be exhausted* I think as I walk home. I know she wants to finish the ploughing before freeze-up.

Geese brake their descent to the pond by flapping desperately, honking a warning as they splash down. I'm glad to reach the comforting warmth and smells of our house. Ruby has soup simmering, knowing Mother will be frozen when she comes home.

There's no sunlight next morning. Dark grey clouds curtain the sky, making a dull sameness of the surroundings— shrubs, fields and buildings all share sombre tones. We dress warmly for our brisk walk to school.

By noon, heavy clouds with white at the edges fill the sky. The first snowflakes of the season fall lightly over the drab countryside, until the earth below is fluffy white. We're delighted with this first snow as we walk home.

Small eddies of snowflakes ripple across the path. I hold up my face to the gently falling flakes and open my mouth to catch the snowflakes on my tongue. They melt to nothing.

What if each snowflake has a magic power? And wherever a snowflake lands will be white forever? Then I can stand here and have snowflakes fall all over my face until my freckles disappear and my face is white and beautiful. No more freckles!

Winter lies upon the land.

THIRTY-TWO

Orphan

Granddad with horse (Ol' Tom center) with Uncle Lawrence. 1946.

"Ardith," Mom says softly. "Look what I brought you." I blink in surprise. Then I roll off the bed where I was lying, chewing on my fingernails.

"What's wrapped in the sack, Mom?"

Rolling the cover back, Mom exposes a tiny newborn lamb. A perfect miniature, covered in fleecy white wool, its brown liquid eyes plead for attention. It bleats tragic sounds, terrified by everything.

"Grandpapa says you may have her," Mom tells me, "if you're willing to care for her. Her mother died when she was born. None of the other ewes will adopt this little thing. Their lambs are half grown and won't share with such a tiny creature. Poor wee lamb, born out of season! And her mother died because she was really too young to be a mother. But the lamb seems normal. She's just a runt. You'll have to feed her from a bottle. Often, too. Would you like to have her, Ardith?"

"Oh, Mom! What a precious wee lamb! I'd love to have her. I'm going to call her Bo-Peep. Because she lost her sheep. Oh, come here, you sweet wee lambie."

I fetch a cardboard box and line it with the sack. But Bo-Peep looks so forlorn that I roll her up in the cloth and tuck her under my arm as I bustle about, heating milk and finding the baby bottle. I search through the junk drawer until I find the rubber nipple kept for feeding baby pigs. Testing the milk temperature on the inside of my wrist, I settle myself to feed the lamb.

Mom, smiles in quiet satisfaction. "That'll keep you busy," she says. "It's kind of Papa to give you the runt. Now you have something to think about. And I love the name you came up with—Bo-Peep!" Mom smiles again as she watches me with the lamb.

Everyone loves Bo-Peep. Although she's supposed to stay in her box, she follows us around the house as soon as she gains strength. I cheerfully clean puddles and droppings and feed the lamb faithfully. Now that Mom's indoors for the winter, she gives Bo-Peep milk while we're at school. The little lamb grows. She develops a friendly disposition and seems to think she's a person. She curls up with Noël's cat to sleep in her box, but insists on attention from some member of the family during her waking time. Butting her head persistently into someone's lap, she begs to be petted. And she grows bigger.

Granddad laughs at Bo-Peep's antics when he visits us. I cuddle my lamb and sing:

Poor Bo-Peep lost Mommy sheep
And can't tell where to find her.
Bo-Peep's alone. She moved to our home
Leaving her worries behind her.

Mommy Ewe died. How Bo-Peep cried.
She's lost without her mother.
I'll give her feed. Care for her needs—
Clean her. Train her and love her.

Bo-Peep continues to grow all through October. By the middle of November, she drinks from a bowl.

"I have a special surprise for you, Douglas," Mom announces. "Nan is coming to your birthday party. We're going to have your celebration in our new house, which Nan is anxious to see. So Grandpapa will bring her over right after she listens to *The Happy Gang* on the radio. She'll be here by the time you young people get home from school. Let's tidy the house tonight and get a cake baked. What kind would you like, Doug?"

"Chocolate!" he replies instantly. "With chocolate icing, please."

"I'll stir up the cake right now," Ruby offers. "Before I head over to Nan's. And I'll stay overnight with them, to get Nan ready for the birthday party."

"Fine," agrees Mom. "Be sure to put the rocks in the oven, so they will be heated for her feet. And hang the buffalo robe in her kitchen tonight. Spread it over the backs of two kitchen chairs, so it will warm up nicely. I think you should take her black coat out of her closet and hang it over a kitchen chair, too. It may feel really chilly. It's so long since Nan was outdoors; we certainly don't want her to catch a cold."

Douglas is pleased with the news and grins as he disappears to do chores. Ruby whips up a cake, and then heads to

Nan's place. Noël and I sweep and dust the house. I meticulously arrange the photographs and vases on the piano. I'm upset when things are untidy; I like to arrange everything in perfect order. It distresses me when Mom leaves clutter on the kitchen countertop.

I'd better not criticize Mom, I think, while rearranging the cupboards so they look decent. Look at all these bread crumbs. Must be from the sandwiches when Mom made lunches. I twirl my cloth in circles, gathering crumbs.

"Supper," Mom calls. We three children know there's a treat in store. Potato pancakes. We pour Roger's Golden Syrup over them. Delicious.

"I'll leave the dishpan on the back of the stove while I wash dishes," I tell Noël. "That syrup sure makes the plates sticky. Hurry and dry them, Noël, so we can draw straws."

"Ha, ha!" Noël gloats. "You got the long straw, Ardith. Now you have to wash the dirtiest half of the floor. Ha, ha."

I smile ruefully as I fill the bucket half full of warm soapy water. I fetch the floor cloth and scrub brush.

"I'll sure be glad when we can afford linoleum," I mutter, giving an especially hard scrub to the area under the slop bucket.

"Finished my half," I announce with a flourish of the cloth. "Here you are, Noël, exactly half. Right up to the edge of this middle board."

Noël eyes her side of the floor. "I think washing in front of the door is just as bad as scrubbing under the slop pail," she claims. "I have to lift all the boots up to wipe under them. And some awful stuff drops off. Ugh!" But she works briskly, and after finishing the chore, she dumps out the filthy water.

"Let's wrap Doug's present before he comes in." giggles Noël. "Nan showed me how to knit and I've been struggling for weeks now. I finished this up last night."

She holds up a long, colourful scarf for Doug. "Look, Ardith. I did it all by myself." I admire the scarf, which we wrap in grocer-paper and tie with colourful yarn.

"Well," I say, "I made Doug a card." I show my sister a folder with a picture of our family painted on the front. Inside is a verse:

We all have a wonderful brother;
We have only him and none other.
He's kind and he's true,
We really love you,
Say his sisters and his loving mother.

"Oh, Ardith, that's great!"

"Race you home from school," I challenge. Douglas beats all three sisters and is first to greet Nan with a kiss the next afternoon. We girls follow suit. Nan sits in her rocker near the heater. Bo-Peep's head is on her lap. Nan's fingers trace lazy circles in the fleece, and the lamb enjoys all her attention.

"Have we time for a game of Chinese checkers before lunch?" asks Douglas.

"Certainly," agrees Mom. "You little people may have a game with Nan. Ruby, will you help me get the lunch?"

We're careful to select the darkest marbles, although even those are difficult for Nan to see. But the game is a merry one.

Ruby takes her place at the piano as Mom enters the front room carrying the cake with lighted candles. Striking a chord, Ruby leads the singing:

Happy birthday to you; happy birthday to you;
Happy birthday, dear Douglas; happy birthday to you.

"Make a wish, Doug," cries Noël.

"Blow, Doug," I laugh.

Ten candles wink out at once.

"Here's Grandpapa," calls Ruby, as the family enjoys the cake. Grandpapa ties his team securely and takes time for a hasty cup of coffee and some cake. Ruby helps Nan into her long black coat. When Nan settles back into her rocker, Grandpapa, Mom, Ruby and Douglas pick it up and carefully carry her to the sleigh. Noël and I follow with the warmed buffalo robe, while Mom runs to the oven and rolls the hot rocks into their sack. These are set near Nan's feet, and the robe tucks around her. Ruby and Mom go along in the sleigh to help carry Nan into her own home. There Ruby stays, while Mom walks home. Douglas is doing chores and we girls have finished dishes before Mom returns.

"Nan really loves our house," Mom reports. "She noticed how tidy it is, too, girls. Thank you both. But do you know what she liked best? Bo-Peep."

"Great party, Mom," Doug thanks his mother. "It was so nice to have Nan over. We haven't had her here since our house burned down. How long ago was that, Mom?"

"Almost five years," Mom replies. Five years since we had a proper house. Five years of war. How much longer, dear God? How much longer?

I see Mom's face convulse more rapidly than usual. "Mom's tired," I whisper to Noël. "Let's go out to the barn." We still spend long hours there because we know Mom needs a quiet space.

Wisps of fluffy clouds lie against the yellow evening sky like whipped egg white on a bread pudding. "What a perfect evening. Would you like to go to town to meet the mail train?" asks Mom, knowing Douglas longs to hear from his Dad.

"Sure, Mom," says Douglas casually. "Will Dad remember my birthday?" He disappears down the trail in the gloom. Noël and I are in our pyjamas listening to Mom reading to us when we hear the squeak of Doug's boots on the snow.

"Hi," he calls out. "I got a postcard. Dad's been to Scotland for a furlough. And he says, 'Wish I could be with you on your birthday.'"

Bo-Peep becomes a nuisance in the house. "That lamb is too big to be indoors," Mom tells me.

"But Mom," I protest. "What shall we do with her? She can't go out to the barn. The cows might step on her. She's still so little."

"Nonsense," replies Mom. "She'll be just fine in the barn. I'll show you something. See, I'm putting this little bell around her neck to warn the cows when she's underfoot. She'll be all right, Ardith. You'll see. The cows won't hurt her."

Sadly, I carry Bo-Peep through deep snow to the barn. Placing her little box safely behind an unused stanchion, I arrange the sacking carefully. "I'll check on you in the morning," I whisper. "And I'll bring your milk. I love you." I kiss Bo-Peep and run away, tears streaming down my cheeks.

The little lamb thrives in the barn. She grows bigger and follows the cattle across the field to the stack for shelter, Bo-Peep always last of a single file.

"Now Bo-Peep thinks she's a cow." I mourn.

"She's fine," says Mom. "She's perfectly content with the cows." Mom smiles as she hears the steady tinkle of the sheep bell.

Dark blue clouds seem to sweep into a clear sky like huge blots of ink that seep into blotting paper.

"What a perfect evening to go riding," I say a few days later. "Come on, Noël. Let's take Nipper for a spin."

"Can I come, too?" asks Douglas.

"Three on a pony?" I stare in astonishment. "Oh, Doug, I don't think ... "

"Just a minute," says our brother mysteriously. He disappears and returns with a long rope. "Bring the hand sleigh, Noël," he calls. I put the bridle on Nipper. Then Doug mounts behind me and loops the rope around his waist.

"Okay, Noël, you ride on the sleigh." Away we jog down the lane, with Noël trailing behind, buffeted by drifts. When she gets cold, she trades places with me. We're even able to give Douglas a turn on the sleigh. We come home with rosy cheeks and snowy clothes; sleighing was great fun.

The next evening, Mom tells us over our meal of clapshot and sausage, "Today is Nipper's birthday. Grandpapa has it written on his calendar."

"Really?" We bolt our food, anxious to go to the barn.

"Hey, kids," says Noël. "Let's have a birthday party for Nipper."

"All right," I agree. I scrape the leftover potato and turnip mixture to the slop pail. "Here's some clapshot for Bessie," I say. And away to the barn we run.

"I'll make a cake," I offer, dipping out a generous measure of chop, and spreading it into a shallow pan.

"I'll get the candles," says Noël. "How old is she?"

"Four," I tell her. So Noël sticks four straws into the chop. Then we sing the birthday song to our little pony. Nipper seems delighted with our attention, and certainly enjoys her cake. We sit on her broad back, playing checkers while Douglas finishes the milking and feeds the pigs. Then we walk to the house together. The lantern casts eerie shadows across the snowy yard and shines on the lonely cabin, forsaken beside the shelterbelt. Our old cabin looks forlorn and forgotten, I think.

Cpl. William Ray as aircraft ground mechanic. 1945.

Suddenly Douglas blows out the lantern. We stop in surprise.

"What happened, Doug?" asks Noël. Doug points upward. The heavens are awash with dancing coloured lights. Arcs of brilliance swirl and swish in ever-changing patterns against the northern sky, twinkling with a million stars. We gaze in awe at such splendour.

"I wonder if Daddy can see the northern lights tonight?" asks Noël. It's a sobering thought. We creep quietly into the house.

I can't even remember Dad, I realize. I remember things he did … , but what does he look like? I can think only of flashing teeth when he laughed. Oh, I wish the war would end, so Daddy could come home.

THIRTY-THREE

A Quarter at a Time

Mom says I sing like a bird.

I can read from encyclopedias, dance the schottische and polka, and chord on the piano when Grandpapa plays Red Wing and Golden Slippers.

"Time for music lessons," Mom says. I am ecstatic. To learn to let my fingers fly over those yellowish keys, bringing out a whole orchestra of sounds, I can hardly wait.

My lesson time is two o'clock, Friday. I'm excused from school, to walk alone to Mrs. Rozko's house. But she isn't the music teacher. Oh, no. Mrs. Rozko gets free lessons for both her kids for letting the music teacher use her house in town to teach in. And use her piano. And even eat lunch there. A good deal.

I have a quarter tied in my hanky. And I carry a brand-new book, a dictation book, with blue-lined pages and every second page ruled with black staff lines.

I knock on the tattered screen door. Mrs. Rozko leads me into her living room. It's a beautiful room with dark brown wood carvings of elegant design around the French door and a tall brown, shiny upright piano with a stool that goes around and round until I feel tippy and spinny. The piano has its name BELL written above the keyboard.

Mrs. Sim sits on a sofa surrounded by music sheets. Her grey eyes look solemn and serious. She wears silver-rimmed spectacles on her soft grey face and her thick grey hair is rolled into a bun. She wears a pretty blue dress.

"Sit down," she smiles. "Let me see your fingers."

I hold my skinny pink fingers stiffly, glad I've scratched away the dirt from under my nails. Mrs. Sim sighs. "Ve'll see." She has a Latvian accent. Her husband is called Captain. There's something about his disgrace because he didn't go down with his ship. I don't see why. But they had to leave their country. Now he's a farmer but doesn't know how to farm. His wife makes the living, a quarter at a time. She was a concert pianist.

She plays for me. Her fingers flutter up and down the keyboard like busy butterflies, and the old piano sounds magnificent. I'm spellbound and stand twisting my hanky round and round in my sweaty fingers.

"Now ve begin."

She makes pencil spots climbing uphill and downhill on my black-ruled page. "Notes," she calls them. "With a nice FACE, Every Good Boy Does Fine," she claims. Not always, I've noticed. But I don't correct her.

She plays C scale, pointing out the mountains. I play C scale.

Mrs. Sim slaps my thumb with her pencil. The second time I do it correctly. She gives me a sheet of music. Twinkle Twinkle Little Star. Baby stuff. I'm seven years old. But I decide to humour her. I rattle it off, plunking a chord with my left. It sounds rich. Full. Rounded.

"Wrong."

I hadn't followed the notes. I didn't fold my finger over. I just thumped out that song in perfect timing.

Slap. Slap goes the pencil. She hits my folding finger.

"Practise. All veek. C scale and Tvinkle Tvinkle."

I fork over the quarter. Gather my book and the sheet music and trudge back to school. I had hoped to learn Flight of the Bumblebee.

Time passes.

I can run off my new selections easily, first asking Mrs. Sim to play them for me at lesson time. I simply imitate.

She reports to Mom that I play by ear. How silly. I use my fingers the same as she does.

She reports to Mom that my left hand is heavy as a galloping horse. Of course. I'm left-handed. If I could just twist and turn my right fingers as quickly, I'd be in sync.

I have to practise for weeks for a dreaded piano recital. Everyone will be there. Mom and Ruby and Doug and Noël. All the kids who are taking lessons. My brother practises Happy Farmer. He can rattle it off. Ruby works on He Leadeth Me with four flats. It's tough, but she masters it.

I'm playing La Paloma. It's my turn. I sit at the keyboard in the town hall, hearing whispering and snotty sounds and scuffing shoes and coughing. I stare at my fingers. What did Mrs. Sim see in them?

I look around. Mrs. Sim stands beside the stage, wringing her hands. Does she think I'll make a mistake? I can hear her gentle warning in my mind, "If you make a mistake, just start over. No one vill notice." I'll bet! Suddenly I begin to play. My left hand thumps out the rhythm. Tum-de-TUM-tum. Tum-de-TUM-tum. Von-and-TWO-three. Von-and-TWO-three. I play La Paloma as it has never been played before. Then I rise from the piano bench and curtsey, amid a thunder of applause.

I never do learn to play Flight of the Bumble Bee.

THIRTY-FOUR

White Christmas

Cpl. William Ray at work RCAF. 1945.

I'm thinking of our white Christmas.
Everything here is topped with snow.
But where Daddy lies
Under foreign skies
He sees dark grey ground below.

I'm praying on this white Christmas
That World War II will cease to be.
That the fighting ends,
Everyone makes friends,
And Daddy comes back home to me.

I compose this little verse at school in my spare time.

The Christmas concert is the highlight for the Ray family this year, because all of us kids are participating for the first time. Ruby practises her music lesson after school every day before going to Nan's for the evening.

After completing chores, Noël and I practise our singing. Douglas reviews his songs with Annette, keeping time by a rhythmic swish in the bucket as he milks. I watch the unborn calf shudder inside Annette's body while the cow twists her head in the stanchion and looks at us with large, liquid eyes. I hunker down with Bo-Peep. Full-grown now, the sheep no longer needs her cardboard sleeping box, and rests in a stall with the yearling heifer. I groom Bo-Peep, using Nipper's currycomb to sweep straw from the shaggy back and tail. Bo-Peep hasn't been docked, so her long woolly tail needs grooming regularly. Noël brushes Nipper's sleek sides; the pony loves attention and nickers softly.

"Mom says Nan and Grandpapa are coming to our house this Christmas," Noël reminds us.

"And Granddad, too," I add. "And Uncle Lawrence."

"Isn't it grand to have enough room for our whole family again?" asks Douglas. "We can put both boards in the table so we'll all fit around at once and we kids won't have to wait until all the adults have eaten."

"Well, we're almost adults ourselves," I say self-consciously.

Time passes with us busy preparing for the festive season.

"Who wants to help choose the Christmas tree?" calls Douglas.

"I do!" I cry.

"Me too!" calls Noël.

"Dress warmly then," says Mom. "The snow is really deep in the pasture."

Filmy white streaks swing from heavy sullen clouds banking the northern sky. The mercury is well below zero. Noël and I pull the hand sleigh and Douglas carries the axe. It seems much farther to the pasture through the drifts. I see tufts of coarse slough grasses poking in jagged clusters through the crust.

"Here's a pretty tree!" says Douglas at last. We girls check the spruce.

"Yes, it's well shaped."

"And not too tall. Okay, Douglas, chop it down."

But springy branches make the tree keep jumping off the sleigh until Douglas says, "I'll drag the tree home."

The wind's blowing right through my coat. My fingers tingle, my toes sting, and I feel like crying. Why does cold affect me more than the others?

A flock of partridges explodes from a snowbank and takes wing, which startles us as we hurry home.

"Come see the tree," calls Noël.

"That's a beauty," Mom agrees. "Just the right height. Let's leave it out until Christmas Eve. I feel uneasy with a tree near the heater while we're away at the concerts. I'm deathly afraid of another house fire."

Few attend the United Church Sunday school concert in the hall that afternoon. Lutherans, Catholics and Baptists all have their own concerts.

Finally, the last day of school before Christmas arrives. Early that morning, Miss McPhillip sends Normie and John to light both stoves in the town hall. By noon, the building warms enough for us to decorate. Billy's dad drops off a tall spruce tree, which Normie and John set up. My group decorates the tree. Ruby's grade transforms the stage ceiling into a splendid night sky by completely covering it with dark blue crepe paper tacked up with large foil stars. Spanning the entire width backstage is a wire on which one huge metallic star is suspended. A fish line attached to the star allows Normie to reel in, making the star slide magically through the sky.

Everything is ready by three o'clock, so Miss McPhillip dismisses early, allowing us time to do our chores before returning for the evening program.

Every family finds a spot in the crowded hall since it's the most exciting time of year. When the curtain rises, there's stunned silence. I look with dismay at the stage. Heat rising from the two stoves has stretched the crepe paper sky. It hangs in billows; sagging blue paper obliterates the foil stars. The class performs perfectly in spite of the lowering sky. Our parents sit on backless benches and applaud with gusto.

A single gas lamp hangs from centre stage to light the hall. It has a flat shield on one side, and when we're performing the lamp is turned so that the light shines on the stage, leaving the audience in shadow. A half turn of the lamp at the end of each act gives the audience house-light to gossip while we set the stage for the next act.

Ruby plays her piano solo flawlessly; Mom's mouth smiles like a crack in the johnnycake. And last comes the nativity pageant. I glide solemnly on stage with other cheese-cloth-clad angels, my bare feet blue with cold as I stand with the alto angels. The soprano angels stand together behind us. Ruby stands at the very top of the ladder, taking the role of Gabriel. Lizzy is Mary and settles herself centre stage, while John takes a Joseph stance beside her, almost unrecognizable behind his bushy beard. Miss McPhillip rearranges Billy beside the other shepherds, and creeps off stage, before she signals for the curtain.

The curtain rolls up; but only halfway, and then it sticks. The audience chuckles, seeing the angels' curling bare toes, their uneven cheesecloth hemlines, and their shivering blue ankles, but they can't see their faces. They can see Mary sitting with an astonished expression, and Joseph kneeling beside her.

Normie yanks and tugs, but the curtain refuses to rise. Finally two men from the audience come and fold the curtain around its heavy roller and stand holding it on each edge of the platform. The show goes on. Although Gabriel is completely hidden from view, her heavenly music wafts down from the ladder-top. It is really Ruby, singing her heart out.

"Behold! I see a star. We must follow it," cries a Wise Man, and points to the huge hanging star, Normie's cue to reel it in. He tries, but the star refuses to budge. Normie reels and the star threatens to buckle, but still it doesn't move. The Wise Men are dumbfounded, not knowing whether to enter the stable, or wait for the star. They glance around uncertainly, looking for directions from the teacher. She picks her way through children standing beside the stage, and tries to get backstage to direct the Wise Men. But Normie saves the play. He throws his reel down in disgust, marches across backstage, grabs the star and drags it along the wire by hand. The Wise

Men trail uncertainly behind, and thus discover Mary and Joseph, looking as dignified as possible with faces red from suppressed laughter. Everyone agrees it is the best pageant ever.

After intermission, Santa Claus arrives with candy bags for all. I'm thrilled to receive a Jap orange in my bag, my first orange of the winter.

Christmas Day at home is exciting. We wait for our grandparents to arrive before gift opening. When Nan is finally settled in her rocker beside the decorated tree, Douglas hands around the gifts. "Because he's the man of this house," explains Mom.

I'm delighted with a doll that can stand alone, has real hair, two pearly teeth and a generous sprinkle of freckles across her nose.

"Looks like you, Chickie," roars Uncle Lawrence. I smile politely, but I know better. My doll is pretty; I'm ugly. There are very few gifts under the tree, although everyone is remembered with something handmade. Finally only one large, mysterious box is left to open. As Douglas lifts it, Granddad steps forward to help him.

"Careful," he says. "We can't tip it." They set the box in front of Mom, who peels away the cardboard, exposing a wet battery. From the grandparents.

"Oh, how perfectly wonderful!" exclaims Mom, her tears sparkling. "Now we can hook up our radio. Look, you little people. We'll have our own radio, here at home. We needn't walk over to Nan's for news anymore. Oh, thank you, Mama and Papa and Granddad and Lawrence. What a thoughtful gift for us all!"

"I'll hook it up right now," offers Lawrence gruffly, noticing Mom's tears. "Then we can catch the King's message."

I listen to the King's soft, stammering voice over the radio. I'm deciding what name to give my new dolly, and don't take in his message of hope.

Everyone fits around our square kitchen table. I'm placed where my left arm doesn't interfere with Douglas on the back bench, and Nan's rocker is drawn to the side with Grandpapa and Noël. Uncle Lawrence and Granddad sit opposite, while Ruby sits nearest the stove to help Mom serve.

"Lucky the hail didn't kill all my turkeys," chuckles Granddad. "The poults just stood there till they were knocked flat, but the adults made a run for it. So I have a turkey for you as usual, Edith."

"Yes, thank you," smiles Mom with satisfaction. "Everything on the table is home-grown. We're fortunate to have wonderful root vegetables despite the storm. The potatoes, turnips and carrots made a comeback, although the beets took a beating. And Ardith picked these cranberries from the muskeg."

"I thought about your carrot pudding when I was in England, Edith," Uncle Lawrence says. "No one can make such good pudding." Mom flushes with the praise, glad her first banquet in the new house is a success. Then she sighs. "I wonder what Will is doing today."

"And I wonder how Martha and my two little girls are," adds Uncle Lawrence.

"Here's to 1945, a new year of peace!" Grandpapa holds his glass for a toast. Everyone raises a rosy glass full of bright red tomato juice. I can see right through the clear liquid. I would rather have half a glass of pure tomato juice than a full glass watered down, I think defiantly. But Mom thinks it adds colour to our table to have red juice. Of course, she'll never serve liquor—strictly taboo!

The day ends as we gather around to hear Bing Crosby sing his latest song, White Christmas. Then Nan is bundled up and carried off. I snuggle into bed with Noël, holding my precious new doll. I'll call her Marilyn, I think, as I drift off to sleep.

THIRTY-FIVE

Radio Broadcasts

Scottish dances. 1945.

"I despise these new stockings that Nan knit for our Christmas present," I declare as Noël and I set off for school after the holidays. "None of the other girls wear hand-knit ribbed stockings. Ours look so thick. I'd like to have thin lisle stockings bought from the store, wouldn't you, Noël?"

"Yes," agrees Noël sadly. "But you know that Nan made these with love and ... "

"Oh, I know that," I burst out. "And I'd never hurt Nan's feelings. Besides, we can't afford to buy any. And Mom would never buy what can be made. And they're warmer. So we're stuck with them. I know, let's roll them down when we get close to school so the kids won't see them. We'll roll them up again when we're walking home." It seems like a good idea, but Billy notices right away.

"Haw-haw!" he teases. "You look like a Clydesdale horse with those big ankles. You have to swing your feet around each other because your socks are sticking out a mile."

I glare at Billy, tossing my head and refusing comment. Trying to be stylish has certain drawbacks, and Billy is one of them.

Ruby smiles understandingly as she watches us roll our stockings up before heading home, never mentioning it to Nan. Nor to Mom. She knows what teasing feels like, too.

Winter holds on grimly. The evenings are too cold to go riding, but Ruby walks to town on mail train nights. Otherwise we're content to stay indoors, playing board games: Parcheesi, checkers or Chinese checkers.

"We may play the radio for a half hour each evening," Mom says. "So you may choose the program. Let's each have a turn to choose."

"*The Lone Ranger!*" breathes Doug, who likes the sound of galloping horses.

"*Charlie McCarthy*," says Noël. "He says funny things."

"*Fibber McGee and Molly*," I choose, laughing to think of all their junk falling from the closet.

"Very well," agrees Mom. "That sound like an interesting week. I'll take *Lux Radio Theatre*. Of course, we'll catch the news at six o'clock so we can keep track of things. My, it's grand to have our own radio. But we mustn't neglect Nan. I'll slip over to see her every morning and catch *The Happy Gang* with her."

When a chinook arches and warm winds soften the snow, we go sleigh-riding on the river hill. Ruby is keen to practise on her new skis, but I'm not fond of them. The straps bite my feet and cut off my circulation soon after I put them on. Then

Lac Ste. Anne School Festival Diploma. 1949.

my feet get cold. Why do I get cold before anyone else? There must be something wrong with me.

Sometimes the river water freezes solid clear to the bottom. Then water from upstream bursts over the surface, and flows along the top until it completely covers the snow with a crisp smooth surface of fresh ice.

"Oh, good! The river's flooded," Doug notices. "Let's go skating."

We glide for miles upstream and down again on this wonderful highway. Everyone plays on the river whenever the ice floods. I'm now a strong, confident skater.

Finally the days begin to lengthen and the snow settles. Drifts harden along the roadside, giving us plenty of new areas to explore on the way home from school.

"Look what I made!" calls Douglas. It's a cunning igloo, carved into a deep bank. Noël and I crawl inside and Douglas piles in behind us.

"Hey, it's warm in here!' says Noël in surprise.

"No wind," explains Douglas gravely.

A few weeks later, the road turns to slush and mud appears on the southern slopes. The snow turns dingy grey but the skies are crystal blue. The air feels moist and soft while pussy willows burst from the boughs, announcing another spring.

THIRTY-SIX

Broken Foot

Douglas loves our dog. 1945.

Fog hangs in pockets and shrouds the barnyard with a ghostly veil, changing the appearance of things familiar. The air holds the earthy scent of damp leaf-mould and thawing manure. We three children rise early Saturday morning; it's too fine a day to waste on sleep. We hurry through chores and by the time we finish our porridge, only a skiff of fog is left.

I laugh. Douglas glances up. "It's a perfect day for riding," he says. "But we'll have to watch for ice under the slush. I'll go get Nipper ready if you bring my gloves."

We meet at the rail fence and climb onto Nipper, taking off at a brisk trot. The pony breaks into a canter down the range line and lopes along. Suddenly she slips on treacherous ice and falls. Heels over head, she turns a complete arc in the air like a wheelbarrow dumping its load while Douglas and I slide down her neck into the mud. The falling pony lands squarely on my foot. Ow! Stars and firecrackers blow up in my head. I feel a wrenching, crushing blow to my leg. Whimpering, I creep to the ditch. Douglas urges the pony to roll from her back, but her four legs thrash in the air. At last, she regains her footing.

"Okay, Ardith," says Douglas. "Nipper is up. We can ride again."

"Oh, Doug," I moan. "My leg! I can't ride. My leg hurts!"

"Don't be silly," he says. "You'll have to, so come on. I'll boost you." Half lifting, half pushing, he manages to push me up onto Nipper, and slowly leads the pony home.

"What happened? What's the matter?" Mom demands as I drag myself into the house by my elbows. "Let me peel off your moccasin and stocking."

Mom exposes a crushed and swollen foot. "Oh, dear! It's a sprain. See how puffy it is. Let's get you to bed."

Noël and Mom help me lie down. I'm in extreme pain.

"You'll be fine tomorrow," Mom assures me. But I'm not. I can't bear weight on my foot no matter how hard I try.

"Never mind," Douglas says. "I'll get you to school. Wait till I bring Nipper around." I hop to the doorway and am boosted up. I ride the pony to school all that week, hobbling around the classroom, leaning on Anita or Billy. Miss McPhillip watches. Do I have a serious injury? On Friday, my teacher visits Mom.

"Surely Ardith's foot needs medical attention," she urges. "I'll drive you both to Mayerthorpe to the doctor." Mom gratefully accepts. They slide me into the back seat of the teacher's car for the ten-mile trip to town.

The diagnosis is that my foot is broken. The doctor applies a heavy cast right from my knee to my toes. Now I know what happens to a mummy, I think ruefully, as I watch the doctor wind the plastery bands around and around my leg.

"It weighs a ton," I tell the women on the way home.

"I can't believe Ardith went a whole week with a broken foot," Mom murmurs apologetically to my teacher. "She seldom complains, and she rode the pony to school every day. That must have hurt. Why didn't she tell me? I had no idea the injury was so serious. She must have a high pain tolerance."

Douglas helps me to school and home again. He faithfully tends to my needs and cares for the pony at school. My perfect attendance record is maintained, a source of family pride.

I lie on my bed, admiring my collection of perfect attendance awards. The books are great, but I'm more proud of my achievement, proud to be perfect in some way.

I love Douglas. He's helping me keep up my attendance. The break isn't that painful. If I concentrate on something else really hard, the pain floats away. But now I feel useless, because the cast is too heavy to move much.

Noël has twice the amount of chores now that I can't help. "I'm glad it's warming up," she tells me. "So I don't have to carry in so much wood."

Mom teaches me to chord on the piano. We sing a song while choosing a pleasing accompaniment. I have a good ear and can hear when a chord change is necessary. The music helps me pass the long spring evenings, while the rest of the family plant the garden and landscape the yard. Douglas can see longing in my eyes. "I'll spade up a small area near the house for your flower bed," he offers. Mom gives me a choice of seeds. Nasturtiums, I decide. They're bright and brave. I sit flat on my bottom on the moist earth and plant seeds in the soil. These flowers will look attractive against the caragana hedge, I think. My crutches lie beside me and I'm careful not to soil my cast.

As I hobble through tall grass along the edge of the lane, I'm startled by a killdeer that flutters pitifully at my feet, wailing shrilly. Oh, the poor thing! It has a broken wing, and I know just how that feels! Maybe I can catch the bird and put splints on it. I hustle on my crutches, but try as I may, the bird flutters away, always a few feet ahead. I can't quite reach it. I follow the fluttering bird to the foot of the lane and am astonished to see it suddenly take flight strongly and disappear!

I laugh ruefully and hobble back home. Douglas is studying at the table and I tell him about the mysterious injury. "The old broken wing trick, Ardith. And it fooled you, too! The poor mother bird just acts injured to lure you away from her nest. Then she flies home!"

I feel mortified that a little killdeer has tricked me. "I guess I'm not very smart!"

After six weeks my foot heals enough to have the cast removed. Miss McPhillip drives Mom and me to Mayerthorpe again and the doctor uses a circular saw to chew away the cast.

My thin, withered foot lies like a scaly serpent shedding its skin. It has wasted away and I'm alarmed. This dingy limb surely doesn't belong to me.

"You'll have to exercise your leg," the doctor says firmly. "It looks fine."

It looks awful! I correct him under my breath. But it feels fine. "Thank you, doctor," I say aloud.

It's grand to have freedom to walk again!

THIRTY-SEVEN

World War II Ends

Wonderful news bursts from the radio—the European war is over! A holiday is declared—no school next day! Everyone celebrates V-E Day, 1945.

The joy persists. There are changes in the air! All the children at school are excited, unsettled. Miss McPhillip understands our restlessness and tries to think of special activities to imprint the meaning of the war's end in our minds.

The school holds a track meet in June. Neighbouring schools from the municipality send their best athletes to compete in racing, jumping and broad jump. At last, the Ray children can excel! Although our vision is so poor that we can't play ball games, we have strong, healthy bodies and are able to run like the wind. Douglas is tough and wiry. He wins a first place ribbon for high jump and marches over to Nan's house with it.

"Here, Nan, let me pin this red ribbon on your chest!" The thought of her excelling in high jump is delightfully amusing to Nan.

"Miss McPhillip promised us an end-of-year picnic on the banks of the river!" I receive a perfect attendance prize—another book in the life story of Anne of Green Gables.

Douglas winks at me, "You'll soon have the whole set," he encourages me, and I give him a grateful smile.

"Now that it's summer holidays, you may all meet the passenger trains every evening," Mom tells us. All the kids are there.

We wave little Union Jacks and long streamers at every soldier who returns home to Rochfort Bridge. We give each one a hero's welcome.

Wonder of wonders! Daddy returns unharmed to Canada. He is different. "He still plays practical jokes, but he never laughs with Mom. They're like polite strangers," I tell Noël. "What's wrong?"

I compose a little poem for Daddy while I rest my leg awhile. I want him to realize how happy I am to have him back.

Waving flags, red, white and blue
Feeling happy, proud and free
Knowing we'll start life anew
Daddy will take care of me.

But Daddy just grunts when he reads it.

The notion that Daddy will stay home to take care of his family is short-lived, because unlike other fathers, he decides to remain in the air force. He's stationed in Edmonton and spends his leaves at home, beginning at once to drill a water well. First he gets a gifted neighbour to test the ground with a pointed forked stick and "witch" for water. We watch the witcher walk solemnly back and forth, back and forth over the area where Daddy hopes to drill. We see the wand dip down every time he passes a certain spot. He checks several times and then smiles. "You'll get good soft water right here, Will," he claims, pointing to the spot.

Daddy understands how to drill for water. Before he joined the air force, he earned money by drilling wells for neighbours who farm near Rochfort Bridge.

Daddy has a huge well machine that is made with a thick rough-lumber frame that holds a powerful engine and has a thirty-foot tower, rigged with sturdy rope with which to lift pipes to be used in the well. The tower folds down over the top of the well machine while it is moving to a new location.

Although Daddy was badly hurt on the job, having a fractured skull, he kept his well machine, and now he intends to drill our very own well near the house.

Daddy strides around the well machine, fixing motors and joining pipes, like his old self. Still, he's changed …. Difficult for me to pinpoint, but my Daddy's different.

Mom notices it, too, I'm sure. I see her wistful, hollow eyes as she looks at Dad. Her face contorts rapidly, and she wrings her hands continuously. They never quarrel and are always polite, although distant, whenever we kids are around. I feel on guard around my dad, although Noël accepts him wholeheartedly and throws herself on his lap.

All through the summer holidays, Daddy works at the well whenever he's home on leave. He puts heavy piping two hundred feet down where he finds plentiful, clear soft water. Next he builds a tall tower of wood above the pump house and mounts a Beatty windmill on it.

The powerful wheel turns with the wind, pumping gallons of water into a heavy galvanized water tank, and a huge new stock tank. I love to gaze into the deep water of the tank. It's so much deeper than our old wooden watering trough. I remember how I thought the old trough was a magic mirror. Who needs a magic mirror anyway? Daddy's here.

And Douglas and I don't have to carry any more buckets of water from Grandpapa's. We drink our own well-water.

By the middle of August, the Japanese troops surrender and V-J Day is celebrated. This means that our new aunt and cousins will be allowed to leave England.

I'm feverish with excitement. I long to meet my two little cousins—the first cousins I've ever had. Auntie Martha arrives by train to Rochfort Bridge with little Aster and Pansy. Why, they're all tiny, I see in surprise. I'm as big as my new Auntie. Bigger, really, because I'm stronger. I try not to stare, as I examine this lady from a foreign land. It's easy to tell that she comes from England—her skin has that fresh, moist, soft glow, and she wears rouge and lipstick in an elegant fashion. Fluffy auburn hair frames a long, thin face, further emphasized by a long, straight nose. Impish green eyes twinkle beneath thick curling brows, and a puckish smile gives Auntie Martha an elfish appearance. She speaks rapidly, but softly, and her accent is intriguing. She's exhausted from travel, and bewildered by the strangeness of everything, but she hugs me warmly, and I breathe in her delicate rose-water scent.

Aster's a frail, frightened four-year-old who clings to her mother; she won't let go. Noël kneels to show her the kitten, and its plaintive meowing finally arouses interest in the solemn blue eyes peering out beneath her bonnet. Aster wears a perpetual pout on her pretty mouth and seems to know only one word: No! This she repeats firmly and emphatically to every offer.

"Just leave her alone," advises Mom. "She has to get used to us. Poor wee tyke has been thrown from pillar to post ever since she left London. She must be totally bewildered!"

Aunt Martha gives Mom a grateful look.

"Cracky!" she declares. "If you want to talk to someone, here's Pansy. She's breaking me bloomin' arm." And she holds out her younger daughter. I slide my arms around the petite child. What a darling! Pansy has rosy cheeks and flaming auburn hair curling in wisps under her cap. She has serious, clear blue eyes. She's wiry and active. Plainly, she wants to be set down so she can explore. Noël takes her to investigate her new surroundings.

Auntie Martha greets her new relatives warmly. She's not

enthusiastic about living at Granddad's house, quickly sensing that there'll be no privacy there.

"I must have a home of my own!" she declares stoutly. "Lawrence, you promised me my own home, on your own farm!" But, in truth, my uncle doesn't own a farm.

However, Granddad owns more land about twenty miles away, so he offers his homestead to Uncle temporarily. "There's no house," he warns, "Just a shack."

"I accept," says Aunt Martha firmly. "I must have privacy."

So they move to the homestead immediately. I'm disappointed, and Mom shakes her head. "A little thing like that," she marvels. "I wonder how long she'll stick it?"

Auntie Martha hasn't anticipated the utter loneliness and isolation of a homestead. Uncle Lawrence works in Edmonton and returns only on weekends. The entire week, Aunt Martha's alone with her two tiny daughters. After five days, Uncle Lawrence comes back and brings his family to visit us.

"Oh, God!" Aunt Martha says. "I can't stand it. There isn't a light to be seen at night except for the stars overhead. And those coyotes howl all the time. I'm terrified of them. There's only a latch on the door so I don't feel safe to go to sleep. I can't even pull up a bucket of well-water. I've never used water that didn't come from a tap. I just can't stay alone. Oh, Edith, what shall I do? I must be brave for the sake of my girls, but I'm not brave. There isn't a sound from one day to the next except those ruddy coyotes. No one comes to see me. I don't know anyone. And there's no radio. I tell you, Edith, I'm going out of my mind. How do you stand such isolation?" And my new aunt bursts into tears. Her face turns red and she blows her nose several times on a pretty wisp of linen, then wipes her eyes.

"I can't believe it," she says ruefully. "Even the sky is different. Look at it." And she sweeps her arm overhead to indicate a clear azure sky. "Not a cloud in the sky. I tell you, Edith, that's getting to me, too. I've begun to keep track of how many clouds I see in a day. And we never get rain. Not even a shower. Sunshine, sunshine, sunshine! I can't face all that sun. Oh, Edith, what am I to do?" And Aunt Martha bursts into a fresh frenzy of tears.

Mother gathers Aunt Martha into her arms. The tiny lady comes only to Mom's shoulder. Over her head, Mom motions for me to push the kettle onto the hot stove. I nod and make some tea while Noël wanders away with Pansy. Mom leads Aunt Martha and Aster to the living room where the two ladies have a murmured conference on the couch. By the time I appear with two china cups of tea and jellied soda biscuits, a plan has been made.

"Ardith, you'll have to live with your cousins for the summer until Uncle Lawrence can stay with Aunt Martha. She simply cannot be left alone. Now, what do you think of that?"

I'm delighted with the idea. I worship my new Aunt Martha and adore my little cousins. I rush to my aunt and hug her closely. "I want to help you, Aunt Martha," I whisper sincerely. "It will be wonderful to stay with you."

THIRTY-EIGHT

Coyote's Cry

Aster (Anne) rides with Ardith. 1946.

L iving with Aunt Martha on the homestead is far from wonderful. Conditions are primitive. I had lived in a granary for years, but Granddad's shack seems somehow worse. It's bigger, making the bareness more apparent and crude.

The shack stands on a hill in the middle of nowhere. The main road is two miles away and a meandering trail leads through a grain field to the homestead. The shack is built of heavy, unplaned lumber, with a shingle roof, plank door and one east window. A small windowless lean-to has been added to the west side. The building is weathered to a dark greyish-brown, with a rusty stovepipe poking from the curling shingles.

The main room is large, stark. The furniture is hand-made of rough lumber—a trestle table, two benches, and board shelving nailed to the walls. Only the black iron cook-stove gives a degree of elegance to the room. There's no sofa, no comfortable chair, no radio, no bookcase, no pictures and no curtains.

A rough lumber countertop runs under the window, with shelves on either side. Aunt Martha places the wash basin on this counter so that she can look across the grain field as she washes. She spends much of her time washing—herself, the dishes, the children, their clothing.

"No matter how often I wash, I always feel grubby," Aunt Martha says. "It's the dust. And that straw tick on the bunk makes me itchy."

"Wait until harvest, Aunt Martha. Then we'll fill the tick with nice fresh-smelling straw."

Aunt Martha's unimpressed. "I'll never live here in the winter. There's absolutely no insulation. Look at that lean-to—pasted newspapers to cut the draught along the walls."

I laugh. "I like reading those old funny-papers: *Katzenjammer Kids, Popeye, Li'l Abner* and *Dick Tracy,* all pasted together. They must have been put on that wall a long time ago."

"And the mice," says Auntie Martha. "I can hear them scampering and squeaking across the counter all night. I know

I'm not imagining them when there's droppings every morning."

"You've got the flour and sugar sacks safely in the old wash-boiler, Auntie, and your tea is in a tin. There's really nothing the mice can hurt."

Auntie sniffs. "I guess not. All the pots and pans are hanging, and I've turned the dishes upside down. But I hate mice. And the mosquitoes. And the flies. They just swarm in when we leave the door open. But the place is too stuffy and dark without the sunlight. That lean-to is always dark with no window at all."

"We only sleep there," I remind her. "At least it's private."

I glance into the lean-to. It's cheerless indeed. A rough-lumber bunk holds a wide straw tick and is spread with a quilt and pillows. Auntie's steamer trunk stands open. Aster sleeps in the trunk and Pansy sleeps in the lid. "Good thing the girls are tiny," I laugh. "I'd never fit into your trunk."

Aunt Martha's suitcase holds clothing safely from mice and provides the only elegance to the room, since she has placed a doily and their wedding photo on top of it. This sole attempt at decoration breaks my heart; my new auntie deserves better. Their few good clothes hang on nails along the studding.

A binder-twine line hangs across the kitchen, usually strung with a few bits of children's clothing. A heavy wire clothesline is strung outside between the biffy and the well.

"If you'll watch the girls, I'll pull up some water," I offer, throwing the bucket into the deep round hole. I winch the full pail to the top, dumping it into the washtub.

Aunt Martha is a frail lady who had been a servant to nobility in London before the war. She's delicate and refined. She has never experienced buckets down the well, lack of electricity, an outdoor biffy and wood-burning stove. She scarcely copes.

"Let me show you how to shine up that old black stove, Auntie Martha. After the heat fades, just take this old waxed bread wrapper and rub the stove all over. See, the melting wax gives it a glossy sheen. Of course, it smokes a bit, but that's all right. The smoke will discourage the mosquitoes. Now doesn't that stove look elegant?"

"It does look better, Ardith. Thank you for showing me."

"I'll just tuck the dirty paper into the edge of the kindling wood, to start a fresh flame tomorrow."

"Fine, dear. But there's nothing for breakfast except the fresh milk and a few leftover potatoes."

"I guess we can have potatoes and gravy, Aunt Martha. Just scorch a bit of flour until it browns in the frying pan. Then add milk and salt. That will make thick gravy. We can cut the potatoes into it—although we're all tired of potatoes for every meal!"

"I sure wish Lawrence would come home with some groceries. He's been in Edmonton for more than a week, and we have no groceries, no money, *no nothing,* on this Godforsaken homestead! He should be getting good money with a taxi."

"I hope so. It's lucky Granddad planted a big patch of potatoes. We can rob the tiny new potatoes from each shaw, and the rest of the plant will mature. So we won't run out of food. And isn't it lucky that Uncle Lawrence arranged for us to get a bucket of milk every day from the Clarksons?" I'm used to living strictly off the farm, and don't miss the groceries like my aunt does.

"Yes, it's very kind of them to provide us with milk. Even though I find it quite a hike walking over there every evening."

"Oh, Auntie Martha! I'll carry Pansy if you can manage the ten-pound syrup pail full of milk. And it does give you a chance to chat with Mrs. Clarkson and hear the news. It gives us something to look forward to every day and it's good exercise, really!"

"That's true, Ardith. If we wait until it's evening, it's not too hot, although I swear there are twice as many mosquitoes."

My days are spent playing with the children, helping Aunt Martha, resting when they nap, and chattering to entertain the family. I sing to the little girls, or tell them fairy tales.

We look forward to our visit with the Clarksons. I carry Pansy on one arm and swat mosquitoes with a leafy branch while Aunt Martha holds Aster's hand and carries the empty milk bucket, swinging it to ward off mosquitoes.

"Look at my welts," Aunt Martha exclaims, showing me ridges of swollen flesh. "Those pesky mosquitoes are poisoning us."

I can see this is true. "You're not used to mosquitoes. The children are really suffering; they're covered with welts. The mosquitoes don't affect me so much. We'll ask Mrs. Clarkson what to do for those bites," I murmur.

"Do you have baking soda?" asks Mrs. Clarkson with concern. "No? Well, take mine. Make a thick paste and smear it on the stings. And Ardith, make a smudge outside the door. Do you know how to make a smudge?"

"Yes, Mrs. Clarkson," I say, feeling guilty that I haven't thought to do this. "I'll make one. We'll keep a smudge going, Auntie Martha." I assure her, and smile at her dismayed expression.

"Come in and set a spell," adds Mrs. Clarkson. "We'll have a cup of tea. You must be tired, walking through that trail in the bush. And carrying this little tyke, Ardith. Come in, come in." Mrs. Clarkson is a plain, sensible farm wife who bustles about making a fresh pot of tea. She sets out a tin of vanilla cake.

I limit myself to two slices of cake, although I feel like devouring the whole tinful. Mrs. Clarkson talks to Aunt

Martha, giving practical advice, her weather-wrinkled face kindly and concerned. She squints as she smokes. Through the blue haze swirling around her head, Aunt Martha looks longingly at the cigarette package.

"Care for a smoke?" asks Mrs. Clarkson, suddenly aware of Aunt Martha's gaze. "Help yourself," and she laughs apologetically at her oversight. Aunt Martha's delicate fingers caress the cigarette before she places it between her lips. Mrs. Clarkson holds a light, and the two women settle back to puff in silence for a time. I watch my aunt with interest. Savouring her smoke, Aunt Martha looks relaxed and content. I didn't realize Aunt Martha smokes. Uncle Lawrence must have told her not to do it in front of Mom 'cause she'd be scandalized. But so what if Auntie smokes? That doesn't make her bad. Many women smoke. I feel loyal to my aunt.

Mr. Clarkson appears in the doorway carrying a huge bucket of milk. A network of wrinkles puckers his skin as he nods shyly to Aunt Martha. His eyes twinkle and he winks at me. He busies himself straining fresh milk into Martha's bucket, and then joins the women for a cup of tea.

"Now don't you worry, Mrs. Ray," Mr. Clarkson declares heartily. "If you have any problem or need anything, you just come right on over. We're glad to lend a hand. And this here milk should put some meat on your bones." Mr. Clarkson chuckles, glancing sideways at Aunt Martha.

He's a restless man. Can't seem to relax with strangers in his house. Taking up the fly swatter, he begins flapping flies, dropping their remains into the slop bucket. This fascinates Aster, who gradually relinquishes her grip on her mother to watch where Mr. Clarkson will strike next. Aware that he's entertaining the child, the awkward farmer begins an elaborate pantomime, stalking each fly seriously and muttering Gotcha! when he connects. All too soon, Aunt Martha glances at the gathering gloom outdoors and says, "Cracky! We'd better head home. I don't want to be out after dark among those yowling coyotes."

Mrs. Clarkson murmurs, "They'll never touch you, Mrs. Ray. Don't be afraid of them."

Still, the little procession scurries home along the narrow path, to the accompaniment of hordes of humming mosquitoes. Auntie carries the heavy bucket of milk.

It's quite dark by the time we reach the shack, and while Auntie's lighting the kerosene lantern, I pick up the huge butcher knife from the shelf.

"I'll show you how to lock the door, Aunt Martha," I offer. "Just stick this butcher knife between these two logs. There! No one can get in now."

Since there's no radio at the shack, I stoke the fire and adjust the damper for the night while Aunt Martha tells wonderful stories about England. I can picture the beauty of that foreign land, the destruction of it by bombs, the arrival of the Canadian soldiers and the romance of Uncle Lawrence and Aunt Martha.

"Tell me more about meeting Uncle Lawrence," I beg. "Where did you first meet?"

"We were at a pub. We met to smoke and drink and have a natter with friends. There were two of us—my best friend, Betty, and me. And in came two Canadian soldiers, your Uncle Lawrence and his pal Roger. Well, we started talking ... "

"But why did you like Uncle Lawrence?" I persist. "What did he say?"

"He said I had the prettiest green eyes he had ever seen. Said they were deep enough to swim in. He liked my size, too. Said I was small enough to tuck under his arm. I am, too. I'm only as tall as his armpit." Aunt Martha laughs ruefully. "Oh, he told me lots of things—all about his big farm in Alberta.

What a wonderful country Canada is. How grand it is to live on a farm."

Aunt Martha rolls her eyes around the room as she speaks, but her thoughts are far away. "Oh, he was generous, too. Gave me smokes and chocolates. He seemed so sure of himself. And we were all scared stiff from the blitz on London. It was a bad time, Ardith."

"So what happened?" I ask.

"So ... well ... the usual thing, dear. I found out I was going to have a wee one. Lawrence and I were married ... I moved in with Betty ... and after Aster was born, we kept her safe in the bottom drawer of the bureau. Whenever there was a raid, we pushed the drawer shut. So she's used to sleeping in a box. We did the same thing with Pansy. Safest way. Though we were never directly hit. Thank God."

"Then what happened, Aunt Martha?"

"Then ... Lawrence got terrible sick. He was a bundle of nerves. He was put into hospital but he just got worse. Shaking and jumpy. So they sent him home. I was really in a fix. Two babies and scarcely any income. Well, we toughed it out. Everyone was in a bad way by then." Aunt Martha has a faraway look in her eyes.

"Then I met your Daddy. Lawrence notified him that he was being sent home, so one day, out of the blue, in walks Will. Blimey! You could have knocked me over with a feather. Thought I was seeing things at first. They're brothers, all right. Only Will's shorter, more heavy set. I figured that out when he shook my hand. But Will was a life saver. Brought me peanut butter—a whole tinful. And coffee. And chocolates, cigarettes and hot cocoa mix. Good food from his canteen. Best of all, Ardith, he gave me money. He could see how it was for us .... He played with the little girls—I was sorry to see him go."

"Was that the only time you saw Daddy?" I ask.

"Yes, over there. After all, he was stationed near Devon. But he gave me his address. So when I got word I could ship out, I wrote to him. Needed money. Your Daddy helped pay our fare." Aunt Martha wipes her eyes. "So the kids and I sailed across the ocean. Took a long train ride. But I never expected this homestead. It's so isolated. I can't see a single light at night. There's all these strange sounds, too. Coyotes, night hawks, owls. Rustling noises in the trees that I can't identify. I think of mountain lions. Wolves. Bears. I can't stand this place, Ardith. And I hate Lawrence for lying to me," she bursts out. "Lawrence lied," she cries. "He told me he had a big farm, and he has nothing. We have nothing except what your Granddad doles out. I feel as homeless as an unwanted fly. If I had the money, I'd go straight back to England. But I have no money. And things have changed there, too. Oh, Ardith, I shouldn't be worrying you with my problems. But I feel so nervous. And I'm tired .... Let's go to bed."

We lie silent for a while. I feel sorry for my new auntie, so afraid and bewildered. I wish I could help more. I compose a verse about the situation:

> Auntie is distressed at night
> by coyote's lonely cry.
> And she feels so uneasy
> In case someone passes by
> And stops to visit her at night—
> three children, and a wife,
> with just a latch to close the door,
> so she takes the big knife
> wedges it deeply in the log
> so it will bar the door.
> Then she can sleep there soundly.
> Intrusion fear no more.

I'm suddenly aware that Auntie Martha is sobbing, her face muffled by the pillow. I roll over and hug her. Gradually Auntie's sobs stop, and she sighs, a long, ragged sigh in the dark.

I press myself against my aunt, absorbing the comfort that her body gives. It takes a while to get settled, although the bedroom is dark. "This straw mattress seems awfully flat. It will soon be threshing time and we can refill the tick with fresh straw. That always smells better." I try to cheer Aunt Martha.

"We'll never survive a winter in this shack." my aunt says. "And you'll have to go home for school."

I hadn't thought of that. "Maybe Uncle Lawrence will get a good job in Edmonton and you can move there," I say. "But gee, Aunt Martha, I don't want you and the girls to move away."

"We'll see," she mumbles. We fall asleep.

A loud hammering at the door awakens us all. The little girls whimper softly. "Who do you think that is?" Auntie's voice is urgent.

"I don't know," I say. "Should I open the door?"

"No. I don't know who it is, but I pray that knife will hold. It's all right, dears," she speaks softly to the children. "We're safe here."

The pounding continues. Louder and more insistent.

"Blimey!" Aunt Martha exclaims. "This is just like a raid in England. I never expected a panic again, here in Canada. What should we do?"

"Listen!" I hear a slurred voice uttering oaths and threats. "That sounds like Uncle Lawrence. It must be him, Aunt Martha. No one else would pound on the door at this hour."

"Cracky! He'll be vexed." Aunt Martha exclaims. "Help me pull the bloomin' knife from the door."

The two of us struggle to remove the butcher knife, and fall backward as the door is pushed savagely inward. Uncle Lawrence stands weaving in the doorway. He's furious. He grabs the knife from his wife's hand. I can smell booze as he comes forward.

"Who is it locks a man from his own house?" Uncle Lawrence demands. It occurs to me that the shack belongs to Granddad, not Uncle Lawrence, but I remain silent.

"Lawrence! Stop! Damn it! Stop!" screams Auntie Martha. "What's wrong with you? Put that knife down! Put it down, I say!"

But Lawrence steps forward, closer, slicing the air with the big knife. "Shut up! Shut up!"

The little girls gaze at their Daddy in terror. I go to them to reassure them. I feel sorry for my aunt. Somehow I feel I'm to blame. I'm humiliated by my uncle's behaviour. I know I must take charge, must stop my uncle. My knees buckle but I step forward. "Give me that knife," I tell him. "Don't scare the little girls. Give me the knife. You're frightening all of us." I touch his arm. "Let me have that knife."

Uncle Lawrence blinks his eyes and shakes his head as though to clear it. I pull the knife from his grasp and thrust it deep into the flour in the sack in the old wash-boiler.

Uncle turns on his heel and stomps out of the shack. I'm aware of the sound of an engine as he roars away in the taxi. We all huddle together, hugging the little girls on the bunk until they settle down and we fall asleep at last.

When I waken from a tormented sleep, I meet a determined aunt. After we straighten up our hair and drink all the milk, we trudge along the dewy trail to Clarksons'. They listen to Aunt Martha's censored account of the previous evening. (Aunt Martha and I agreed to keep the real events a secret.) Mrs. Clarkson bustles about, making breakfast, while I dry the children's feet and rub ointment from Mrs. Clarkson on their mosquito bites. After a hasty coffee, Mr. Clarkson packs us into his pickup and drives to the shack, where Aunt Martha collects her few belongings.

"Goodbye, sweet dreams!" she cries. I feel guilty again when I see my aunt's bitterness. I listen to her explain her plan to Mr. Clarkson.

"I'll take the afternoon train from Rochfort Bridge to Edmonton," she says. "I have the address of another war bride who lives there. She'll take us in and help me find a place. I just can't stay on here. And I can't depend on Lawrence. Thank you so much for all your help, Mr. Clarkson. I can't even pay you for this ride. And then, there's the milk ...."

"Now, now. Don't fret none!" Mr. Clarkson says. He looks worried and a bit nervous. "Hope I done the right thing," he says. "That big lout musta' done something to get your dander up like this. I'll just drop you here at the train station and head for home. Least I know, the better." He smiles at me and adds, "Now, you stay with your auntie until she gets safely on that train, won't you, Ardith. Then you can skedaddle home." And he waves, "Goodbye, Mrs. Ray."

I wave and wave to Auntie Martha and the children as they pull away from the station platform, and I watch until the train is gone, and even the smoke disappears. Then I walk home to tell our family.

THIRTY-NINE

Flying

Dad and Ruby fork hay into the loft. 1946.

All summer Mr. Williams is busy building our house. He works upstairs making bedrooms, fitting closets, shelves and cupboards, and spends a few days every week on the project.

So Noël, Douglas and I move out to our hayloft for summer sleeping. We tolerate the droning mosquitoes and their stings and enjoy the soft cooing sounds of pigeons roosting in the eaves above us. It's cool and airy in the empty loft with both doors flung wide.

On clear nights, we study the constellations from our perch on the doorsill. Gazing into the vast canopy of stars,

Douglas tells us stories, while we listen wide-eyed, captivated by Greek myths of gods and goddesses. Douglas says, "The stars are so thick that it seems as if the whole universe lies before us. Shooting stars burst like firecrackers. It's dazzling."

The stars look pale and wan to me; I think the universe is fading, sinking away. My whole world is changing. Ever since I came back from the homestead, things look different to me. And I feel different. I worry about how my Aunt Martha is doing.

It's great to be home again, swept up in make-believe worlds. "I love to stare out into this pitch-black sky and ... "

"This sky is not pitch-black, Ardith," corrects Noël. "There's lots of stars shining tonight."

"Really? I can't see them. Something's wrong with my eyes."

I reveal my problem to Mother that evening when I pray, "Dear God, please don't let my eyes dim over like Nan's."

"What do you mean about your eyes, Ardith?" Mom asks as she looks directly into my eyes. "They look healthy and normal."

"Oh, Mom," I burst out. "I can't see the stars any more. Am I going blind?"

Mom smiles. "I doubt it. I guess your glasses aren't suiting your eyes anymore. I'll have to make an appointment for you with the doctor in Edmonton to get them checked. I'll have Doug's checked, too. Do you think you two can manage to go to the city by train?"

Douglas and I travel to Edmonton, a real adventure. After seeing the oculist and finding that we both require new lenses, we explore Jasper Avenue until it's time to meet Daddy, who gets off duty at four o'clock. We have plenty of time to window-shop.

Daddy meets us at a little café called Bob-Inn. He looks handsome in his summer uniform. I'm proud to be seen with my hero.

He buys a hearty lunch for us kids. "We have to eat early," he explains, and lays three tickets on the counter, his eyes twinkling as he watches our reaction.

"The circus!" Douglas breathes. "Dad has tickets for the Barnum and Bailey Three-Ring Circus tonight!"

This is the most thrilling night of my life, I think, as I'm caught in a kaleidoscope of coloured lights, blare of music, blast of loud announcements and the magic of the Big Top. I don't know which ring to watch; all are equally entertaining. I laugh at the antics of the clowns, marvel at the grace of the horseback riders, shudder as a beautiful lady is shot from a cannon, and am delighted with the animals: lions, tigers, monkeys and bears. I particularly love the awkward yet graceful elephants. Their gross, wrinkled bodies made to balance in unnatural positions make me long to set them free to be wild in their own familiar jungle again. Surely God doesn't intend animals to be misused, I think seriously.

Suddenly the spotlight swings high above our heads—a daring act on the high trapeze. I'm spellbound. It's the most amazing acrobatics I've ever seen. Never in my whole life will I forget this moment.

Here are modern gods of the sky. Their glittering costumes and agile bodies thrill me to my very marrow. The exhilarating music, the drum rolls building to a climax, and the flips and turns that seem to defy gravity completely capture my imagination as nothing else can. Oh, to be earthbound no longer! Oh, to be free to soar through the sky!

We linger at the midway. Dangerous rides, guessing games, gambling tables, freaks and magicians. It's a world I've

Mom, Aunt Martha, Ruby. 1946.

never before seen. I seem to inhale the entire experience. Douglas says, "Can we wait to watch the Big Top come down?"

We stand in awe as the elephants are guided to carefully lower the tent. The circus is over.

When Douglas and I reach home, we're possessed by our circus experiences. Douglas builds trapezes that suspend from the loft rafters, using ropes and iron rods he pulls from the skeleton of the bedstead that has burned in the house fire. We children become so adept on the trapeze that we can swing by our knees and change to the next trapeze in mid-air.

"It's all a matter of timing," Douglas explains gravely. "Now let's try to pass Noël back and forth between you and me." We practise for days. It's exhilarating.

Once I move hand over hand along the loft rafters from one end of the barn to the other. I tire and decide to drop to the hay below. But my silver signet ring catches on a knot in the wood. When I let go, I hang suspended by my ring.

"Help me! Oh, please help me!" I scream. Douglas and Noël arrive, hand over hand from each end of the loft.

"Lift her up, Douglas," says Noël. "I'll unhook her ring." They pry my hand loose, and I fall, groaning on the straw. My ring has pulled to a sharp point, pinching my finger. I run howling to the house where Mom takes the wire snipper and cuts my precious ring from my puffed and purple finger. I rub it ruefully, thankful that my finger is still attached.

While my hand is healing, I make up a little verse about our hayloft adventures:

> We glide through the air
> with the greatest of ease,
> Doug, Noël and I
> on the flying trapeze.
> Our tricks seem like magic ...
> We do as we please
> when up in the loft
> on a homemade trapeze!

"Let's stage a circus and invite the family," Noël suggests.

"Sure," says Doug. "We've mastered our acts."

While Ruby stays with Nan, Mom and Dad, Grandpapa and Granddad all climb the stout ladder to the loft and seat themselves, gathered by lantern light. The show begins. Douglas and I pass Noël back and forth from the trapezes. As she reaches the height of her swing, her little body disappears out the open loft door, and reappears unharmed, to the gasps of the thankful audience. That's the climax of our performance.

But Dad quickly forestalls criticism by calling out, "Now it's our turn." He contributes his act by swinging the lighted lantern once around his head like a brakeman on the train. "This is a highball," he says. Mom demonstrates turning a summersault and Grandpapa tries to stand on his head.

"I used to be able to do that," he fumes, crestfallen that he can't force his body to remain upright when he's upside down. His face turns such a deep purple that Mom looks at him in alarm. I wonder if the colour is from exertion or embarrassment.

"Never mind, Grandpapa," I whisper. "I've never been able to stand on my head." I squeeze his hand in sympathy, understanding.

"First one down," calls Granddad, wisely disappearing to the gloom below, before he's called upon to make a fool of himself. So ends the circus.

Douglas First

Granddad Ray. 1950.

With berry picking and garden weeding, swimming and horseback riding, singing at the piano and reading to Nan, summer flies by. Uncle Lawrence doesn't return from the city.

Meanwhile, Mother helps Mr. Williams finish the upstairs. She's anxious to have the bedrooms complete so we'll no longer sleep in the living room when the loft becomes too cold.

"Douglas, would you like to go with Grandpapa to pick up a load of coal for our new furnace?" Mom asks.

"Oh, yes," Douglas says. "It'll be interesting to see a coal mine. And I'll help load up so Grandpapa doesn't have to shovel too much."

Mom smiles at Douglas fondly. "I'm sure they have loaders," she says. "But you can certainly help unload. That should be fairly easy, with the coal chute Mr. Williams built. He's leaving us the end of this week. I've run out of money. But we can move upstairs even though it's not completely finished."

"All right, you young people. Time to choose your bedrooms," Mom calls. "Let's go upstairs. Who's first?"

"Douglas," we all cry. "He's waited so long for privacy. You choose first, Doug."

He chooses the room facing south with a large closet and plenty of room for his desk and bed. He's overcome and kisses Mom tenderly. "Thank you, Mom, for this fine bedroom," he says, goes inside and closes his door.

"Ruby next," we call. Ruby chooses the smallest bedroom, with a gable window facing west.

"I'll be over at Nan's most of the time," she explains. "And I'll be the first to leave home. So I don't really need a big room. This is lovely. Thanks."

"I'll pick this bedroom facing south," I decide. "I love the built-in bookcase. It'll hold my whole collection of books. Oh,

Mom, can I have my little wicker set from Granny to use as ornaments on the bookcase?" Mom nods permission.

"I'll put the cot here. And the dresser here. That leaves space under the window to sit and read."

"Then I'll let you have the big trunk to put there," Mom says. "It will be perfect to sit on."

"Great! Thanks, Mom." and I plant a kiss on Mom's cheek.

"That leaves me the biggest bedroom," exclaims Noël. "And I'm the smallest. Oh, lucky me!" And she explores her walk-in closet. "I have two windows" she gloats. "Oh, this is grand!"

"Now, Noël," cautions Mom. "I'm going to slide the double bed into your room with the understanding that this will be the guest room when we have company. Is that all right?"

"It's a deal, Mom. Thank you so much."

It takes no time at all to move upstairs. We all disappear into our own space this evening. It seems strange, I think, as I lie in bed and listen to the sounds of my new surroundings. The rafters crack and I hear Mom move about downstairs. When it becomes silent, I doze off.

During the night, I awaken to the padding of bare feet. "Move over," whispers Noël. "It's too lonely in my big bed. I need a hug." Mom finds us snuggled together next morning, still sound asleep. She has a smile when she wakens us. "I know how you feel, Noël, alone in your huge bed." Mom nods. "Oh, I wish Daddy would get a discharge and come home to stay. We could surely manage without his salary." Mom sighs. Then she squares her shoulders and adds brightly, "Rise and shine, girls! Let's hit the raspberry patch before the sun does."

We kids invent a new game: mountain climbing. We scale a perpendicular cliff, (the log wall of the barn to the loft door high above), imagining it's Mount Robson.

My bare toes search for little ledges on the logs, seeking toeholds and finger holds. I climb steadily, and never look down, or my head will spin and I'll become dizzy and fearful. We rest in the shade and lean against the logs, seated on a patch of quack grass and dandelions. We love the long hot summer afternoons when we can sit and idly talk, argue or dream while comparing our childish impressions of the adult world.

"Race you up the mountain," Noël challenges, and we clamber to the loft.

"Time to start back to school on Monday," Mom says one morning. "Where did the summer go? I'll miss you young people."

But I know Mom is glad to see us go. "We really get on Mom's nerves," I whisper to Noël. "I'm glad school's starting. I love school."

Blood Sisters

Ruby and Mom at Paddle River Bridge. 1946.

A perfect day to start school. I glance at an azure sky, with a purple and orange wash along the horizon.

"Hi, Anita. Hi, Billy. Hi, Lizzy. Hi. Hi. Hi, everybody." I smile as the students gather on the steps. It's great to be back to school. Good to see all my friends again. They look tanned and have grown several inches.

But where's Miss McPhillip? A new teacher prepares for classes at the big oak desk near the front of the classroom.

"Is Miss McPhillip sick?" I whisper to Anita.

"Oh, didn't you hear? She's moved to Edmonton. She's getting married."

I'm stunned. The idol of my life is gone. It doesn't seem possible.

I study my new teacher through half-closed eyes. The woman is pretty in a mature way, probably about Mom's age, I decide. She has brown hair framing her face and her liquid eyes are deep brown. She's elegantly dressed with high-heeled shoes. The teacher smiles a welcome to the class. "She looks nice," I whisper. "I think I'll like her."

"Good morning, boys and girls. My name is Mrs. Warnock." The teacher introduces herself and writes her name on the blackboard with a flourish. Oh, oh, I'm dismayed. This teacher has perfect handwriting. What will she think of mine?

A new girl—Gracie Warnock, looks like she and her mother are daisies from the same bouquet. Another girl to play with. And as pretty as her mother. Gracie wears long brown ringlets around her elfish face. Her brown eyes peek from behind long curling lashes. Everyone's drawn like a magnet to this new student.

"Do you live in town?" Gracie asks me at recess, and thrusts her face right against mine, mockery in her eyes.

"No" I admit. "But we're near town. Why?" But Gracie flounces away.

"We're forming a club," she announces, "called Town Trotters. Only kids who live in town can join." I notice that all the kids from town stand in a tight cluster like a bunch of grapes with Gracie for a vine. I catch Anita's concerned look.

"Who needs their old club anyway?" I say with a defiant toss of my braids. "Come on, Anita, let's go behind the school to watch the boys play football." We move off.

"Who does she think she is, anyhow?" mutters Anita.

But I see that Anita looks like she can worry warts off a frog. I'm plenty worried myself. All the joy of starting school is leaking out, I think. It seems a long, lonely recess.

By the end of the first week, Gracie has organized a pecking order for my age group at Rochfort Bridge School. If you don't live in town, you're a nobody. Gracie's a natural leader and uses bribery and ridicule to keep her troops in line.

I explain the system to Noël on our walk home, as we absorb the sunshine that burnishes the fields with a metallic haze from the dust of countless binders.

"I feel like a fly in church on Monday morning," I tell Noël. "I'm all alone."

Noël glances at me. "What's wrong, Ardith?"

"That Gracie Warnock is taking over," I burst out. "She has all the kids from town organized into a gang called Town Trotters, so Anita and Lizzie and Patsy and I can't belong. They hog the swings and teeters and have special meetings for their gang on the steps and we can't get near. I try to hear what they're planning, but they just whisper and giggle and turn away from me. I have no chance of getting in on their plans. I'm an outcast. What shall I do, Noël?"

"Start your own club," suggests Noël.

I think about that as we trudge home. A soft breeze rustles the dry grasses along the roadside. "You're right. We'll start our own club."

We're upstairs changing from our school clothes when Douglas bursts into the kitchen where Mom's canning raspberries.

"Mom! Mom! Come quick! Nipper is down and I can't get her up!"

Leaving the berry bottles bubbling on the range, Mom rushes outdoors with us girls behind her, but Douglas has already disappeared around the corner of the barn. He kneels beside the pony on the spongy floor of the corral near the south side of the log barn. Poor Nipper lies stretched out on her side. She's as limp as a squeezed-out rag, and I look at her huge swollen belly. The pony moans and struggles to rise when she hears us gathering around her, but she sinks back helplessly.

"Poor Nipper! Whatever has happened?" And Mom kneels down beside Douglas to pet the exhausted pony.

"I think she's been at the oats, Mom. Look here." Douglas jiggles a loose board along the bottom of the oats bin, wiggling it to show fresh oats shower out whenever he bumps the board.

"I guess Nipper pushed on this board with her nose and licked up the oats that fell out. She must have eaten a whole bunch." Doug explains.

"Yes, and she probably took a big drink from the tank, too. Now the grain has swollen her stomach from all the water. Let's get her on her feet. If we can make her really exercise, she's probably pass the gas." Mom and Douglas speak softly to Nipper, urging her to rise. Nipper twitches her ears forward. She hears but can't get up. Douglas slaps her rump as Mom yanks on the halter. Nipper raises her head as high as it will go, but can't tuck her legs under her grotesquely distended belly. She rolls helplessly onto her side, flopping her head onto the ground. Her breath makes strangled sounds. Moans. Grunts. Mom checks the pony's sightless eyes.

"Look," Mom explains. "She's been struggling for hours. Her eye is bruised and swollen and she can't open it any more. Look, she's even worn the hair off around her eye and down her cheek. My goodness, this is really serious. Nipper is in terrible shape. We need help right away. Ardith, run and fetch Grandpapa."

Fear like a stomach punch grips me. Soon Grandpapa arrives, breathing roughly. "We've just got to get her up," he says urgently. "I'll rig up a sling with some canvas and a tripod. Ardith, run get Granddad. Tell him to harness Ol' Tom. And bring his trochar too."

Granddad and I return astride Ol' Tom. We jolt along on top of the harness straps, traces swinging wildly as Ol' Tom trots along. Granddad shakes his head when he sees Nipper.

"She's bad off," he warns. "Doubt if we'll save her. But we'll sure try." He feels around, rubs and scratches, taps and pushes the swollen abdomen, feeling her rock-hard belly.

"Must'a had an orgy of oats," he mutters. "And lots'a cold water to wash them down. I seen this before." He continues to feel around, seeking the right spot. "Never done a horse like this," he drawls. "But it works good on cows. Anyway, we're desperate, so here goes."

With his trochar, he punctures Nipper's hide with one thrust, sinking the pointed needle with a hollow core deeply into Nipper's stomach, allowing gas to erupt in noxious blasts.

Noël giggles at the noises. "Sounds like a bull moose in rutting season," she whispers, but I'm silent, staring at Granddad working over the pony.

He's hurting her, I think, although Nipper seems to groan with relief. We're confident our grandfathers will heal poor Nipper since they do all the veterinary work of the farms. I watch with interest as Ol' Tom does his part and pulls the pony up with the hoist. They suspend Nipper in a sling with her feet scarcely touching the ground.

"Now, then, Edith, we'll leave her like this overnight and check first thing in the morning." The grandfathers leave.

"I'll stay right beside her all night," Mom promises. "Ardith, please go in and make a bite. I'll have mine here. If you girls want to eat out here, we can have sandwiches and call it a picnic. Douglas, before you do chores, can you bring me the old rocker, please? Noël, you bring me a couple of blankets, and my coat, please dear. It'll get chilly out here during the night, I'm sure."

Long after we have our forlorn picnic, Mom keeps vigil, wrapped warmly in the old rocker at Nipper's head, talking, petting and willing her recovery. "Come on, Nipper," she urges. "You're a fighter. Remember when you wouldn't wade into the floodwater and I tried to force you? You fought me then. So you can fight now. We'll fight this together. Please, Nipper. We all love you. We need you. Fight for your life."

For a time the pony puts up a battle, but she sinks into a stupor; her head droops despite Mom's efforts to support it with her lap. Just as the sun rises, the pony gives a low moan and dies. Mom is crying when she tells us, checking the raspberries that Ruby finished canning.

We're brokenhearted. We don't want to go to school, but we go. Douglas reports to Grandpapa and I stop by to tell Granddad; Neither is surprised by the news.

I have a busy recess. I collect Anita and Patsy and we disappear into the tall slough grass. "Too bad Lizzy's not here today," I say. "Because we're going to become blood sisters in our own secret club."

"How do we do that?" asks Anita. I'm prepared.

"See this pin?" I say. "We prick our little finger until it bleeds." Each of us does that. "Now, we'll press our fingers together so the blood mixes. There. This makes us blood sisters. Now we seal our sisterhood by promising never to tell the secrets of our club to a living soul."

I raise my palm, fingers skyward, in a sign of pledge. "Promise?"

"What secrets?" Patsy raises her hand, bewildered by this ritual. Even Anita looks puzzled.

I think quickly. "Nipper died," I whisper. "Tell you more later." The school bell tinkles, calling us indoors. So I manage to arouse interest in a school sisterhood over the loss of our beloved pony.

Grandpapa hauls the carcass across the field to the river bank where he dumps the bloated body. We expect a funeral for our pet, but neither of our grandfathers is capable of excavating the required pit.

"You'll have to learn," Grandpapa explains. "There's a limit to what can be done on a farm. We couldn't save the pony. And we can't bury her either. The coyotes will clean up her body within a week."

Mom makes a favourite supper for us that evening— johnnycake with syrup. We understand that this is her way of telling us she's sorry. Her face contorts as she explains, "We loved our dear pony, but she died. So we'll have to carry on. If you little people wish, we'll have a special prayer and sing a hymn—as a memorial service for Nipper. Will that be all right?"

We file into the living room after our meal. No one has eaten much. Mom opens the prayer book:

> *When our heads are bowed with woe*
> *When our bitter tears o'erflow*
> *When we mourn the last, the dear*
> *Gracious Son of Mary, hear.*

"I wrote a little verse," I say. "I'll read it now.

> *We had a little pony*
> *Her name was Nipper Ray.*
> *We loved her very dearly*
> *and rode her every day.*

She was a friendly pony—
faithful, gentle, true.
Our very best companion—
Oh, Nipper, we loved you."

Mom heads to the piano and strikes the familiar tune:

All things bright and beautiful
All creatures great and small.
All things wise and wonderful—
The Lord God made them all.

"We were blessed to have such a faithful little pony. We'll remember her always," Mom tells us.

After kissing Mom, we separate to our own bedrooms for a quiet time. Later that evening, I hear the howl of coyotes. I imagine the meal they're having—our precious pony. I cry bitterly.

The details of this death, and the prayer service that followed holds the sisterhood's interest for several days. Being farm children, the girls have experienced losing a pet, so as we mourn, the club bonds.

Spotty

Noël, Doug and Ardith feed Spotty. 1940.

Mom writes to Daddy of our loss and unhappiness. When Daddy next comes home on leave, he brings a large crate with him on the train. "What is it, Daddy?" asks Noël, while I peer through the slats.

Sorrowful brown eyes appeal to me from behind the bars. I draw back in fright, but Daddy opens the crate, revealing a large, ugly, spotted puppy dog.

"Oh, Daddy, what a funny freckled dog. What kind is he?" asks Noël.

"He's a great Dane," says Daddy proudly. "He'll be a really big fellow soon. Maybe not quite as big as Nipper, but I'll bet Noël can ride him when he gets full grown," Daddy chuckles. My heart sinks. That dog is just as spotted and ugly as I am. Awkward, too. He'll never replace Nipper in my heart.

Daddy doesn't notice my lack of enthusiasm. "I'm sure he'll be strong enough to pull a sleigh," he says. "Look how big his feet are already. He's going to be a real dandy. What shall we call him?"

We look at the pup. "He must have a million spots on him," says Doug. "Shall we call him Spotty?"

"Hello, Spotty." Noël rushes off to find some scraps to feed our new pet.

Spotty has four hollow legs; he's always hungry. "There aren't enough table scraps to satisfy that appetite." Mom moans. "Whatever shall I feed him?"

"Just make him a mash," Grandpapa advises. "Use chop."

"Ugh," says Douglas. "That sounds awful."

"Well, if he's hungry enough, he'll eat it," returns Grandpapa. "After all, we thrive on porridge. Of course, if you make the mash with milk, it'll be more nourishing."

The dog grows to an enormous size. But as the cold weather arrives, he shivers constantly; he has sort hair. His flat ears flop when he jerks his head, he slobbers badly, and his tail is a weapon as he increases in height. Finally, after Spotty sweeps all the teacups off the table with one wag of his tail, Mom explodes, "That dog can't come into my house anymore. He's a monster. Look at my good china."

Noël and I gather the broken bits, frightened by Mom's anger. What will happen to Spotty?

"Come on, boy," says Douglas, ushering the dog to the barn. We can hear our pet's mournful protests during the night. He hates the barn and wiggles with delight whenever Douglas releases him in the morning.

Mrs. Warnock and Gracie appear at the church service on Sunday. Since Rochfort Bridge actually has no United Church building, services are held in the hall, which is hastily swept after the Saturday night dance. Whoever arrives first on Sunday morning has the job of arranging a few benches into rows and sliding forward a portable pulpit. Now that it's chilly, the big heater is stoked up, too. So it's cosy near the stove by the time we settle in. I choose to sit next to the fire and soon feel as hot as the ginger root Grandpapa sucks during the service. Mrs. Warnock glances around curiously, then chooses a seat behind me with Gracie by her side. I sit primly, careful not to scuff my freshly polished oxfords across the smooth wooden dance floor. Everyone waits for the minister, who has a circuit of churches to preach for each Sunday and is often late, depending on road conditions.

Mom shakes hands with Mrs. Warnock and smiles toward Gracie. "I've heard a lot about you already," she says. "Welcome to Rochfort Bridge United Church. Our minister should be here any minute."

The pews are half filled by the time Reverend Halley enters. A dumpy, elderly gentleman, he has sloping shoulders with all his weight in a bundle below his waist. He has tired grey eyes and his hair looks as though it has been left in the rain too long. Mr. Halley is past retirement, but when the war caused a shortage of preachers, he stayed on. He puts his papers and Bible on the pulpit and gives Douglas a bundle of folders to pass around.

Then the service begins. It's long. I love to sing the hymns and read the psalms in unison, but the prayers are never-ending. I'm interested in the announcements, and hear the visitors welcomed. I drop my dime into the collection basket and settle for the sermon. I hear shuffling of feet and stifled coughs throughout, and entertain myself by counting how many times the minister says "resurrection" during the sermon. I reach thirteen when there's another short prayer and a closing hymn.

Mrs. Warnock goes directly to speak with Mom. "The service was interesting," she says, "but I can't help noticing that no one plays the piano. Is the pianist sick today?"

"We usually just make our own music," Mom explains. "No one plays the piano."

"Well … ," Mrs. Warnock offers. "I would love to play for you, if these young ladies would be interested in forming a choir? I'd be happy to instruct them and play every Sunday."

A dream come true for Mom! Voice training for us—how wonderful. "Oh!" Mom's eyes sparkle with excitement, her face contorting. "Let's ask them right now."

While Douglas and Grandpapa push benches to the walls and slide the pulpit away, Mom and Mrs. Warnock arrange a suitable time to practise each week, and a new choir forms. Gracie has a beautiful clear soprano voice and reads music.

"She's not so bad," I whisper to Noël.

I learn to sing alto, loving to harmonize.

The weather cools rapidly. Crows cluster for weeks. They caw and crowd each other among the shelterbelt trees, until suddenly they're gone.

A shrill wind bends the treetops forward as though they're searching for something below, as leaves rattle across the ground. Clouds like giant laundry stretch across the sky and now begin to sift snow down. Winter has arrived.

King of the Castle

"The snow still hasn't let up." I check out the window. "I'll have to break a fresh track to the biffy again." No one shovels a path. We simply tramp a trail wherever we go and pack down the next layer. On open stretches our path is soon obliterated by blowing snow.

After a hot porridge breakfast, we line the snowbank to brush our teeth, spitting carefully with the wind. We've learned from experience that spitting against the wind isn't nice. Mom smoothes my braids and combs Noël's curls. Douglas flattens his cowlick with water and we set off for school, books and lard buckets swinging.

"I'll break trail," says Douglas.

"I'll bring up the caboose," calls Noël. We leave a single straight path down the lane. My thighs are sore from lifting my legs so high, trying to clear the snow.

"Only the first of November and look at this snowfall!" Douglas says. "I wonder what the kids did this Hallowe'en. Bet it was tough wearing a costume and trick or treating in this stuff. Gee, I wish Mom would let us try it once."

"Me, too," I say. "Mom says it's a pagan custom, but the kids sure have fun."

"I'd like to beg for popcorn balls and apples," says Noël.

"That sounds great." Mom never allows us out of her sight on Hallowe'en night. She doesn't believe in such foolishness and is determined that we will never destroy the property of others as a Hallowe'en lark.

Ruby catches up to us as we walk down the range line. "Wait up!" And she strides through the deep snow with long, strong legs. "Nan wants to come to your birthday party, Douglas. She's glad there's lots of snow so she won't be jolted in the wagon. The sleigh will glide like a swan over all this stuff. She says she's coming, even if it's cold."

Ruby still stays with Nan most of the time, although she has her own bedroom at home.

A few days later, true to her promise, Nan arrives by sleigh to help celebrate Doug's birthday. She enjoyed his last party so much that she's been looking forward to such pleasure again.

It's bitterly cold. Nan arrives all bundled, a buffalo robe rolled around her body, hot rocks warming her boots and a heated Eaton's catalogue on the seat of her rocker to keep her hip warm. She has on her heavy black coat, woollen muffler, thick felt hat, and warmest mittens.

We're covered with snowflakes when we return from school. It's coming down so heavily that my brown jacket is almost white.

"It's so thick it almost blinds me." Ruby digs the snow from behind her glasses. We greet Nan.

"My goodness!" says Nan. "We'd better hurry with lunch so Grandpapa can get me home. You people look like snowmen. It'll get dark early tonight."

It's a simple party for a young fellow, but Douglas is pleased to have Nan here.

"Did you put on make-up for Doug's party?" Noël teases. "Your cheeks look like apples."

"No, no. I'm not a painted hussy," protests Nan. "You know I never wear cosmetics."

"Are you feeling all right, Mama?" asks Mom in alarm, noticing the flush on Nan's cheeks. "Do you feel feverish?"

"I'm fine, dear. Go ahead, Douglas, cut your cake. All the lighted candles bring me out into a sweat."

We munch the cake quietly. Nan looks different today. Her cheeks blaze and her eyes are very bright. Even her soft skin seems smoother, as though her wrinkles are shaken away. She's animated, her hands move restlessly instead of lying patiently crossed on her lap.

A sudden gust of wind rattles the windowpanes to the west. Snow sprays across the glass; the sound startles us.

"Looks like the wind is coming up," mutters Douglas. "I'd better get at the chores." He stuffs the last of his cake into his mouth and heads for his chore coat, hanging in the basement stairwell. After bundling up, he lights the lantern and disappears to the barn.

"Shall we sing for you, Nan?" asks Ruby. "We're learning some beautiful pieces with Mrs. Warnock." We sing several hymns with Mom accompanying us. "Oh, I love to hear you sing," Nan murmurs. "But can you stop, now, please? My head has started to pound."

"Oh, Mama!" Mom says. "Why didn't you say so? We didn't realize. I think you should lie down for a few minutes, until Papa comes. Wouldn't you like to try my bed?"

Nan allows herself to be led away and soon falls asleep on the wide bed. When Grandpapa arrives with the team and sleigh, I run out to invite him to tie the team and come for coffee. "I really think you should leave Mama here for the night," Mom whispers. "She seems a little feverish."

"Well, all right, Edith. If you don't mind, I will. It is such a blustery night that I'm sure she'd be chilled, time we carried the rocker into the house. Sure you don't mind?"

"Of course not, Papa. She can sleep with me. It's no trouble at all. Ruby can stay home too, unless you need her?"

"No, no. I'll be fine alone. I'll just slip on home, and you can explain the plan when she wakens." And Grandpapa leaves the house.

We wash up the party dishes and settle at the kitchen table to do our homework. Our only gas lamp is suspended from the ceiling so everyone can study together under the soft light. An hour later it begins to wink, a signal for us to go to bed. The lamp is running out of fuel. Its warning wink allows us time to light the coal oil lamp wicks, so that each of us has a small light for our bedrooms. We're extremely careful when carrying the kerosene lamps because of fire hazard.

Mom worries about house fires. She has planned a fire exit from each bedroom and drills us regularly. I hope I never have to crawl out my bedroom window in my night clothes, and creep across the porch roof to drop onto the clothesline stand. This upstairs is high.

Everyone settles quietly. It's nice to have Nan spend the night. But a week passes and Nan's still not well enough to leave.

Ruby skis over to Grandpapa's every evening to cook his supper, and returns to spend the night with us. We all expect that Nan will soon return to her own place. But she doesn't get better, and the weather's punishing.

Finally, just before Christmas, Nan, Grandpapa and Mom have a conference with us all. "It's foolish to heat two houses," explains Mom. "And the weather is so miserable. Why don't you both move in here? I'll give you the downstairs bedroom and move upstairs with the children. We have plenty of room. You can keep your horses and cattle in our barn, Papa. Now that Nipper's gone, we have an empty stall. The pigs can snuggle up in the pig house. So what do you say? Will you join us?"

"Dear Edith, I don't know what to say," says Nan, quite overcome. "What will Willie think?"

"I really don't know what he's thinking about anything anymore," says Mom sadly. "He never expresses opinions and he seldom comes home now that it's cold. But he'll be fine upstairs with me anyway."

We all smile at our grandparents.

"Well, Edith, we really are up against it," said Grandpapa. "It'll be a great help to stay here. I'll move our beds over so you can have your own bed upstairs. Thank you, dear." After a few more plans on how to arrange things, Grandpapa goes home to pack.

"We'll move their furniture and stuff tomorrow." Mom looks pointedly at Noël. "Well, dear, you'll have to give up your bedroom. Remember our understanding?"

"Yes, Mom," replies Noël. "You can have my room. Should I move in with Ardith?"

"That's right, girls," Mom smiles. "And I have a surprise. Grandpapa will buy a double bunk bed for you girls, so you'll share a bedroom and still have your own bed. We'll set it up tomorrow."

I make a verse to honour Nan's joining the household:

> *The north wind doth blow*
> *We have too much snow—*
> *And what will our Nan do then,*
> > *poor thing?*
> *She'll move to our place*
> *Where we have much space*
> *And gather us under her wing!*

After we go to school next morning, Mom and Grandpapa take apart her bedstead and lug it upstairs to Noël's room. They take up the bedroom suite, too. Mom sweeps and scrubs the wooden floor in the downstairs bedroom, careful not to wet the boards too much. "I don't want them warping and curling before I can afford linoleum," she explains.

While the floor dries, she and Grandpapa go over to his house to dismantle the beds, pack the blankets and clothing, and carry the dressers into the sleigh. Only one trip is necessary. They leave tables, cabinets, stove and couch behind. Nan already has her favourite rocker, so by mid-afternoon they've finished the move.

We return from school and find Nan in the rocker knitting a bedspread. She works on each square separately, feeling the flowery design with her fingers, and checks constantly to get her pattern right. Her long sensitive fingers are the most nimble part of her anatomy.

She calls out, "If one of you can give me a wee boost, I'll go to the kitchen and help start lunch in this house."

Mom appears at Nan's side. "Are you sure you feel well enough, Mama?" she asks. "I don't want you overdoing it."

"Nonsense," laughs Nan. "I'm just fine, and I'm anxious to check inside your beautiful new cupboard. Just give me a wee boost."

It takes more than a wee boost to raise Nan from her rocker. But long practice has shown Mom exactly how much strength is needed. Once Nan's leg is beneath her and she's properly balanced, she can shuffle across the floor unaided. She goes to explore the kitchen, and soon has bread and cheese laid out and the kettle singing.

"Come now," Nan calls, mashing the tea. "Before this gets too strong, or it will grow hair on your chest." She chuckles at the old joke, and says, "I wouldn't be surprised at all if Edith grew hair like a man. She surely works like one."

Nan stands at the table, waiting to be lowered into her chair. She doesn't trust herself alone; her balance is so poor that once her body is bent, she has to drop, so she's careful to drop where she intends.

Nan is proud of herself for finding all the necessary lunch items. "If I'm going to live here, I want to do my part," she says firmly. "Let me do what I can, Edith."

Nan's heavy glasses dig deep furrows into her nose on either side of the bridge, giving her a stern look. "All right, Mama," Mom says gratefully.

It continues to snow every few days. Soft flakes fall straight down with no wind. Visibility is limited, and there seems to be no horizon; everything looks the same soft grey.

By week's end, Grandpapa has moved his stock and harnesses into the barn. Spotty is somewhat mollified to have horses in the barn with him, since he hates the cows and Bo-Peep. Pat and Dolly sniff Spotty, nuzzle his nose and nicker softly.

Noël and I are pleased to have horses to sit on while we watch Grandpapa and Douglas do the chores.

"I'll take Pat and you can have Dolly," I offer. "Look how high we are on these horses—I can touch the ceiling from here." It's true. Grandpapa's team have sleek long legs.

Every Friday evening the family scramble through supper and keep dishwater ready on the back of the range so there'll be no delay. But sometimes our hands are still busy when Mom switches on the radio. *Lux Radio Theatre* begins. We slip into the living room to hear the first section with Nan, Ruby and Mom. Then we scurry back to do a few more dishes during the commercial.

Nan also enjoys the hockey broadcasts with Foster Hewitt. Although she has never seen a live game in her life, Nan cheers whenever he cries, "He shoots! He scores!" regardless of which team scores. Douglas listens to these games with his grandmother. Mom says, "We'll play the radio for two hours every evening during these long winter months, since Grandpapa is sharing his wet battery with us."

Grandpapa is a church elder, and attends monthly meetings in town. One evening while he's gone, Noël and I are playing in the barn while Douglas finishes chores. He suddenly realizes that Flossie, Grandpapa's cow, is about to give birth.

"Quiet, girls," Douglas warns. "Flossie's in labour, and you can watch if you promise not to make a sound." Noël's eyes are round with interest, and watch the red cow's wide sides heaving. As the cow moves about restlessly, she heaves again. She lifts her tail and I see a black bouquet of tiny triangular hooves emerge. The next heave pushes out long legs, and a final push brings the calf onto the straw like a shiny cellophane bag. A membrane is plastered on head and shoulders, although the legs are free, and sprawl in four different directions on the straw.

Douglas yanks off his mittens and runs to assist. "I'll scoop this stuff off, Flossie, so your baby can breathe."

Douglas digs his fingers into the calf's nostrils, clearing the passage. Flossie moves forward, and gives soft encouraging sounds as she begins licking with long, sure strokes. The little creature shudders and comes to life, then bawls as his mother boosts him to his feet. By this time, Noël and I slide from our perch on the horses, and edge toward the door. We linger a few minutes more.

"There, Noël, looks like he can stand. He's even starting to nurse. Let's tell Mom."

We rush to the house. The thermometer registers thirty degrees below, and a sharp wind comes up. "Mom! Mom! Flossie freshened. The calf is really cute—all red with a white star on the forehead. Can we call him Star, Nan?"

Douglas follows us to the house about twenty minutes later. He's done for the night.

We do our homework and then play checkers. We're all in bed before Grandpapa returns from his meeting.

By morning, it's forty-two degrees below zero. The house heaves and pops with the cold; beams protest the temperature. Mom's surprised to find Spotty shivering on the step in the morning. "Douglas! Didn't you latch the barn door?" she cries. "Here's Spotty."

"Yes, Mom, I certainly did. I was very careful to latch the door because of the new calf."

"What new calf?" Grandpapa thunders. "Did Flossie freshen already?"

"Yes, Grandpapa. A nice little guy, too!" Grandpapa snatches up his mackinaw and rushes to the barn. He returns a few minutes later with the new calf wrapped in his coat. He kneels onto the kitchen floor by the stove to unwrap the baby.

"Oh, Grandpapa. What happened?" we ask. The calf's ears are all crinkled and its tail is frozen stiff.

"That damn dog!" mutters Grandpapa. "He must have lunged and lunged at the door until he burst the latch. Both sides were flung wide and my poor calf is half frozen. I tell you, Edith, your dog is good for nothing!" Grandpapa begins rubbing the calf briskly to get circulation flowing again. "Now I know why the muskrats built such thick houses last fall," Grandpapa adds. "This is one of the worst winters for a long time."

The little calf recovers, but half its tail falls off. "We should really rename that calf," Doug says. "We should call him Shorty."

The winds never cease. Blizzard follows blizzard. All the spruce in the muskeg list slightly southward, as though longing for a warmer climate.

"Now you little people must be very careful never to leave anything on the floor," warns Mom. "I mean *never*. If

Nan falls over your dirty sock or old shoe, you would feel terrible, wouldn't you?" We nod agreement.

"Also, I want you to be sure that all the chairs and the footstool are placed in exactly the same spot each day, so that Nan can depend on their being there if she needs to steady herself. Can you remember that?" Of course, I decide. We don't want Nan to fall either.

"One more thing," adds Mom. "If we spill water, or potato peelings, or anything slippery, we must wipe it up immediately. Onion skins are especially dangerous because they stick to the floor like glue. So let's all be extra careful from now on, so Nan can navigate with confidence."

We understand. Our Nan is truly handicapped. We must be both legs and eyes for our beloved grandmother.

Meanwhile, snow drifts into mounds and ridges along the west side of the range line, where trees catch it sweeping across the field and trap it along the edge of the road. Drifts like long fingers reach halfway across.

"I'm king of the castle. You're a dirty rascal," Noël taunts, and we scramble and slide on the packed and glistening snow.

Crossing Borders

Ardith and Ruby join CGIT,
a girl's United Church group. 1946.

Christmas together in our new house is a quiet celebration. Daddy comes home for the holiday and welcomes Nan warmly. He loves and respects her and is glad we can give her a warmer, more comfortable home.

But Daddy's not pleased to have Grandpapa living here. Daddy hears Grandpapa criticize Spotty, and takes it as a personal affront. The two men are coolly civil, with Granddad trying to keep conversation running smoothly during our family gathering.

Noël brings a laugh by saying, "Granddad, why do people call you Baldie? You have more hair than either Grandpapa or Daddy!"

"It's a joke," Granddad explains. "When I was born, I was covered with hair. So everyone called me Baldie, and the name stuck!"

Daddy returns to Edmonton soon after Christmas. The cold weather continues well into the New Year. It's still far below zero when classes at school begin again.

Attendance at church drops sharply. Mrs. Warnock questions the choir girls about their attendance. We had all been so keen. After the thrill of blending our voices together in the beautiful Christmas carols, it's tough to get the choir girls together for regular services in the new year.

"It's too cold to stay after school for practice," protests Lizzy.

"It gets dark so early now. I gotta get home," says Nancy.

"This cold weather makes me hoarse," jokes Anita. Only Ruby, Noël, Gracie and I show up at the hall for the four o'clock practice.

"Let's face it, Ruby," I say, as we walk home late. "Reverend Halley's sermons are as dull as dust. I almost fall asleep when he starts—it is the exact same sermon he ground out last year at this time, and the year before that. I don't blame the girls for quitting, but I feel sorry for Mrs. Warnock. She tries to make it interesting, and we're learning a lot. I even like Gracie. She's really talented, and she's not bossy, now that she knows all the kids like her just the way she is. She dropped the Town Trotters club, and the Blood Sisters don't meet anymore either."

"There's nothing we can do about Reverend Halley—we're stuck with him," says Ruby.

Then suddenly news has it that a new minister is coming. Reverend Halley, tough as beef jerky, has finally been put out to pasture. The girls all show up for choir practice the next Wednesday, giggling and shoving, and it isn't hard for Mrs. Warnock to figure out that they've heard the same rumour she has—that the new minister coming to save the souls at Rochfort Bridge is young, handsome and unattached. That'll pack the pews.

Mrs. Warnock chooses a joyful selection that she has up her sleeve, and we pitch in and learn it in one practice, so we can all be on hand for Sunday. We know we'll have a ringside seat if we're on the choir benches.

That Sunday morning, Noël and I wake up early. We listen for sounds downstairs to indicate what time it is, since we have no clock. But no one is stirring. We peek out through the frosted windowpane, and a pale moon peeks back at us.

"It's still kinda dark," Noël says. "It must be pretty early. We'd better keep quiet until Mom lights the fire in the kitchen. We don't want to disturb Nan."

"Let's play cards," I suggest. "What will we play? Old Maid or Rummy?"

"Rummy," Noël says. We sit cross-legged on the bottom bunk, deal cards on the bedspread and feel sanctimonious for our consideration of Nan's comfort. Finally, when the stove lids rattle and the shaker is doing its job with the ashes, we make up our beds and dress. We come downstairs as Mom is stirring up porridge with her spurtle. Nan is settled, tidy and fresh, at the kitchen table.

"I just beat Noël three games straight in Rummy," I announce proudly. Nan's eyes get very round behind her thick lenses, making her eyeballs look twice their normal size. Her mouth gapes and she draws in her breath with a shuddering gasp. Then she chokes out, "Och, Edith! To think you allow your girls to gamble on the Sabbath!"

All the pleasure slides from my face, and I feel like I've been caught breaking the strongest commandment. Mom glares at both of us, saying, "You've upset Nan with your non-sense. You know better than to make sweeping statements like that!" And I do know better. In my pride of accomplishment, I'd forgotten.

We glance at our grandmother and see shiny tears leak down her wrinkled cheeks, dropping onto her freckled arms. I turn and run up the stairs as if the devil were after me. I grab the pack of cards from my bookshelf and fling them under the bed as if they're poisonous.

"I'll never play cards again as long as I live," I vow. "I'm so ashamed!" We're shaken by Nan's reaction. We dress for church, our breakfast forsaken. We just can't face Nan after seeing her cry.

When we finally creep downstairs, Nan has disappeared to her bedroom. "What were you thinking of?" Mom scolds, her eyes spitting sparks as she serves crusted porridge. "You know Nan never approves of card playing. And to play cards on Sunday upsets her twice as much. Don't you *ever* pull a stunt like that again!"

"Sorry, Mom," I say. "We won't." I feel wicked beyond measure.

Mom combs my hair and static crackles around my ears. Then she yanks my head and swiftly braids it, passes her comb through Noël's tangled curls, and we're ready. Ruby appears from her bedroom, looking like a fashion model. She's grown into a mature young lady. She wears a skirt and blouse she's sewn herself and her hair's piled up on her head. I appraise her. "You sure look beautiful, Ruby. Bet the new minister'll notice you."

"Oh, hush up!" laughs Ruby. "Are we ready? We don't want to arrive at the last minute all out of breath and not be able to sing."

Mom checks on Nan, easing her into her comfortable rocker. Grandpapa and Douglas set off first, across the snowy field to break a fresh trail for the girls.

"Sure you'll be okay alone?" Mom asks Nan. "One of us can stay here with you. I guess we're just excited about having a new minister. I'll turn the radio on for you, if you wish."

"I'm just fine, Edith. Run along with the girls. But yes, I'd like a bit of music—turn on the radio, please."

By the time we chuff through the soft snow to town, we're a bit out of breath. We peel our coats off and stand around the heater awhile.

"Wonder what the new minister will look like?" asks Nancy.

"We'll soon see," says Anita.

"Look at Ruby, all dolled up," teases Lizzy.

I watch Grandpapa and Doug arrange benches for the service. Finally everything's in order, and the clock shows a few minutes past eleven. Mrs. Warnock plays through the new anthem, so our choir'll get the tune into their heads. She's just starting the third verse when the door opens and the new minister steps into the hall.

He's strikingly handsome. He has a godly appearance: tall, slim, with a finely shaped head topped with soft brown curls parted straight down the middle of his head. His curls sweep back behind his ears but little wisps flop forward when he bends to remove his heavy overshoes. He wears a neat black suit with creased trousers and a jet-black cotton shirt, and his white collar is turned backward, in the manner of priests. He shrugs off his long coat and flings it across the ticket table near the door of the hall. Then he moves directly to the pulpit, arranges his books in order and smiles at us all, displaying a perfect set of teeth.

Brown! Brown! I'll bet his eyes are brown. I can't see directly because the choir benches angle toward the congregation, and I mustn't crane my neck or I'll risk Mom's wrath. Mom can curdle cream at a glance when she gets her dander up.

"Good morning," the minister says in a voice that sends shivers up and down my spine. His voice sounds rich, cultured, vibrant. "My name is Gordon Morton, but my friends call me Gord."

I adore the name Gord, I breathe reverently, with half-closed eyes, savouring the new name in my mind. Reverend Morton glances at us in the choir. He smiles at each girl individually, slowly passing his eyes along the pew where we perch.

I knew it! They're brown. Oh, he's the handsomest guy I've ever seen. Oh-h-h, Gord! Gord looks like a god of the night sky, wearing that black suit, with his hair all ... At this point, Anita elbows me rudely, and jolts me back to reality in time to stand on cue and sing the opening hymn. The choir's contribution is spirited, although a bit shrill with excitement. I wonder if Gord's curls have electricity in them, and fly up over his head when he combs his ... Again comes the elbow, this time for the psalm reading.

No pimples on his face—a perfect complexion. Och, I'll bet he hardly has to shave. It looks like his cheeks are downy and smooth, like a ... Anita's elbow again! I feel faintly vexed. I am *so* paying attention; I'm indignant as I dig out my dime and fork it over when the wooden plate passes. It's just that

I've never seen such a heavenly hunk of manhood. He looks really pure, and innocent, and holy and ... An elbow digs into my ribs—the doxology this time. I can rumble it off by heart, dropping my chin as my voice breaks into the alto part for the last three notes. Our choir holds the end in quivering harmony until Mrs. Warnock nods, and finishes off with a resounding thump of the bottom keys. Then I settle for the sermon, which I follow raptly. It's extremely interesting; Gord seems to speak directly to me.

He speaks of how suffering forms character and brings us nearer to Jesus, and how God never places more upon us than we can bear. The anthem's well worth the effort it has taken to learn, since Gord nods graciously to the choir, and I think he smiles a smidgen. A final prayer and hymn wind up the service, and Gord is a winner. Everyone's jovial as he makes acquaintance with his flock.

"This is my second daughter, Ardith," says Mom proudly, pushing me slightly forward so that I'll shake his hand. I gaze with rapture into liquid brown eyes, drowning my soul in their depths.

"Hello, Gord," I say clearly.

Mom yanks me so sharply by the back of my belt that I spin around in surprise, almost sprawling on the waxed dance floor.

"Get your coat!" Mom hisses. Her voice is like a sweet rattlesnake, controlled but so choked that if Mom were fed wire, she'd spit out nails. I climb into my coat and hover near the door, ready to run if that's what it takes.

Mom marches briskly out the door, head held high, and strikes off down the path, with us four youngsters stringing out at intervals behind. I'm trying to keep pace. I know I'm in for it, and wait for the axe to fall. Noël and Ruby are lagging, and Douglas waits to walk back home with Grandpapa.

Finally, Mom decides she's out of earshot, and begins her lecture. "Ardith," she says, "whatever possessed you to speak like that to the new minister?"

"Like what, Mom?" I ask.

"You know perfectly well what I mean," sputters Mom. "Calling a stranger by his first name …. An adult stranger … and a minister! How dare you!"

"But Mom!" I protest. "He said his friends call him Gord. I know I'll be his friend."

"You'll be no such thing!" Mom retorts. "He's a man of God and your elder. Don't you ever, *ever* be familiar with your elders, Ardith. I can't imagine what got into you." Her voice breaks and I realize Mom's going to cry.

Oh, no, that's the second time today that I made my elders cry. I must have the devil in me today. Aloud I say, "I'm really sorry, Mom. Don't cry." I rack my brain for something to say to change the subject and get the heat off.

"Say, Mom," I say, "don't you think Reverend Morton looks just like Jesus?"

Another error, I realize, as I listen to Mom's uncontrolled sobs, which continue all the way home.

Everyone likes the new minister, who treats us with respect and dignity, and can soon name everyone who attends his services. More each Sunday, too, as news spreads that Mr. Morton's a great speaker, a magnificent singer and anxious to work as a leader. He organizes the teenaged boys of the church into a pack known as Tyros. Doug's proud to be the secretary of this group, delighting in this strong male leadership while his own dad's still away in the armed forces. Reverend Morton becomes his role model.

A corresponding group of girls called Canadian Girls in Training (or C.G.I.T. for short) is formed with the teenaged girls. I manage to get in under the wire by being allowed to join at the age of twelve. "After all, I'm taller than most of the other girls," I argue.

"Yes," agrees Ruby. "But you're always bawling. You'd better straighten out if you intend to be in the same club as I am; I won't put up with that baby stuff."

Fortunately, Mom intervenes and insists that Ruby allow me to be included in the C.G.I.T. group. Fortunate for me, that is. Ruby isn't pleased.

The group are to serve at a Valentine tea to be held in the hall in mid-February. "Do I wear my uniform?" I ask, crossing my fingers that I can. I love the crisp white blouse with navy-blue pleated skirt and thin blue socks. There's an emblem embroidered in red on the pocket of the blouse.

"Mom, can I have red hair ribbons on my pigtails to match my pocket stitching?" I ask. "Please, Mom!"

"Good heavens, no, child!" Mom says sharply. Then, seeing my crestfallen face, she adds, "Red ribbons will clash with your hair, dear. Redheads never, ever wear red or pink."

"Do I always have to wear green, blue or brown?" I ask. "No one else wears brown at school. Why me? I look drab as dirty water in the tub."

"Brown matches your complexion," Mom replies. "Your freckles are brown, Ardith. You look lovely in brown."

Like a bean pot that boils over, I think. I hate brown. I want to wear pink and red, like my sisters. Mom is mean! Just then I see Mom with blue ribbons in her hand. "Thanks Mom." I feel ungrateful.

The town hall's transformed into a tearoom with card tables decorated in red and white dotting the floor. The C.G.I.T. girls hover over the tables.

"Oh, Anita," I whisper. She and I are responsible for the same table at the Valentine tea. "Look who's coming in now."

"Who?" Anita wonders who has caused me such excitement.

"Reverend Morton, of course," I say. "Shh, Anita, he's coming this way. Do you think he'll choose our table?"

"Oh, I hope not," giggles Anita. "I'm so clumsy I'm apt to spill cream down his neck or upset cake on his curls."

"Look. He's coming this way." I smile and pull a chair for him. "Here's a chair, Reverend Morton!" He sits down and nods to us politely.

"Would you prefer tea or coffee?" I ask importantly.

"Tea, please." I rush off and return with a full cup, which tinkles faintly on its saucer as I walk. I'm very careful not to tilt the cup near the minister. Nor do I spill it on my uniform. I manage everything promptly, properly and proudly while fluttering eyelids continuously.

In the weeks that follow, I grow more enamoured of the new minister. He radiates goodwill like a solar heater; his smiling face shows interest and concern with the problems of his flock. I can't keep my eyes off him. I'm careful to guard my secret admiration for him by lowering my lashes and fluttering them to capture flicks of pleasure which fill me with rapture.

Finally it pays off. Reverend Morton says quietly, "Ardith, could you stop by at my office after school on Monday? I need to talk to you."

Could I? I'd walk over hot coals to be there, if necessary. I can scarcely wait for the morrow. I dream of this interview— of melting into his arms like mushy snow sliding from the school roof.

Of course, I compose a limerick about the minister:

All the girls really adored
The handsome new minister Gord

They love his cute grin
And idolize him.
He acts and looks like the Lord.

Next afternoon finds me beside the desk in Reverend Morton's office. Instead of sitting behind it, the minister chooses to seat himself on top of his desk, legs hanging intimately beside me. He smiles at me.

"Ardith, do you know what boundaries are?" he asks.

"Of course," I say.

"And do you understand that sometimes boundaries are crossed?" persists Reverend Morton.

"Yes, I guess so," I agree. "My Granddad crossed a boundary."

"The minister frowns. "What do you mean, Ardith?" he asks. "What happened?"

"Well, he moved from the United States to Canada, and that's crossing a boundary, isn't it?"

"Oh," the minister lets out a long sigh as if relieved of something. "I think I understand what you're saying, Ardith. Do you mean your Granddad crossed the border?"

"Oh, yes," I giggle. "I guess I got border and boundary mixed up."

"That's all right," says the minister. "You're on the right track, and the words do mean much the same thing. I was really referring to personal boundaries, not those on a map. You see, everyone has rules for themselves ... about what they may or may not do ... that are known as personal boundaries. Now, as a minister, I have personal boundaries about my behaviour ... and I wonder if you understand that?"

Of course I understand. After all, I'm almost thirteen. What's he really trying to tell me?

I tilt my head to one side and look up at Gord, fluttering my eyelids to capture little flicks of image. I catch a serious frown on his handsome face.

"Ardith," says Reverend Morton firmly. "I'm not going to become involved with any of the young ladies in my congregation. That is a vow I took before I was ordained. So, despite being friendly, a friend is all I'll ever be, to you, or to any of the choir girls. Do you understand that?" he ends gently.

"Of course I understand," I mumble miserably. And I'm out of here.

"Thank you then, for taking the time to keep this appointment," smiles Reverend Morton. "And keep up the good singing, Ardith. I can pick out your clear alto."

I mumble thanks and shuffle out into the darkening afternoon.

Although the days are beginning to lengthen, it's already dusk, and the sky is hanging out its first stars against a dark blue curtain. I feel so confused that I scarcely know which side of my head my face is on.

What was Gord telling me? That he likes me but can't act on it? That he likes all the choir girls but can't tell them? Or worse, that I'm a little kid who doesn't know the difference between boundaries and a hole in the ground?

I wish there were a hole in the ground, so I could sink into it and disappear. I'm so ashamed. I must have crossed Gord's boundaries.

Now he doesn't like me. No one likes me. I'm ugly. I'm just a freckle-faced nobody. As useless as brown chaff on the granary floor. No one understand me. I'm flawed. Everyone treats me like a child. I'm almost thirteen. Almost a teenager.

The Flood

Hay racks from Pete Cornelis' crew wait to throw bundles to the thresher. 1942.

The weather turns balmy and suddenly the yards and roads are awash as snow changes to mush and melts to water—water in which garbage from last fall floats: mottled beer bottles, crumpled cardboard boxes and old newspapers. The air is moist in a soft blue sky with not a cloud marking the expanse from horizon to horizon.

I dig out my high-topped rubber boots and Granddad's felt insoles, and trim them for liners. They protect my feet as I squelch in the sloppy mud.

I roll down my itchy stockings, relieving the bite of rubber sealer-rings garters while my stockings become knee-socks, so I'll have no chafing from flapping rubber boot-tops.

Sunday's a beautiful day. The air is soft and moist, and Noël and I dress in our lighter clothing to go to church.

"Oh. Oh, look, I have a rip in my skirt waist," I say. "It'll hang crooked when I'm in the choir. Everyone will notice. Should I ask Nan to tack it up for me?"

"On Sunday?" asks Noël. "You know what Nan says— for every stitch you take on Sunday, you'll have to pick that many stitches out when you get to heaven."

"I know," I laugh. "Pick out the stitches with my nose. Only I thought that was just if you went to hell. Och, I'll pin my waist. I'm sure Nan will mend it for me tomorrow."

So I keep body and soul together all day Sunday with the help of an enormous safety pin.

The next day the Bible almost slips from Nan's fingers, but she catches it, smoothes the pages carefully and picks up the thick satin ribbon marker.

"Of course I'll fix that," she chuckles, smoothing the marker into place. The Bible makes a satisfying plop as the pages fall shut, making a faint musty smell of old binding waft to my nose.

"Thanks, Nan." I set the Bible carefully onto the shelf. Nan has a delicate lavender scent. I love to burrow my nose deeply into her lap to inhale it. But this morning I pick up a distinct urine odour. I'm surprised. Nan's always particular about her person.

Douglas strolls into the living room. "Time for the *Green Hornet.*" He switches on the radio.

"That music!" I imagine a huge hornet hovering above me, its wings singing as it waits ready to sting. Terrifying!

"Must you listen to that?" I ask. "I was planning to read to Nan."

"Go ahead," says Douglas, switching off the radio. "I should be outside anyway."

That evening Grandpapa announces that he feels like fiddling a little. He checks Nan's face to catch her reaction, and she nods. So he rosins up the bow while the whole family gathers in the living room.

The dancing begins. The piano stands in a corner and we push the couch back. Grandpapa plays Golden Slippers, Cotton-Eyed Joe, Red Wing, and Marching Through Georgia. Then he plays Sailor's Hornpipe and Crooked Stovepipe. We skip and march and dance Gay Gordons and two-steps until everyone is tuckered out. Mom chords at the piano until she goes to prepare lunch, and then I try chording. Grandpapa patiently tells me which key he's going to use, and I soon recognize chord changes. It's a lively evening.

Several days of sunshine follow, and it seems like spring is here. Just as the roads crust so that I can pick a dry trail along the ridges, the sun goes out. Swollen grey clouds gather overhead, and the warm winds turn chilly. The clouds grow heavier and rain begins to fall. All night I hear a steady drumming on the roof above me as I lie on the top bunk. At first light, I peer outdoors to a dismal scene. Perched on the top of the woodpile is a wretched rooster with half his bedraggled harem around him.

I see Spotty plodding through knee-deep puddles near the barn. It's all desolate.

The windows are steamy and the upstairs smells musty. The smell of wet plaster alarms Mom for fear the place is leaking. Her face begins to twitch as she makes a frantic check around, but Mr. Williams has done his work well. Not one leak is located. There's an overall dampness in the air, like mouldy mushrooms in a jar.

The yard is awash, the lane a lake, and still the rains come down. By the end of the week, the downpour has changed to heavy mist hanging in low spots and on top of the shelterbelt trees. Dampness chills to the bone.

"Come on, Ardith," calls Douglas. "Let's see if the river is over its banks." We squelch along the rain-slicked road, trying to keep to the shallowest puddles. If we choose straight down the middle, we gather a ton of mud on each boot, to be shaken off about every third step. If we take the verge, strong saplings and bushy rose-briars attack our legs and hinder our progress. We keep our eyes to the ground, choosing the best footing, and hope we don't get mired. The mist burns off, and a sickly sun shines.

Streams of water gurgle along the ditches. The culverts are still frozen and deep pools of swirling water foam around the ends. Douglas checks each culvert as we pass. We finally reach the river hill, and stare at the chaos below. The Paddle has burst its banks and the whole valley's covered with dirty floodwater. Floating slabs of rotten ice floes half the size of a piano spin in lazy circles in the sluggish current. Ice chunks stack against the pilings of the range-line bridge and grind like giant molars trying to chew the girders. More ice piles in behind them. One or two chunks swing free and sail in isolation, but most lie trapped, like huge white turtles turned on their backs.

"An ice jam! Look how the ice is backing up the floodwater. I'll bet the men will have to blow it up with dynamite to get it moving again." Douglas' eyes sparkle with excitement.

"Funny no one's here," I remark. "The guys usually stay by the bridge to keep ice from building up."

"Listen. Did you hear that?" We strain our ears above the roar of water.

A faint BOOM! sounds downstream, like a cannon at Fort Knox. "Dynamite!" Doug cries. "There must be an ice jam at the trestle, too. Let's follow the banks to the trestle and see what's happening." Although I'm cold, I hate to disappoint my brother.

We head eastward along the tops of the cut banks. Snow has melted in sheltered spots, but across our path lie huge drifts, which we must plough through. We wallow along slowly.

The valley below is desolate. Half-submerged Balm of Gilead trees shudder as ice floes scrape them. Slabs caught in their branches glisten like slanting prisms. The riverbed has vanished. The whole valley is filled with sluggish floodwater.

We can see the huge CN trestle ahead. Another BOOM! sounds and a plume of water shoots skyward as a crew blasts with dynamite.

Douglas and I join some town kids lining the bank like spectators at a ski slide. "Hi, Billy." I say. "What's happening?"

"The bridge is blocked," he explains. "There's such a jam that the ice pressure is pushing the trestle out of line. Those guys are trying to free the ice before it ruins the trestle. They say the track is closed until the bridge can be inspected by some engineers coming out from Edmonton. So Rochfort Bridge is isolated. I hope that means the school's closed."

"I doubt it, Billy." I secretly hope this isn't the case.

We hang around the trestle until I'm so cold and miserable I can't take anymore. Doug's keen on watching the crew although not too much progress has been made, so I head home alone.

The mist has changed to rain before I reach our farm, and my coat is freckled with damp spots by the time I get into the house.

The radio announces the isolation of Rochfort Bridge and all areas west that evening. It's thrilling to have such importance that the whole world hears about the plight of our town. But the practicality of plodding through muck in the barnyard and mud on the roadside is wearying, and long before the rains stop and things begin to dry, I'm sure that this has been the granddaddy of all floods.

We hear the pile driver slamming new pilings to reinforce the trestle, which has been forced six feet out of line.

Our little village remains in isolation for weeks. Heavy bags of mail finally come through, delivered by a farmer using his wagon.

Daddy comes home on leave, travelling by train as close as possible, and then walking across the trestle to reach Rochfort Bridge. He's glad that the heavy rains haven't affected the well-water. No seepage creeps into the new well. But our new basement holds a foot of water. Mom's dismayed. "The house is standing on a hill, so why didn't the water drain away?"

"No eavestroughs," was the answer from Dad. The large roof collects the downpour and drops it along the edges of the wall with such force that it's driven straight into the ground.

Mom's disappointed. It seems almost a personal affront that her projects don't withstand the weather, while Dad's do.

"I feel betrayed," she claims. "We'll dip this seepage up and haul it outside. Ardith, bring the berry pails. Come on, you young people. We'll all have to work. Let's make an assembly line."

Mom fills the buckets from the basement pool, passes them to Ruby, who carries them up the steps to the doorway, where Noël takes them through the veranda to Douglas and me, who carry the pails away from the house before dumping them.

Daddy estimates the amount of eavestroughing required, orders the material, and installs them himself with some help from Douglas, so there's never a repeat of the wet basement. But long after the water has drained, the coal pile in the far corner of the dark basement makes strange noises as it dries—crackling, pinging, soughing sounds which unnerve me whenever I pick potatoes from the bin nearby. It's easy to imagine a monster lurking in that coal bin.

Where the Lame Walk

Nan hand sewed a log-cabin quilt top. 1945.

There's a smell of paint, glue, and turpentine in the air, as Mom gets spring-cleaning fever and begins clearing out the closets and corners. The sharp smell stings my sinuses and clears my nostrils. But it never quite camouflages a distinct and frightening odour that pervades the bedroom downstairs. Nan's being eaten alive by cancer.

Grandpapa is hard-working, but he's kept penniless by Nan's illnesses. She's assailed by the weaknesses of her body.

Now Nan has to endure searing pain. She's failing fast. Although Mom spares us the details, we all realize that our beloved grandmother is dying. Nan grows gaunt and drawn, her flesh blanches. Then networks of veins purple her skin as though scribbled with indelible pencil. Her fluffy white hair gets matted, hanging like stockings on a wash-line, stuck against her thin neck. Her molasses-slow movements become stiff and even slower.

The doctor is notified. Since the roads are still impassible, he takes a handcar and pumps himself ten miles on the railroad, then walks another mile through the mud. He gives Nan morphine to ease her pain, and instructs Mom on how to give injections. Nan's soft cinnamon brown eyes sink deeply into their sockets and she moans continuously. As soon as Nan gets morphine, her personality completely changes. She, who has never cursed in her life, now rants and raves, curses and swears. It seems as if every evil of which Nan has been aware is now exposed. I'm horrified at Nan's babbling. Mom tries in every way she can think of to ease Nan's suffering. The old lady is tucked onto the couch. She's propped in the big armchair. She's eased into her rocker. And as the evenings grow warmer, she's bedded overnight in the porch. Mom attends her mother constantly.

The family in turn reads to Nan, chats with her, listens to her favourite radio programs with her, and quietly holds her hand. Grandpapa plays his fiddle for her while I chord on the piano with him. Ruby plays the piano and sings. I sing while strumming my new guitar. The whole household revolves around Nan's needs.

Nan summons her grandchildren around her to say goodbye. To each she presents a treasure, a token of remembrance. I receive a delicate fluted china dish on pedestal feet that has been hand-painted. "It was my wedding present," Nan whispers to me. "I always mixed dry mustard in it."

"Thank you, Nan," I say brokenly. "I'll treasure this always."

Finally, the ambulance carries Nan away. Mom rides along and stays in Mayerthorpe Hospital with her until Nan dies a week later. Nan is seventy-six years old. When Grandpapa breaks down and cries, Douglas is reminded of poor Jippy's death.

Nan's body is taken from the hospital to the funeral parlour. Mom takes Nan's good clothing there, but it isn't until the following day that she brings us children.

It's a dismal twilight place. Everything is grey. Grey velvet coffin, grey mottled rug, grey painted walls and grey pleated drapes—a cold, grey room. I shiver as I step silently forward to view Nan.

But it isn't really Nan. This skin is shiny and waxy, the face muscles relaxed and pain-free. Two purple grooves are trenched on either side of a nose where glasses have gouged her face, and there's a sunken look, unlike Nan's lively face. She's wearing her long lavender dress with the beautiful pearl buttons and her ivory necklace. I wonder if Nan is wearing her extension boot, but I don't dare ask Mom.

Shared moments with Nan come back powerfully, unexpectedly, as I gaze at my grandmother's corpse.

The following day is the funeral. I'm surprised when Uncle Lawrence shows up with Aunt Martha and the children, but there's no time to chat before the service.

We sit on the front benches reserved for us in the gloomy community hall, while slow, tedious funeral music seeps into our thoughts. Our music teacher is donating her musical talent. Other friends bring fresh flower arrangements gathered from their early spring gardens and tied with fluffy silken ribbons. There are a couple of stiff, artificial flower wreaths too.

The entire hall is filled with friends who are seated on the benches or standing against the walls. It seems as though the entire population of Rochfort Bridge district crams into the service. The overflow fills the street outside. Neighbours stand around in the mild afternoon sunshine; small children push their way between adults. Everyone's sorry to lose a good woman.

"Ardith's going to look just like her, with that carroty hair and pale freckled skin," I hear someone say. "Let's hope she gets the quiet wisdom, too."

I keep gulping down the sadness that is like a living creature crawling up my throat. Death is still frightening to me, although I'm twelve years old. The mournful music makes me uneasy. It's a dirge, but Nan never wailed nor complained. She wouldn't like this funeral. Reverend Morton begins to speak from behind the portable pulpit, which has been pushed to the left to leave room for the long grey flower-decked coffin at the front.

"Mrs. Black" he begins solemnly, "has gone to her Lord. To be at the right hand of God. Where the blind see, and the lame walk … "

I'm lost in thought. I picture Nan stepping sprightly from cloud to cloud in her bare feet, no longer dragging her heavy extension boot. I picture Nan stooping to pick tiny, brightly coloured flowers, able to see them all, and reach for them with ease. Nan, no longer wearing the heavy spectacles that have trenched purple gouges on either side of her nose.

Reverend Morton continues. He speaks of her unselfish life, her generosity when knitting for the war effort, her exemplary Christian life. For Nan's sake, I try to concentrate on the service, but my thoughts drift. I remember the soft fuzzy hairs

Nan (while she could walk outdoors) with Grandpapa. 1939.

on Nan's chin, the shuffle of her footsteps across the floor, her gentle chuckle.

As he approaches the coffin, Reverend Morton lifts a flap at one end of the long box, and there lies Nan, for all to see, looking as if she were asleep. I half expect to see Nan open her eyes and rouse herself. I have to remind myself—this is only Nan's old body, thin now, her flesh eaten by cancer. Nan's soul is above us. Probably floating somewhere near the ceiling. That means that Nan can see us all right now. She can see Mom sobbing into her lace-trimmed hanky. She can see Grandpapa sniffling, with red eyes and purplish cheeks, wearing his best suit, his white cotton shirt-collar buttoned so snugly under his knotted tie that his eyes seem to bulge from the pressure. She can see Ruby, broken with grief, tears coursing down her cheeks and dropping onto her hymn book. She can see Douglas, solemn as an owl, blinking rapidly behind thick lenses, and wiping his tears with the backs of his hands. She can see Noël sobbing in disbelief and despair. And she can see me. What must Nan think when she looks down at me? And I raise my eyes and begin to search the ceiling for movement or shadow that will indicate Nan's presence. I see nothing. Nevertheless, I smile and wave my hand in salute to my Nan, who must be hovering above. Mom catches the movement out of the corner of her eye and strikes my hand to my lap. I sit huddled and humbled, and secretly exalt that I had a chance to say goodbye to my idol.

Now Grandpapa rises stiffly and shambles forward, first to file around the coffin, and back to his place, followed by Mom, Ruby, Douglas, Noël and me; then Granddad, Uncle Lawrence, Aunt Martha and their children. Six pallbearers, heavy-footed farmers, neighbours all, are next. There are shuffling feet, muffled coughs and quiet weeping as row after row of neighbours file by. A black-garbed undertaker, his snowy shirt contrasting his black tie and black pinstriped pants, like a stuffed penguin, acts as usher. A smell of moth-balls and sweat hangs in the chill air.

Death is grim. I listen to the final hymn, Oh Love That Wilt Not Let Me Go. And as the words give promise of life beyond the grave, I hear a squeaky protest of turning wheels, as the undertaker rolls Nan's coffin slowly toward the door. Grandpapa and Mom follow, with Daddy, Douglas, Ruby, Noël and me.

At last we're outdoors where the fresh spring air seems to give promise of new life. We children ride in a second car behind the hearse, with Grandpapa, Mom and Dad in the first car.

At the cemetery, I stand back to allow the pallbearers to stagger along the uneven ground, carrying the pearly grey coffin; somehow it looks prettier in the sunlight. They set it on rollers above a deep hole camouflaged with fake turf. While the minister talks and prays, I count the mourners. Two hundred and fifty-six, not counting relatives. I didn't realize Nan had so many friends.

I stand on stiff unnatural turf draped over the black clay, nervously watching the coffin sink smoothly into the cavern. "Ashes to ashes, dust to dust," chants Reverend Morton. Someone thrusts a clod of clay into my hand. As the coffin disappears, I drop my clod onto it. Thud!

Thud goes my heart! Death's angels claim my beloved Nan.

I wander off. I don't want company. I prefer to be alone with my pain. Is it better to be like Nan? Asleep forever? No more anguish—no more hell on earth—just peace?

Everyone goes back to the community hall. It is trans-formed into a teahouse—card tables with chairs arranged around them. Plates of sandwiches and cakes are on each table. Pickles too. Neighbour ladies meet us kids and lead us to a table, getting coffee, clucking over us. I sink gratefully into a chair.

I watch our neighbours. Feeding like sharks, talking and laughing! How can they, and Nan only freshly into the ground?

I try to eat but the food won't force its way past the huge lump in my throat. The neighbours have brought their favourite cakes and goodies as their way of honouring their friend and neighbour, Mrs. Black, and of showing their respect.

During the funeral and the days that follow, I weep. Why did Nan have to go? She had never been anything but kind and gentle. Why are the meek taken? No one answers my question because I don't dare ask.

To add to my turmoil, Mom disappears. She's near breaking point from grief and exhaustion. She's gone to Edmonton for a change of scenery, in hopes of drawing strength from Daddy who is still stationed there.

I wander in the evenings to visit the fresh mound of flower-covered clay in the cemetery. Staring up at the stars, I imagine Nan with God now. Oh, how I miss my Nan.

All the moisture makes the trees leaf out early, and by the first of May a green sheen changes the drab mud flats into a fairyland. The migrating birds return, stopping off to rest in the brimming sloughs and the subdued Paddle River before heading north to the nesting grounds. I love to hear the gabble of geese feeding on the stubble, gleaning the grain left from last fall's harvest. Spring is a beautiful season. New life is everywhere.

Jesus Saves

Noël at the garden gate. 1948.

Evangelist tents are raised on the ball diamond so everything will be on the level. Two sincere young preachers bring promise of new life. Mom allows Noël and me to attend. They being men of cloth, what could possibly go wrong?"

The idea of worshipping God in a tent seems almost blasphemous to me. The soft canvas walls puff faintly out and in, as though they are the giant cheeks of God, breathing the warm evening air. Does God approve of the noisy beat of this revival music? Apparently not too many townsfolk do. I glance around at the sparsely filled benches as Noël and I take in the services. They're exciting, so both of us girls feel compelled to "go to the rail" and turn our lives over to Christ. As we stand there, heads bowed in submission and shame, some kids outdoors are attracted by the singing and shouting and begin to hoot and pelt the canvas with stones. This reminds me of the stoning of Stephen. I listen to the stones striking the canvas and recognize the voices as those of my school friends.

"The work of the devil," cries the preacher, "is in those poor innocent children outside. You are put to this test, Ardith, because you've turned your soul to Jesus. Be strong. You will overcome. Jesus will hold your hand forevermore, leading you to salvation!" If I weren't so bad, I wouldn't be standing here at all. I'd be outside throwing stones!

Noël begs Mom to allow her to attend Good Life Bible Camp at Lake Hope; she would continue her religious training. "I want to be a missionary and serve in Africa," she pleads. Mom smiles at Noël and allows her to attend the camp.

I have reservations. I'm past saving, I know. I can't swallow the doctrine; I feel I'm damned to hell, flawed and unacceptable.

Noël goes to Lake Hope alone. I miss my little sister, and my big sister, Ruby, who is now earning wages at Jasper Park Lodge for the summer.

Ruby. 1948.

Daddy provides distraction for me in the form of a brand new bicycle. Douglas gets one too. What a wonderful gift to usher me into my teenage years. Douglas and I pump for miles along the country roads, marvelling at the ease with which our bicycles eat up the distances.

That summer polio sweeps the country. A quarantine is put into effect so we stay pretty much to ourselves. Our friend, Normie, dies of polio, while both Anne and Frank end up in iron lungs. Three other friends have crippled limbs following the outbreak.

"I'm sure thankful that our family escaped polio," I tell Mom, "and I'm glad Noël came home safely from camp. I missed her!"

As fall wears on, with crisp, invigorating air, Noël grows

listless and pale. She seems to lack energy, and often lies moaning on her bunk with stomach cramps.

"Growing pains," Mom decides, although I notice that Noël isn't growing. She's very petite, and now her skin takes on a sallow shade. She grits her teeth in her sleep and moans piteously during the night.

"Och, Ardith," she whispers. "I feel all crawly. What do you think is wrong?" I have no idea. Mom's busy with harvesting and doesn't really keep track of her kids. And Noël never complains, although her eyes are doleful.

The dust of harvest hazes the horizon. It's a beautiful Indian summer. The grass withers and browns as sharp frosts touch the trees, but the afternoons are still hot.

"Take your sweaters," Mom instructs every morning as we set off for school.

"A sweater is what you wear when your mother feels chilly," I mutter. We kids don't think about weather changes; we're enjoying it now.

Mom and Grandpapa complete the harvest, and only the fall ploughing remains. The bountiful garden produce is put away, and all is in readiness for winter.

Soon there's ice on the water trough every morning, and Spotty's water in the bowl is a solid oval shape. But there's no snow yet.

One crisp Saturday morning, the peace ends by a piercing shriek from Noël. I rush outdoors and am horrified to see Noël burst from the biffy holding a long string-like object in her shaking hand.

Mom examines it closely as it weaves in her palm. I look at the evil thing and nearly vomit. Ruby stares at it open-mouthed. Noël fidgets, her frightened eyes round as robin's eggs as she waits for Mom's verdict.

"Fish tapeworm!" identifies Mom. "When did you eat

raw fish?" She stares at Noël in shocked disbelief. Mom never, ever feeds her family half-cooked foods, knowing full well the results of such folly.

Noël shakes her head. "I don't think I've ever had fish at all—except at Bible Camp," she ends lamely. "If we caught a fish by ourselves, we could have a fish fry on the beach. Like Jesus feeding his disciples, Mom. That's all." Noël pleads to be understood. Surely that isn't wrong.

Mom shuts her lips primly. She looks disgusted and bitter; her forehead convulses violently. "Och, Noël," she croons, and hugs her briefly. Then she drops the worm into an empty quart sealer and pours wood alcohol over it to preserve it, using the tin of gas-lamp primer fluid.

"I'll take you to Mayerthorpe tomorrow," she says. "We'll show this to the doctor."

I cuddle with Noël on her bunk. "No wonder you felt crawly, Noël." I comfort her.

She sobs and murmurs, "I still do!"

"I'll pray for you, Noël," I say. And a prayer rolls from my lips as we kneel by our bed:

> *Dear God, please guard our family*
> *Death may strike so many ways—*
> *Polio and cancer, we*
> *are frightened of so much these days.*
>
> *Protect my sister Noël, please*
> *She needs strength, away from harm*
> *I pray, dear God, on bended knees—*
> *Guard her safely in your arms.*

Noël is promptly hospitalized. A repulsive medicine is poured into her digestive tract via a tube down her nose, since she can't bear to taste such a concoction. Noël is then placed in an open adult ward with eleven women. There she sits, enthroned on a bedpan which soon brims with odorous wastes.

"Och, Ardith," she explains later. "I knew the nurses' job was to poke through the segments, measure the worm, and watch for the head to pass. So I can understand their disgust, but it made me feel so humiliated when they had disgust written all over their faces. I couldn't help it. I couldn't help the disgusting stink. And I couldn't help having a tapeworm. When I grow up, if I get over this, I'm going to be a nurse. And I vow I shall never, ever show disgust to a patient, and mortify them about their condition, no matter how repulsive it may be."

I nod. It must have hurt Noël's feelings terribly. Kids have feelings too.

Noël needs two purges to pass the tapeworm's head, since the parasite has attached its sucker-like head to the lining of her small intestine. It's capable of losing all its sections and still surviving to grow more, using nourishment meant for Noël. No wonder my little sister wasn't growing.

She passes six feet of worm with each purging—twelve feet in all. Our family very nearly loses our little Noël.

Skipping

Douglas and Ruby. 1948.

"Hey, Gracie, looks like you and I are the only girls in grade eight this year," I laugh, "with a whole parcel of boys."

"Too bad about Sal," says Gracie. "But it's lucky she can go to Edmonton for therapy on her arm. Polio is a terrible disease."

"Yes," I agree, "and Lizzy quit school. So, here we are, stuck with ten boys."

"They're just marking time until they're old enough to quit, Mom says," adds Gracie. "They skip school for harvesting, and hunting season, and spring planting, and hauling wood. Or any other exciting chore that they can line up."

Mrs. Warnock knows I'm not academically challenged. Gracie gives me a run for my money, but that's about all. The teacher encourages me to continue writing in my spare time, but she can see I'm waiting for my classmates. Mrs. Warnock tries to interest the boys of the class by giving sensible, practical assignments to which they can relate, although the work isn't particularly inspiring for either of us girls.

I complain to Gracie about this, and of course, she tells her mother privately, so I'll bet I'm in for it.

Mrs. Warnock says in class, "Ardith, please stay after school this afternoon. I want to talk to you."

Oh, oh! What's coming now? Bet I'll get heck. But Mrs. Warnock surprises me. "Ardith," she says, "I've been thinking about you. I know neither you nor Gracie is motivated to excel with that bunch of boys. The assignments are too simple for you. You're an extremely intelligent young lady, and I have decided to accelerate both you and Gracie to the grade nine class, where you will find academic challenge. Now, your classmates might not appreciate your and Gracie's skipping. Do you think you can handle it?"

I'm totally flabbergasted by this turn of events. "Oh, Mrs. Warnock!" I cry. "Thank you! I'm sure the kids won't mind—the boys know we're good students. I'd love to go on to grade nine. Oh, thank you, Mrs. Warnock."

I'm delighted, and feel like hugging the teacher, but of course, I know it'd be out of line.

There's mixed reaction to our skipping at school. None of the boys in grade eight is upset; they continue to treat me well. They respect my intelligence. The boys are fair. They know I love to study, and they're glad I'm getting a chance to apply myself. It doesn't worry them at all, since they're quitting this year anyway. And we'll still all be together in a multi-grade classroom.

But the girls of grade nine don't welcome me with open arms. Their clique is difficult for Gracie and me to break into. These girls are older, some a full two years older than I. They attend dances. They have boyfriends. They're with it. I'm still in pigtails. I don't fit in socially.

So that makes me doubly pleased to be invited to a isolated area of the schoolyard with Patsy and Anita during noon break the following week.

We scrunch down into the long slough grass where it's deliciously cool. Patsy casually produces a cigarette box. Carefully she draws out three rumpled cigarettes, smoothes one and sticks it into her mouth. "Here," she says, handing Anita and me the others. I straighten mine and place it between my lips. I'll show Patsy, I think slyly, I've seen this done before.

After we get our smokes burning, Patsy says, "Watch this." She puts the lit end of her cigarette into her mouth and closes her lips. The cigarette is still burning, nestled under her tongue when she reopens her mouth. I'm amazed.

"Hey, that's nothing," says Patsy casually. "I can make smoke come out my ears. Want to see?"

"Of course." I'm excited. "I've seen it come out of peoples' noses, but never their ears."

"I bet you can't," says Anita. "That's impossible."

"Watch closely then," cries Patsy. "You're in for a big surprise." She sucks in a long drag, removes the cigarette from her lips, and presses them firmly shut. I stare at Patsy's ears, watching for smoke. Just as I'm sure I see a wisp escaping, I feel a sharp pain, and jerk my hand away. Ouch! She burned my hand with her cigarette tip. Smoke pours from her mouth. I smell hair and flesh scorching.

"Got ya that time." She catches Anita's eye and both girls bray like donkeys, while I ruefully rub my burnt hand, trying hard to smile. I'm an easy mark—so gullible.

Patsy has just slapped me like a bug; I swallow bile back down my throat and chide myself. She's paying me back for being smart in school. The bell clangs and we run back to the classroom. I sit down and write a verse:

School days. Days of golden rule.
I love the subjects taught at school.
But some scholars are not sincere
They only come to play, I fear.
Our teacher will accelerate
Grace and me. We think that's great.
We're skipping from grade eight to nine.
The other kids all say that's fine,
Although a few may laugh or jeer
It saves us both a whole school year.

Someone has written a foul word in perfect printing on the schoolhouse door. I stare in horror. Who dares to do that? I certainly wouldn't be suspect—I could never print that neatly.

On Friday afternoon, Mrs. Warnock allows the class to have a spelling match. The last two up from the previous match are captains, and they choose their teams with great calculation. My mouth goes dry with fear that I might not be chosen until the end. It's a disgrace to be the last chosen. "You get Ardith," I imagine the other captain smirking.

This never, ever happens. I'm chosen by at least halfway through the draw. The kids have more confidence in my spelling ability than I do.

I enjoy the challenge of more advanced school assignments, and Mrs. Warnock builds my confidence as a student.

"Do you realize," I ask Noël, as we walk home from school, "that this is the last year for me at Rochfort Bridge School? Most of the kids here don't plan to go to high school. But I sure want to, even if it means travelling to Sangudo."

Mom has done her groundwork well. All of us kids have a real thirst for knowledge, and Ruby and Douglas are presently attending high school at Sangudo. A squatty little school bus picks them up at Rochfort Bridge Main Street each morning, and hauls a small group of kids to high school.

Only the very academic young people continue their education past grade school; most of the students phase out after grade eight to begin their adult careers.

"I suppose I'll take high school, too," Noël says.

It's a cool, crisp afternoon in late October. The trees are completely stripped of leaves, except for the Russian willows' bowers of olive leaves, which border the bare cultivated fields. We dawdle along home, enjoying our chat. The sky has that bright sharpness that makes us squint to cut the glare. Sunlight reflects off a shiny vehicle in our driveway.

"Hey, whose car is parked beside the house?" I ask.

"No one we know." Noël can identify friends by their vehicles.

We rush indoors, and meet Uncle Lawrence with Aunt Martha, Aster, Pansy and a precious baby.

"Hello, girls," Aunt Martha smiles, deftly detaching the baby from her breast and holding her upright. "Meet Daisy.

We'll soon have a full bouquet." She laughs nervously, glancing at me.

I hug Aunt Martha. When had she gone back to Uncle Lawrence, and why? I smile to my aunt and admire the baby, who is nine months old. She's a bonny baby with straight dark hair and pale blue eyes, like Granddad's.

"We're just waiting for you to get back from school," Aunt Martha explains. "Now we must head back for Edmonton. But we'll try to get out this way again before the snow blows. You girls have sure grown, and it's so nice to see you."

They leave amid a flurry of well-wishes, with my questions unasked.

After the car disappears down the lane, I turn to Mom. "When did they get together again?" I ask.

"Just after Daisy was born, apparently," Mom says. "Uncle Lawrence promised not to drink anymore, and Aunt Martha agreed to live with him if they can stay in Edmonton. They seem happy. Maybe it'll work out for them."

I sure hope so. I review bad scenes in my mind. Seeing my Uncle Lawrence again rips the scab right off my memories. They expand like an internal haemorrhage. But I wrap my brain around the pain, and smother it to silence. I often wonder about my frail aunt, living with that huge, mean man. But I can't speak of it to anyone.

Always Room for One More

Jock, Dad display freshly-killed turkey from Granddad. 1948.

I write, seated near the stove:

> *How the wind is howling as it swoops around the eaves*
> *While the clothes out on the clothesline dance,*
> *and stiffly wave their sleeves.*
> *The gangling calf is gambolling knee-deep in fresh new snow.*
> *She doesn't seem to realize, it's 32 below!*

But we are snug and cosy as we work within the room—
Making plans for celebration of the Christmas coming soon.

"Time to make out the Christmas order," Mom announces, thumping the Eaton's catalogue onto the kitchen table. "Christmas is just around the corner. Now, what do you young people need? I am sending only one order to Eaton's," warns Mom. "So you had better be very sure of what you want."

I agonize over the coloured pages trying to choose the perfect gifts from a bewildering array of choices. Finally, the finished draft is mailed.

"I know it takes at least a fortnight to process that order," I whisper to Noël. "But I can hardly wait. I wonder what our gifts will be like. Aren't you excited, Noël?"

"Of course," she agrees. "But it's kinda thrilling just waiting and thinking about the parcel, isn't it?" We giggle together. Not a day passes without our speculating on the contents of our Christmas parcel. It's a time of happy suspense and anticipation.

A few weeks later, Mom gets a letter written by a very shaky hand—spidery letters scrawling across the envelope and scarcely decipherable. "My goodness!" exclaims Mom. "Who do we know that writes like this?"

She slits the envelope neatly. "Uncle Jim," she cries. "It's from Uncle Jim."

"But Mom," I protest. "I thought we have only one uncle. You're an only child, and Dad has only Uncle Lawrence for a brother. So who's Uncle Jim?"

"Not your Uncle Jim," explains Mom. "He's *my* uncle. My dad's brother, Jim."

"Why did he write, Mom?" asks Noël.

"He wants to come and stay with us," explains Mom through stiff lips. "He's been sick and can't work. So he thinks he can stay with Grandpapa. Well," Mom looks at her, "luckily we have a big house. I guess we can pack in Uncle Jim. But where shall we put him? And what will Daddy think?"

"He can have my room," my brother offers. "I'll sleep on the cot in the sewing room. 'Cause I don't think Uncle Jim and Grandpapa should have to share that bedroom, even if they are brothers."

"Thank you, Douglas. We'll see what Daddy thinks of all my relatives moving in. But what else can we do?"

The first snow has fallen before we meet Uncle Jim. He's a short, tidy man who resembles Santa Claus. A summer Santa Claus. He has a flowing, thick white beard, thick curly white hair and twinkling blue eyes. When he hugs me, his beard tickles my neck. His vest has an odour of mildew, which makes my nose twitch until I sneeze the smell away. There's also a sweet fruity odour to his breath.

Uncle Jim has palsy and shakes constantly and violently. The medication he requires is called Beef, Iron and Wine Tonic. He likes it mixed with hot water in a shot glass.

"I'll bet it's the wine in that stuff that makes Uncle Jim feel better." Douglas is serious. "He sure uses a lot of it. Spills a lot too, trying to reach his mouth with the hot toddies."

"Mom! Mom!" Ruby calls from upstairs. Mom hurries up the steps.

"Look!" Ruby is horrified. "Bedbugs! Uncle Jim's case must have a million of them! Oh, look, Mom!"

And sure enough, his battered old leather case is crawling with bedbugs. Infested again! Mom's afraid everyone might find out, but luckily DDT is now on the market. "Doug, can you run to town for a container of DDT?" calls Mom. "Ruby, help me gather Uncle Jim's things. We'll hang them out on the clothesline. This freezing weather should discourage the bugs. Ardith, you carry Uncle Jim's case outside, please. I'll not have our beautiful home overrun by these pests. We'll make short work of them."

In no time at all, the house is bug free. Uncle Jim's clothing is whipping in the breezes, and his case remains in the frozen veranda all winter.

Uncle Jim settles in quite comfortably and soon adjusts to the family. He's very fond of Noël and enjoys playing checkers with her, or listening to the radio programs. His favourite is *The Shadow,* but such diabolical laughter gives me the creeps. I bury my ears in a cushion, while Noël laughs with Uncle Jim.

"Let's go down to the old riverbed and watch the muskrats," my little sister says. "There's not much snow yet, so we can track them under the ice by following their bubbles."

"All right," I say. "It shouldn't be too cold. The sun is out today." Actually there's a dazzle of sunlight streaming through the double kitchen windows.

When we reach the old riverbed, we find Billy and John running and sliding on the ice. "Hi, girls," Billy calls. "We're drowning muskrats."

"But how can you drown them when they're under the ice?" I want to know.

"It's easy," explains Billy. "Just follow their stream of bubbles but don't let them breathe at their push-up. See these little domes built of underwater plants? They've frozen and been insulated with a bit of snow. We're each standing beside a push-up, and every time the muskrat comes to breathe, we stamp the ice so it leaves without a breath. It'll finally drown because it can't get fresh air. Then we break the ice and get the body."

"Och, that's mean! What do you want it for?"

"The pelt," says Billy. "We get twenty-five cents a pelt, stretched and dried."

*Mom, Ardith, Douglas, Noël, Dad and Ruby
at front door. 1949.*

"Come on, Ardith," says Noël. "Let's go home. I hate to see those poor muskrats drown."

"I'll bet you'd love a muskrat fur coat, though!" calls John. "Someone has to kill the muskrats." I look at him with reproachful eyes.

Soft grey clouds form in the western sky, and soon the first large flakes begin to sift across the drab landscape. No wind rearranges the snow as it settles softly across the countryside, as though a duvet of giant proportions has been laid over the land. Blue shadows cast upon the white expanse. The weather turns cold, and sun dogs glittering in a crystal sky warn of worse changes coming.

"I'm hiding Uncle Jim's pipe here in my bed," chuckles Noël. "He'll look all over for it, and then offer me a nickel if I find it. So don't you tell him where it is. I want to earn some money, and this works pretty good. I've already made fifteen cents."

I shake my head at Noël's tricks, but I don't tell Mom.

We girls watch Uncle Jim search through the living room and kitchen. He turns over every paper and book, growing more agitated all the time.

Finally, he says, "Blame it all. I'll give you a nickel if you can locate my pipe, Noël. I can't remember where I put it."

Noël makes a pretence of searching the living room and then skips upstairs. She returns to the living room and continues her search. With a happy cry, she produces the pipe and claims her reward. "That makes twenty cents," she totals shamelessly.

Noël and Uncle Jim are engrossed in a checker game at the kitchen table while Mom prepares supper.

"Mom! Mom! Come quick!" calls Ruby from her room upstairs. Mom rushes up the steps, recognizing panic in Ruby's voice. "Isn't that a fire?"

Mom peers through the west window to where Ruby is pointing. An orange glow looks like a very bright sunset on the horizon, and is flickering and blazing in the sky.

"My goodness!" exclaims Mom. "It's a fire all right. It looks like Sheechucks' house! I'm sure of it!" Mom rushes downstairs, snatching her mackinaw from its peg at the basement stairs. "Douglas, Ardith, come along! We must try to help the Sheechucks. Their house is on fire! Dress warmly and hurry! Noël, please stay here with Uncle Jim and tell Grandpapa what's happening when he gets in from chores. And please watch the stew for supper, dear. We'll all be chilly when we get back! Ready? Let's go."

We rush out into the cold twilight. I run quietly on moccasined feet, padding along with my eyes glued to the glowering sky in the west. Leaping flames illuminate the whole area, and cast eerie shadows along the lane behind us.

As we draw nearer, I can hear snapping, sizzling, and popping as bottles and containers burst from the heat. These small explosions terrify me. They remind me of the fire that destroyed our family home a long time ago.

Must be six or seven years ago, but I still feel the same terror now that I had then. Fire is so devastating! I sure hope Mrs. Sheechuck is all right.

A rising west wind cuts through my heavy clothing and clutches at my face and legs, but I scarcely notice in my anxiety to reach the scene.

We swing up the Sheechucks' lane. Now a dark outline of the doomed house looms into view. It's a torch, showering vivid sparks high into the night sky and outshining the stars that twinkle overhead. Only a dark skeleton of the structure remains. It's too late for us to save anything.

Mom runs straight to Mrs. Sheechuck, who huddles on an oilcan, wailing as she watches her home burn to the ground.

"Are you all right?" Mom demands. "Are you hurt? Did you get hurt anywhere?" Then Mom remembers that Mrs. Sheechuck speaks very little English.

"Are you okay?" Mom abbreviates her questions.

"You okay?" she asks again, dropping to her knees and hugging the disconsolate woman. Mrs. Sheechuck looks up in dazed bewilderment.

"House, she go!" she says. Mom glances at the pile of rubble.

"Yes, house gone!" Mom agrees. "Where's Mike?"

"No got Mike."

"Where … Mike?" Mom persists.

"Mike go bush camp," she mutters and bursts into a fresh frenzy of tears. "Now Mike no got underwear!"

"Oh, Mrs. Sheechuck." Mom gathers the old lady into her arms. "Come to my house."

"No got Mike!"

"We get Mike. Come! Come!"

The poor old lady allows herself to be led away. Slowly we head for home. Nothing can be done here.

I glance back over my shoulder as we trudge down her lane. The white poplar trunks are edged with crimson from the glow of burning embers as the last studs give way to the fire.

Douglas sheds his mackinaw and passes it to Mom. Then he runs ahead so that Mrs. Sheechuck won't refuse the coat. She wears only a house dress with felt slippers that are much too big for her. I watch them flop like snowshoes, fill with snow, and spray the snow out again as she plods along. Mrs. Sheechuck has Doug's coat wrapped around herself. The chill wind increases. Everyone shivers now. Heart-wrenching sobs burst from Mrs. Sheechuck. I glue my eyes on the light from home, willing myself to move on. But my own throat swells as I snuffle in sympathy for our elderly neighbour.

Noël's eyes roll when Mom leads Mrs. Sheechuck to the wooden kitchen table and pulls out a chair for her. As the old lady sinks down, Mom nods over her head to Noël.

"Tea!" Mom whispers. Noël mashes some tea leaves and pours a piping hot drink. Mom drips a huge spoonful of liquid honey into the mug and pushes it toward our neighbour.

Mrs. Sheechuck grasps the mug with mud-encrusted fingers. Only then does Mom realize that the poor woman's hands are blistered and scorched to the elbows. Mom finds some white sheeting to use for bandages.

"Where's the Watkins salve?" Mom calls. I locate the round tin of carbolic salve and Mom dresses Mrs. Sheechuck's wounds by first applying liberal slathers of salve.

"You okay?" Mom asks again.

The old lady shakes her head. Then lifting her cup in her swaddled hands, she sucks her tea noisily. "Ah-h-h-h!" she breathes. Then she begins to sob. "No got house. No got Mike. Mike no got underwear. No got no-ting!" she cries. "No-ting!"

I feel a lump come to my throat. I'm sad for the poor woman.

"You stay here!" Mom says. "You sleep my house. I tell Mike."

Mom scribbles a message on a scrap of notebook and calls for Doug. "Run this message to the hotel, please, dear," she says. "The men in the beer parlour will locate Mike. We'll keep his mother here until he comes home."

Noël serves the hearty stew supper. We eat gratefully, feeling warmth seep back through our chilled bodies.

Then Mom leads Mrs. Sheechuck to the little cot beside the sewing machine. She digs out a flannel nightie for the old lady and sits by her side after tucking her in, until she's settled. Doug can sleep on the couch.

Downstairs, Noël and I do the dishes. "Look, Ardith." Noël holds up a neat square of white. "I was knitting while I watched the stew pot and talked to Uncle Jim." It's a potholder, made of grocery string."

Every bit of string that comes into our house is carefully wound onto that string ball, with each addition tied to the last, so that there's one continuous line of string of several different thicknesses. Noël used this string ball to knit a potholder, lumpy and uneven due to the varied thicknesses of material, but she turned all the knots to the back so that the surface is smooth and flat. And she cast off the stitches when a square shape was achieved.

"That is so neat!" I say. "Who is it for?"

"Mrs. Sheechuck!" Noël whispers. "A start for her new home."

I can hear Mrs. Sheechuck during the night, coughing, moaning and crying as she tosses on the cot. I hope they find Mike soon, so he can talk to her. It must be awful not to be able to speak the same language as everyone else. Especially when disaster strikes!

I settle again into troubled sleep. But my rest is shattered by a horrendous nightmare, in full technicolour, of the fire that had destroyed our farm home. Between Mrs. Sheechuck and me, Mom has very little sleep this night.

Or for many nights to come. Mrs. Sheechuck develops bronchitis and needs constant nursing. Her hollow, rattling cough wracks her frail frame, making her gasp and wheeze. Tears course down her wizened cheeks, and she looks poorly indeed. With grey frizzles of hair around her forehead, she looks like a crimping iron has gone crazy where her hair must have been singed by the flames when she fought the fire.

Mike is not located, but it's unwise to move Mrs. Sheechuck anyway. She's much too ill.

Mom notifies the Salvation Army of the plight of our neighbour and soon a few stout boxes are delivered by train.

These aren't the parcels for which Noël and I are waiting, but we watch with interest as Mrs. Sheechuck examines her gifts. Second-hand clothing—stockings, underwear, petticoats and dresses, sweaters, scarf, toque and mittens, coat, purse, toiletries, towels, sheets, blankets and pillows. There are even a few mismatched dishes.

Mrs. Sheechuck is touched by such generosity and cries again. But I notice that although the old lady's eyelids are still swollen, a faint twinkle appears in the depth of her eyes.

A few days later when her cough subsides, she can be found sitting in Nan's old rocker whenever we return from school. Grandpapa pointedly ignores the old lady, and he privately scolds Mother for sheltering her.

"She's nothing but a bohunk!" he splutters. "Send her to her own people!"

"But she has no one, until Mike gets here," Mom protests.

At last the Eaton's parcels arrive. There are three huge parcels. Mother says, "I must open these myself. You young people can't see everything, because it would spoil your Christmas surprise. I'll bring you the things you ordered, so that you can wrap them yourselves."

Bitter disappointment. But wise. Because it maintains the aura of excitement and suspense.

Mom entertains Mrs. Sheechuck as she sews a dolly's outfit for Noël. It's very elegant. The set has a dress, petticoat, bloomers, bonnet and sweater. The little dress is made of flower-sprigged voile, edged with tatted lace. There's a lace insert at the waistband through which a narrow pink ribbon is threaded. Shiny satin bloomers and slip are also lace trimmed. The bonnet and sweater are crocheted of pink yarn in a seashell design. The little costume is fit for a princess!

Noël and I lay our ordered goods on the bed to admire them. "I'm giving socks to each of our men for Christmas," I say. "Each will get a different colour. See—blue for Daddy, brown for Doug, grey for Granddad, red for Grandpapa and grey with red stripes for Uncle Jim."

Noël smiles her approval. "You look like Nan with all those socks."

"These plaster plaques are for Mom," I continue. "This rayon scarf is for Ruby." I stuff the last parcel behind my pillow. It contains a box of pencil crayons for Noël.

"All my men presents are the same colour! See—a red

handkerchief each, a broach for Mom, a lace hanky for Ruby, and that's about all," Noël hides a present under her mattress. Keeping secrets is fun.

At last school closes for the holidays and the concerts and programs end. Granddad arrives with a huge turkey, freshly butchered and plucked.

"Know you need a big one this year!" he chuckles. "With all these extra people. Like a regular ho-tel here!"

"Oh, thank you," Mom tells him. "It's true. We certainly have a houseful! But there's always room for one more."

"Yes," Granddad says thoughtfully. "But ain't he coming home for Christmas?" He searches Mother's eyes.

"Why, yes," Mom splutters. "I think so …. He didn't really say."

Mom shuts her mouth primly and glances around at us kids. I bury my face in my book. What does Mom mean? Of course Daddy will be home for Christmas!

"Do you want the tree in the living room now?" calls Douglas. He props it up until Ruby helps him stand it up in the pailful of sand.

"I'll put on these paper foil bells." I hold them up.

"I love these twisted tin icicles." Noël suspends one by a string. "See how it glitters as it twists and turns."

"Look, girls." Ruby holds an ancient angel from Nan's treasures. "I'll perch this angel on the very top."

"It seems like Nan is looking down from heaven at us. I feel her loving presence, through the eyes of her angel."

"Yes," agrees Noël. "I think you're right."

Daddy doesn't disappoint his family. He swings off the train on Christmas Eve.

"I've got an extended furlough until January third," he calls out. We eye his bulging duffle bag. It looks mysterious.

Daddy has something to put under the tree for everyone:

beautiful necklaces for all his girls, including Mom, which we find on Christmas morning.

I watch Mother clasp her gift and slip it under the collar of her dress. Smiling, she glances over her shoulder at Daddy, but he's too busy helping Douglas assemble his new model airplane to notice.

Daddy passes nuts in the shell to his father, Uncle Jim and Grandpapa, and nods gravely to each. "Merry Christmas." He yanks Noël's cat along the floor by its tail, until the frantic creature escapes under the couch, hidden by tissue wrapping.

Noël presents her potholder to Mrs. Sheechuck, who smiles at her and nods to Mom.

Grandpapa gives us a beautiful gift. It's a handmade bobsled. "I've tested it carefully—ropes, runners, hinges, springs—all working perfectly. It should be safe. But it's swift!" he warns. "Do you think you can handle it?"

"Sure!" cries Douglas. "I'll steer. The girls can ride behind. Don't worry!"

"Let's try it right now," I say. "That's a wonderful Christmas present."

"Thank you, Grandpapa." We all scramble over to kiss him on his cheeks. Grandpapa beams. Proud of his accomplishment.

With a rising feeling of excitement, I bundle up to test the bobsled. Doug pulls it easily, with Noël riding all the way to the river hill.

"All aboard?" Douglas takes his place in front, gathering up the ropes, and steers the bobsleigh down the long, curving hill. The whirling snow blocks my view and the wind whistles a shrill wail as the sleigh increases in speed. It flies down the slope. We scream. We'll miss the bridge, I think in alarm. But Douglas manoeuvres the ropes expertly, and the bobsled shoots across the bridge and flies on until the valley levels out and the sleigh slows to a halt.

"What a ride!" Noël dusts snow off. "I'll bet we were going a hundred miles an hour!"

"Not quite," says Doug seriously. "But this bobsleigh sure is swift. Grandpapa did a fine job of making it." We slide until we're cold, and then head home, rosy cheeked and exhausted. By the time we dust off our snowy clothes, the adults have unwrapped their gifts. We admire every item on display under the tree. Ruby has tidied the living room while Mom continues with meal preparations.

"We're having a real crowd for Christmas." Ruby sniffs the air. "That turkey sure smells good! I'd better set the table. Let's see ... six of us, two grandparents, Uncle Jim, and Mrs. Sheechuck. That makes ten. No problem. We need to add only one board to the table."

Mom says, "You go ahead and lay the table. Take my good white tablecloth. I pressed it and it's on the buffet, all ready to use. Now, how does this recipe for dancing snowballs work? I found it in the *Western Producer*. It says to put moth-balls into coloured water in a pretty jar. Let's use Nan's crystal pitcher, dear. We may as well enjoy our beautiful keepsakes. All right! In go the mothballs. Phew! I hope the water drowns that awful smell. Fill the pitcher, Ruby. I'll find some food colouring. Would green be pretty? How do we make the mothballs dance? They are just lying like stones at the bottom of the pitcher. Where's that recipe? Oh! You add two table-spoonfuls of baking soda and one of this citric acid. Oh, look. They're moving already."

"That's amazing, Mom! I'll set the dancing snowballs as a centrepiece. If we can't think of anything to say, we can watch the snowballs dance. Look at them rising and falling."

"I can't imagine us not saying anything." Mom motions to Ruby. "But, fine! Put them as a centrepiece."

"Wasn't Noël cute about her new doll clothes?" I say.

"She's a bit self-conscious because she still loves dolly clothes. So what! I love them myself, when they're handmade like those. All that tatting on them, Mom. You must have spent hours doing that!"

"Oh, I suppose I did," Mom chuckles. "But it was just a few minutes now and a few minutes again. Just to keep my hands busy. Remember what Nan always said, 'Idle hands are the work of the devil'!"

"Yes. Oh, how I miss Nan!" Just then a horn beeps outside. Ruby peers through the steamy window and exclaims, "It's a taxi. It looks like Uncle Lawrence! With his taxi full! Their whole family is here! Whatever shall we do?"

"Pull the table wider, dear. We'll put another board in, and set more plates."

"We'll do it, Mother. You welcome them in," mutters Ruby.

"Come in! Come in! What a surprise." Mom claims the baby from Aunt Martha's arms. "Hello there, Aster. How are you, Pansy? My, my, how you've grown!"

Mom's eyes snap with excitement as she takes coats from the youngsters. Noël and I each take a child off to admire the Christmas tree and gifts.

"I knew it, Sis." Lawrence sniffs the air. "You've got the turkey roasting. I knew we'd make it in time for dinner!" He rubs his hands together, chuckling.

"See, Martha. Sis has lots to eat!" He ambles into the living room where the men are sitting.

"Hello, everyone," he booms. "Thought we'd surprise you and drop by for Christmas!"

"I hope this won't put you out, Sis," whispers Martha to Mother. "There was no money left for groceries after buying the girls' presents, and Lawrence was vexed that we had no turkey. He said, 'Why should I eat Spam for Christmas when my dad grows turkeys?' So we roll the girls into their coats and drive out to the farm. I do hope you don't mind?" she ends anxiously.

"We're happy to have you." Mom is sincere. "Always room for one more! Ruby, can you set up the little table for the children? I'm sure Noël will sit with them and help them with their meal."

As Ruby rearranges the table settings, I fetch the basement bench, and soon everyone's got a space to eat.

Mom mashes the potatoes into a fluffy mound, while Ruby digs the baked yams from the oven. Grandpapa carves the huge turkey while Mom stirs up gravy. Ruby measures tomato juice into crystal shot glasses. "There's not enough juice," she whispers. "Add a bit of water." Mom says behind her hand.

"Please, come to dinner," she calls to the menfolk, who patiently wait in the living room. They file quietly to their places.

"Let us be thankful that our whole family has gathered here, and for this Christmas celebration we meet in good cheer," prays Grandpapa, and we murmur, "Amen!"

"To a happy New Year," toasts Uncle Lawrence, raising his glass and sniffing it hopefully. "May nineteen forty-eight be good to you!"

"Happy New Year." We touch our glasses across the laden table. I smile at Aunt Martha, and the feast begins.

We linger around the table, cleared of dishes except for the cups. Mother's famous divinity fudge, Yule log candy, fresh nuts in a bowl, and a platter piled high with mandarin oranges are placed on the table. Feasting continues as stories are swapped, and everyone compliments Mother and comments on the amazing dancing snowballs.

Noël delights the little girls by dressing her cat in the beautiful doll clothes. The patient old pet seems to enjoy her finery, and is much admired by the children. She lies calmly in their arms like a contented child.

As soon as we finish washing the dishes, we move into the living room, where Grandpapa rosins up his bow. He strikes a tune on the fiddle, Mother plays the piano and I accompany them on my new guitar. Everyone sings the beautiful carols and then more lively music continues for a couple of hours. The children skip and jig until they're tuckered out.

"I think this one will be a boy," whispers Martha knowingly, as she pats her expanding tummy.

"Do you?" smiles Mom. "That's what you said last time!"

"Yes, but I feel different this time," declares Martha.

Noël reads *Thornton Burgess Bedtime Stories* to the three little girls. Their heads nod. "Come, dear." Martha speaks to her husband. "We must head back to Edmonton. The girls are falling asleep, and it'll be late by the time we get home."

As Uncle Lawrence reluctantly leaves the group, Mom scurries into the kitchen and packs a hamper of food for the city cousins. She tucks in jars of preserves, cookies, cakes and candy. And last of all she includes the remaining turkey and gravy, for Uncle Lawrence.

Martha's eyes glisten as she hugs Mom goodbye. Then the taxi leaves the snowy yard, heading back to Edmonton.

"Where are the turkey scraps?" asks Daddy just before bedtime. "I think I'll have a sandwich."

"I gave them to your brother," Mom apologizes.

Daddy shakes his head as he reaches for the peanut butter tin.

"Him!" he mutters in disapproval. "He sure has problems caring for his family!"

FIFTY

Blackmail

We all celebrate
1948
With health and good cheer
For a prosperous new year.

"Amen," everyone concludes the grace.

We've half finished the turkey dinner when there's a knock at the door.

Mom rises to answer. "Why, it's Mike! Happy New Year! Come right in. Your mother is here."

Mrs. Sheechuck gives a choking cry and flings herself into Mike's arms. She bursts into speech—like water pouring from a broken dam. Mike keeps patting and hugging her.

"Thank you for helping Mother," he says humbly. "I will take her to Auntie Helen's. She can stay there until spring when I can get a new house."

"Oh, stay and eat, Mike, before you go!" urges Mother. "There's always room for one more!"

But by the end of New Year's Day, Mom has one less mouth to feed and Douglas gets his cot back to sleep on.

The weather's milder, so we girls go outdoors without toques or mittens. "Look what I have," I whisper. I unfold my palm to expose two slightly battered cigarettes. "I sneaked them from Uncle Lawrence's package. Let's go to the barn and smoke them." I'm as cool as cream down the well, sharing delicious secrecy.

Noël eyes the cigarettes with misgivings. "Better not." Her lips tighten into a stern gash. "We might burn the barn down."

"Och, Noël. Well, let's go into the A house. I want to try smoking. It looks so elegant."

"Do you have matches?"

I open my other palm to display a pack of paper matches. "I also filched these." Noël could think of no further objections.

We clamber over the corral fence, heading for the A house in the pigpen. We crawl on hands and knees through the low door, but once inside we stand upright in the centre, since the farm building is constructed in the shape of an A. It houses the pigs, now away munching mash at their troughs.

The A house is chilly and smells piggy, but at least it cuts the wind and provides privacy. I hand her a cigarette.

"Now, first you tap it with your finger, like this," I demonstrate. A small shower of dry tobacco sifts to the floor onto bits of straw, dust and dry manure litter. "Now, I'll get a match going and light yours first. Ready?"

After a few fumbling attempts, my match flares and I hold the flame to the tip of Noël's cigarette. The match extinguishes before the cigarette is lit. "You're supposed to suck on the cigarette," I tell her. "Here, I'll show you. I'll light mine."

Again I fumble with matches, light one at last, and hold it to the tip of my cigarette, firmly trapped between my pursed lips. I suck until it seems air is entering through every pore of my body. Suddenly I burst into a frenzy of coughing, exhaling great clouds of smoke. "See, Noël," I choke. "I'm smoking!"

Noël's impressed by the clouds of smoke I produce. She hurries to light her own cigarette, which glows in the darkened shelter. She pulls in the smoke and holds it in puffed cheeks before exhaling.

We face each other, toss back our heads to see who can exhale the most smoke. By the time our cigarettes burn half way, I decide I've coughed and spluttered enough. I fling my stub through the low doorway into the snow outside where it gives a satisfying sizzle as it disappears through the crust. Noël's stub follows, arcing through the air.

"I hate to give up my feeling of maturity," I say uncertainly.

"Me, too," Noël agrees. "It's good to be defiant—sort of satisfying. But we'd better head back to civilization."

With a gust of giggles, we drop to our knees and crawl outdoors.

"Did you girls have a good smoke?" Daddy asks slyly, when we get into the house. I stare at him in amazement. How does he know, I wonder, unaware of the smoke smell permeating our clothes. I glance furtively at Noël, and see my sister's eyebrows singed off.

Daddy chuckles to himself but never mentions the episode to Mom. His furlough's over and he leaves by train the next day.

Back to school where there's action. I admire the fresh border of beautifully handwritten alphabet along the top of the blackboard. "I resolve to write more neatly this year," I vow.

Anita runs up to me at recess and begins to speak gibberish. I stare at her. "What did you say?" I watch Anita's lips closely.

"I said, 'Can you talk pig Latin?'" laughs Anita. "It's easy, Ardith. I'll teach you."

I soon master the trick of dropping the initial consonant from each word and adding it to the end of the word with an additional *ay* sound to complete it. "Listen, Anita." I try. "How's this: Ancay ouyay alktay igpay atinlay?" I chew the words with precision.

"You've got it!" laughs Anita. "Now we can speak in our secret language right in front of everyone!"

Our classmates are impressed with the new language, but they soon crack the code and it's a secret no longer. But it's still fun.

"Ardith, please bring in the clothes before you take off your coat," calls Mom after school. I unsnap the stubborn wooden clothespegs that hold the frozen clothes to the steel line. Even after I release the pegs, they keep their frozen shapes. I stagger through the door with the underwear, stiff as a rigid corpse. Mom rescues me by claiming the clothes. She spreads them on the bars of a wooden drying rack. A wonderful fresh smell of outdoors fills the room as the moist clothes slowly dry.

After supper, Noël and I argue over our chores. "I don't want to do the dishes," Noël announces. "I hate doing dishes!"

"I'll do them all, Noël, if you pay me a nickel," I offer with the cunning of Eve.

"Okay," agrees my little sister. "But I haven't a nickel right now. Can I owe you?"

"Sure." I busy myself with the job. This works so smoothly that Noël begins skipping her work frequently, simply offering me a nickel to do it.

"You young people look peak-ed," Mom decides. "There isn't enough Vitamin D in our northern sunshine. That sun just feebly pushes through. I bought this bottle of cod liver oil tablets from the Rawleigh dealer when he called in this afternoon. I'd like you to take one tablet a day."

"Ugh!" I tell her. "Cod liver oil! I hate that taste. And I keep burping it up again and again, just like I swallowed the whole cod and it's leaping, trying to come back up my throat."

"Don't be coarse, Ardith," says Mom sharply. "Besides, these pills are candy-coated. You simply swallow them, and

they'll keep you healthy. Here you are now. Down the hatch!"
She passes one to each of us. Ruby and Douglas swallow theirs
and continue studying. They have lots of assignments in high
school, and spend every evening with their books at the
kitchen table under the softly hissing gas lamp.

"Did you manage to swallow yours?" Noël whispers. I
produce my pill. I've sucked the coating off, leaving brown
patches showing on the pill like a round face with freckles. I
wrinkle my nose. I'm tasting cod!

"Let's ditch them in the sofa," I suggest.

January is never-ending. Noël and I grow petty over our
chores. We're quarrelsome as carrion crows.

I blackmail Noël. "If you don't pay me a nickel, I'm
going to tell Mom that you didn't do your share."

"But I already promised you a nickel for doing it for me,"
Noël protests.

Thwack!

Both of us get a smack over our arms and backs with the
wooden mixing spoon. Mom glares at us with glittering eyes,
her forehead contorting as she warns, "Not another word or
you'll both get punished more. I simply won't abide quarrelling."

Mom's indignation and her fierce wielding of the spoon
makes us giggle nervously. I try to stifle my laughter by pushing my head into the depths of the cupboard.

Thwack!

More flailing for our provocation. Mom's driven to her
wits' end by our nonsense.

At last, the longest, coldest, darkest month, January,
ends.

Valentine's Day is fast approaching. Something exciting
to think about. Even the air seems softer, more moist to the

face and easier to pull into the lungs. The sun makes sparkles on the fields of crusted snow.

I wonder—will I get a Valentine from John? I daydream. He's so handsome ... even if his face is covered with pimples. He has adorable eyes, soft as chocolate sauce. I wonder—does he like me? He smiles every morning across the aisle at me. We're having a Valentine box at our party—will John post a nice card for me? I'm falling down the Alice in Wonderland hole where my worries grow enormous while I myself shrivel.

Noël and I hurry through the dishes so we can address our cards. We each have a whole book of Valentines. Then I make a sweeping statement, "Noël, you owe me four dollars and thirty-five cents and I want it now, so I can buy a few special Valentines tomorrow."

Noël stares at me in horror. "What do you mean, I owe you four thirty-five? I do not."

"Yes, you do," I say calmly. "I've been keeping track. And that's what you owe. So cough it up!"

Noël knows something. "Mom hides the funds she collects from her Ladies' Aid group in a cardboard shoe box in her closet. I found the stash a few weeks ago, when playing hide and go seek with Aster and Pansy." My little sister counts out the money for me.

"Here you are," she says grandly. "Now are we square?"

"Girls!" Mother announces from the living room. "We have the healthiest couch in the country. I discovered a whole pile of cod liver oil tablets under the cushions. Mind you, the couch sucked the candy off. How do you suppose that happened?" Her eyes flash like rainbows.

I know better than to inquire if the couch had the burps from cod liver oil taste. We got off lucky on that, I guess, since Mom really has a sense of humour.

Not so a few days later when she goes to her Ladies' Aid

meeting and discovers she's short of change. In front of all her friends, she has to confess she "lost" four dollars and thirty-five cents, and she has no idea how.

But she has one idea! Mom confronts Noël and me. "Do you girls realize how mortified I was to confess to all my friends that I am short of funds? Funds they trusted me with? I could see their eyebrows rising, but no one was rude. They trust and respect me, girls. Now, how could this disgrace have come upon me?" Mom gives a long level look to each of us.

Noël crumples under her gaze. "Och, Mom, I borrowed your money. I didn't mean to steal it, but I needed money. So I just took it. I'm really sorry, Mom. I didn't know you'd have to account for it." Noël makes a contrite confession. My part in the drama isn't disclosed.

"Well, Noël, you've broken the Lord's commandment. We must pray that you be forgiven for stealing."

My flesh crawls as I watch Noël and Mother sink to their knees. I know full well that the theft is my fault for demanding payment.

But worse is yet to come. Mother takes her father's razor strap, and says, "Noël, go to your room. We mustn't disturb the menfolk."

I hear the swish of the strap as Mom lashes Noël. I suffer over her flogging. All three of us cry long before the punishment ends. Mom looks distraught and exhausted when she returns to the kitchen. I notice grey hairs poking through her brown, like dark socks darned with white. Mother's whole face contorts as she flings herself onto a high-backed wooden chair.

"I have no idea how to make up the missing money," she moans. "Your dad won't be home again for ages. And it has been so cold that the hens have stopped laying, so I haven't eggs to sell. Oh, dear God, what shall I do?"

I'm guilt stricken. I go to my hoard and count two dollars and fifty cents. Gathering it in my fist, I offer it to Mom.

"Here's some money, Mom. And I'll try to earn more, because Noël was giving money to me, Mom, for doing her chores. We didn't mean to get you into trouble. I'm really sorry." Freckles of teardrops fall on my dark sweater, as I gaze into my mother's drawn and wrinkled face.

"What's wrong, Mom?" asks Ruby when she comes home just then. "What's all the fuss about?" Mom explains what happened.

"I just hate to ask the menfolk for handouts," Mom says stoutly. "I should be able to manage my own children."

"And you do." Ruby hugs her. "Here, I made some money during the summer. Use what you need. And, please, don't worry anymore."

"Och, Ruby, I hate to use your hard-earned savings," protests Mom. But Ruby is generous.

"We should work together and stick together."

"Thank you, Ruby," comes a chorus from us three. Mom makes a pot of hot chocolate so we can share the companionship and comfort. I feel love and warmth radiate from my mother, and I respect Mother's doggedness.

What Nan always said is really true, I realize seriously. Trouble binds families closer. We should accept God's plans for our lives and execute them to the best of our capabilities.

I glance at Noël's woebegone face and feel a stab of shame; I'll never use blackmail again, I secretly vow.

FIFTY-ONE

Approaching Spring

Doug, Ruby, Ardith, Noël with Spotty. 1948.

It's too cold to play outdoors so Noël and I stay in the barn. We sit backwards on Grandpapa's tall horses, as the animals calmly munch hay in their stall.

"Guess what I'm playing?" Noël pats a rhythm on the rump of old Pet. I listen intently.

"Jingle Bells?" I guess.

"Right! Now it's your turn."

I pound a rhythm on Dolly's rump, as dust rises in the air.

"Silent Night?" guesses Noël.

We spend hours on the warm horses, laughing and singing. The animals seem to enjoy the merriment, too.

By New Year's the weather moderates. Temperatures hover above zero. Thin rays of sunshine cast purple shadows across the yard, causing the surface of the snow to crust like glass, sparkling and glittering in the sunshine. I have to squint to protect my eyes from the glare.

Mom's busy in the house and I notice she's wearing a headful of steel curlers.

"Mom and Dad are going to the New Year's dance," Noël speculates.

I overhear Mom speaking to Grandpapa over breakfast on New Year's Day. "Will danced with every woman in the hall," she reports sadly. "Except me. I felt like I was painted to the wall. It was worse than going to dances alone while he was overseas, because I could see him swinging around, having a great time. But not with me!" She chokes back a sob as I stroll into the kitchen.

"Are we having turkey again, Mom?" I ask pretending not to notice Mother's puffy red eyelids.

"Yes, dear. Can't you smell it?"

"Are we having a big crowd again?"

"Just our family and Uncle Jim and your two grandfathers." Mom looks miserable.

Mom knows about misery too, I realize. What's the new year going to bring for her? And for us all?

The weather remains bitterly cold, and the snow lies deep on the orchard. Grandpapa notices snowshoe hare tracks in profusion. "Those wretches are ruining the apple trees," he complains. "I'm going to see how many I can shoot."

"Too bad you have no dog to help you," says Mom. "Spotty'd never flush rabbits."

"That dog is too bullheaded to learn anything." Grandpapa stomps off with his rifle.

He returns in late afternoon with a half-dozen rabbits slung over his shoulder; dangling rabbit heads slowly swing back and forth as he trudges along.

"Ugh! I'm not cooking those rabbits. They look as though they're half starved." Mother turns away.

"Douglas," calls Grandpapa. "Hang a couple of these carcasses in the henhouse to give protein to the chickens."

Their bodies twirl slowly next day, suspended on strings as sharp beaks peck at the meat. The rabbits are now merely pendants of protein, being torn to shreds by carnivorous birds.

Douglas flings the remaining rabbits to Spotty, and I watch with horror as the huge dog rips and gobbles the limp bundles of fluff until nothing's left but a few crimson stains on the snow.

"It feels like spring," declares Douglas when he and Ruby come from the school bus. "It's only the end of February, but it feels like April weather. Just look how the snow's melting."

It's true. Long icicles hang like giant jagged dinosaur

teeth along the edge of the barn roof. The sky beyond the barn is clear blue with only a skiff of wispy white clouds like baking powder sprinkled across the sky.

"Come on, Ardith." Douglas holds the dog harness. "I'm going to put the harness on Spotty and see if he'll pull the dog sleigh. You can have a ride."

"Okay, I'll get ready." We get the dog collar fastened with no trouble, but it's hard to make Spotty stand so we can snap the traces to the sleigh.

"I'm afraid we're too heavy for the poor dog," Douglas tells me. "Maybe we should lead him with the empty sleigh until he understands what we want. You run into the house, Ardith, and ask Mom to watch us and call the dog when we wave. We'll walk down to the foot of the lane, and then Spotty can haul us back."

Mom agrees to watch for our signal, so we walk down the lane. Douglas turns the sleigh toward home. "Maybe it'll be too heavy for Spotty to start," he worries. "Let's let him start pulling the empty sleigh and we'll jump on."

"All right," I'm poised, ready to pounce, with Douglas ready on the other side. He waves. Mom pokes her nose out the upstairs window and calls, "Here, Spotty! Here, Spotty!"

The dog takes off like a shot. Both my brother and I dive for the sleigh, and land together on the snowy road. Spotty and the empty sleigh vanish up the lane.

"How did you enjoy your ride?" Mom teases, when we walk in, disgruntled.

"Old Spotty can sure move when he thinks it's chow time!" Douglas says ruefully. "I doubt if he'll ever understand that we want to ride behind him. As soon as I sit on the sleigh, he's all over me, and the harness gets tangled up."

"If you're going to keep on trying, count me out. I really don't like Spotty. Take Noël next time."

FIFTY-TWO

Love Bug

Ruby at Paddle River Bridge. 1946.

I wonder if John will give me a Valentine? I don't mind if he has a polio limp. After all, Nan had a bad limp, and we all loved her. I hate it when the kids call John Gimpy. It's not his fault he's lame.

"Come outside, girls." Douglas stands in the doorway. "There's a full moon and it's so mild and clear tonight. It's a perfect evening to play fox and geese. If you'll all come out to play, I'll make a new pie in the pasture where there's fresh snow. Coming?"

"Count me in!" Noël starts pulling on her ski pants.

"Me, too!" I wind my scarf around my neck.

"Okay, I'll play for a while." Ruby seldom plays with us, but can't resist Doug's invitation.

While we're dressing, Douglas stamps out a new pie on the unmarked snow. First he makes a large circle. Then, he cuts the "pie" into quarters and stamps each line into a thick trail. In the very centre is a small circle called the safe zone. Everyone starts from this spot.

"Now, I'll be the fox!" he explains. "You geese run in any direction to escape, but you can't step off these paths. The centre circle is the safety zone. Whoever gets tagged is the next fox. Ready? Go!"

We run from him until we're exhausted. I always elude him, but finally, Noël's tagged. She becomes the fox and runs after the geese. It's a great game—out in the moonlit pasture.

"What's in the box, Mom?" I come downstairs to breakfast. A large cardboard box sits on the open oven door. Strange sounds come from inside. I peek in. Two tiny pink piglets lie side by side, small and delicate.

"Och, piglets! Look, Noël, tiny piglets. What happened, Mom? Why are they in the kitchen?"

Mom explains, "Old Bessie had a huge litter—twenty-one piglets. Surely that must be a record! But one was trampled to death, so that makes twenty. And the old sow has only eighteen nipples. Grandpapa was going to knock these two on their heads, but I asked him if you girls could raise them on bottles. Do you want to try?"

"Oh, sure, Mom."

"I want one, too," cries Noël.

"Fine. You may choose your own. You know how often they'll need feeding. Here are two bottles with black nipples. I've already tried to feed them but they don't like the rubber in their mouths. Maybe we'll lose them after all." Mom sighs.

"Look, Noël, I like this one. It's so soft and pink. Look at its cute little ears! And long white eyelashes. I'll keep this one. I'm going to name it ... Runty!"

"All right! This one is just as cute. I'll name it Grunty! 'Cause they're twins. Runty and Grunty. How does that sound?"

"Kind of repetitive. Glad we don't have to think up eighteen more rhyming names!"

"One each is enough," laughs Noël.

We teach Runty and Grunty to suck and soon their box is set on the floor because they're too warm at the oven. A week later, the piglets live in a tiny cardboard pen lined with newspapers behind the kitchen stove. They thrive on the milk and grow rapidly.

I think of John as I tend my piglet. Does he like me, I wonder, cuddling Runty in a towel. Will I get a nice Valentine from him? I worry, as I freshen the newspaper lining the pigs' pen.

Meanwhile, Noël dresses Grunty in doll clothes and carries the pretty pig around in a blanket. Grunty lies quietly in her arms, his long curling lashes half closed as he snuggles contentedly.

Poor Runty wails forlornly in the pen, nudging the cardboard walls and peering out, trying to get attention from me. I don't disappoint him, and cuddle his pink body closely. I much prefer my pet pig to that clumsy dog. His slobbering and heavy-panting breath really distress me.

Noël's playing with Grunty again. She has dressed him in dolly clothes and is pushing him around in a macaroni box. The little pig lies on his back with his front feet sticking out over the tiny quilt. A bonnet covers his silky head, and his floppy pink ears protrude from the edges. Grunty lies contentedly as long as the box continues to move. But when Noël stops pushing, Grunty opens his eyes and raises his head to see why the action has stopped.

Runty squeals in protest at being left alone in his cardboard corral. His inquisitive face peers out over the edge. He wants attention, too. He finally bursts down the box and wanders forlornly into the living room. He snuffles at the rugs, until he finds one to his satisfaction and then relieves himself.

Mom appears from the kitchen just in time to see this. "That does it!" she sputters. "Those piggies have got to go! They're much too big to keep in the house any longer. Out to the barn with them!"

"But Mom," Noël pleads. "They hardly know how to drink from a dish yet!"

"They'll learn quickly enough, when that's the way they're fed," says Mom heartlessly. "The place is starting to smell piggy, girls. You've done a fine job of raising them, but they're almost a month old now. So out they go!"

"But Mom," Noël begins again. "They're so tame. The other pigs will bunt them all over and trample them!"

"Noël's right," agrees Grandpapa. "I'll fix a separate pen for these two hogs. Then they can be petted whenever you want, Noël. But your mother is right. It's time to put them out. So enjoy them tonight, dearies, because tomorrow they'll have new quarters."

"Oh, Uncle Jim," says Noël. "I'll miss Grunty. He's so gentle and tame. Look how he cuddles in my arms." Uncle Jim nods in sympathy.

"I'll be glad to send Runty outdoors," I say ruthlessly. "I hate changing these newspapers all the time. Mom's right. It smells piggy in here."

"Let's bake cookies for the party tomorrow," I suggest. "I'll mix the dough while you find the heart-shaped cookie cutter and grease the pans."

Noël finds the tomato soup can that Mom has squeezed into a heart shape at the edge. It cuts out perfect little hearts in the soft sugary dough. I bake them carefully and only one batch gets a bit scorched. "We'll scrape the bottoms off these and serve them for supper," I giggle. "Our menfolk won't mind if the cookies aren't perfect. Now, can you find the red sugar crystals while I mix some icing? And do we have any cinnamon hearts?"

We spend hours decorating, and the little cookies look very attractive drying on waxed paper salvaged from the cornflakes box.

The misshapen, broken, or scorched hearts I arrange on a plate for supper. "This is my pile of broken hearts!"

Noël admires the glittering crystals of little red hearts nestled in a bed of icing on the cookies.

"Let's clean up this mess and get to bed. I can hardly wait for the party tomorrow!"

The icing hardens enough to stack the cookies. "If we leave this cornflakes box on its side, we can slide the waxed paper right in, and it won't disturb the cookies. Then I can have the box to bring home my Valentines," I say with satisfaction.

Finally, the kitchen's back in order, and we light our kerosene lamp and pad quietly up the stairs to bed.

At school next day, Noël comes to my desk to see why I'm just sitting there, staring into space. I've scooped my Valentines into the cornflakes box and cleared my desk completely. Noël sidles up to my desk and whispers, "Ardith, what's wrong?"

At first I don't answer. But then I moan, "Och, Noël, I feel awful. I guess I'd better ask if I can go home."

Mrs. Warnock smiles sympathetically when I ask to be excused. "Too much party food?" she guesses. "Certainly, you may leave early. All we have left to do is clean up this mess," and she glances at the disarray of her normally orderly classroom.

I trudge along the snowy trail, swinging my cornflakes box with total disregard to its contents. I feel like a bad smell, I think. No Valentine message from John. Nothing. He doesn't like me at all. Not even a little bit. I feel as though an enormous wet, heavy canvas is sinking on top of me. Life is a misery, everything's useless, and nothing can be done about it. No one likes me. I guess I'm flawed.

Hot tears course down my freckled cheeks. I feel good for nothing.

FIFTY-THREE

The Mad Moon

Uncle Lawrence. 1945.

Monopoly
With Doug's new game
We love to play.
It entertains
For hours each day.
Monopoly
requires skills—
good management
for us instills.

Bang! A loud explosion sounds from the depths of the basement. Noël and I look up from our Monopoly game in alarm. "What's that?"

"Oh, no," moans Mom. "Another mess to clean up. I'm afraid one of my sealers just blew up. Probably the peas. I'll light the little lamp and go see. I've already lost six sealers this year. Those peas aren't keeping well. Perhaps I should just open them all and dump them. It'd certainly be easier than picking broken shards of glass and smashed bits of green peas off everything."

Mom sighs and goes slowly down the basement steps with the kerosene lamp. Douglas follows her. "What blew up this time?"

"Peas!" says Mom flatly. "I was afraid of that. I'll get a bucket of water and a cloot. I'll have to wipe all the jars on this shelf. Oh, dear."

"I'll set them off onto the floor for you, Mom. Then you can clean the shelf and wipe each jar as you put it back."

Douglas busies himself in the basement while Mom goes upstairs for water and a rag. I decide to go down and help Douglas.

"Poor Mom," he says. "She worked so hard growing and picking the garden stuff. And canning it. Just look at all the jars of jams and fruit—three shelves full. But we really shouldn't be eating these peas if they're explosive in the jars. I'll carry them upstairs for her. I might as well check over every jar while I'm here. We certainly don't want to poison the family. The safety of our family is my responsibility while Daddy's busy. Here are three jars of saskatoons with rhubarb that are sizzling," Doug adds. "Those must be fermenting. Let's take them upstairs, too, before they blow up."

Soon we have the basement in order again. Doug dumps all the peas down the biffy. "We'd better not fling them to the pigs," he explains, "in case the peas are building toxins. It would be terrible to poison Old Bessie when she's got that huge litter to feed. Or the shoats!" he adds. "We don't want to poison anything!"

Douglas flings the fermented fruit over a snowbank in the backyard where it lies like a purple decoration on the crusted pile.

I love to lounge in the biffy, reading the comics. Dick Tracy's so smart, always outwitting his adversaries. But sometimes I feel most like the gloomy guy in *L'il Abner*, who always has a cloud hanging just above his head. I often feel the same!

"What's the matter with the chickens?" I ask as I return later from the biffy. "Mom, come and see the chickens. They're acting funny."

Mom flings her mackinaw over her shoulders and steps outdoors to check the chickens.

They're acting peculiar, indeed! A few are moving in circles, one foot planted on the snow, while the other totters around it, so that the birds turn lazy circles. Other old hens are lying on their sides, slowly kicking their feet up in the air. But they don't appear to be in pain, since their eyes are bright and shiny. The old rooster is strutting strangely sideways, chuckling to himself as he checks his harem. He bursts into a melodious crowing, lists to one side, flaps his wings wildly, but finally loses his balance. He falls on his face, driving his beak deeply into a snowbank. He remains in this undignified position, and I hear him give a distinct hiccup. The young chickens are singing, with occasional hiccups, and the old biddies are clucking, punctuated by burps and belches. They all have wide-open beady eyes, giving them astonished expressions.

Mom's astonished, too! "Whatever has happened to my hens?" she marvels. "I've never seen the likes of this before. Ardith, what do you think is wrong with them?"

I capture a chicken as it circles around me. I lift the bird and feel how limply it lies on my arm, its head dangling loosely across my sleeve. A sweet, heady smell comes from its beak.

"This hen is drunk!" I announce. "They're all drunk, Mom!"

"Drunk?" cries Mom in dismay. "But how is that possible?"

I point to the purple patch of snow. Not a single saskatoon is left. Even the snow has been pecked up where the fruit was spilled. The hens are intoxicated from fermented fruit.

"My goodness!" says Mom. "I suppose they're all right. They'll get over it." She turns and heads for the house.

"Now I know what a hen party is," I tell Granddad. "You never saw such happy hens."

He laughs and laughs at my story. "And your mother is so dead-set against liquor," he says. "Then she makes her hens drunk!" He laughs until the tears run down his cheeks, and roll across his stubbled chin.

I return home in time for supper. A beautiful red sunset marks the western sky with crimson splashes dotted by dark blue blots. "Red sky at night, shepherd's delight," I quote aloud, remembering Nan's wise sayings. "I guess our good weather will continue. Great! I'm tired of winter. I hope we have an early spring." I stamp the soft snow from my feet and step into the steamy kitchen.

The warm weather persists. The snow settles more each day, and the heavy air feels moist and invigorating.

"Let's go riding," I say. "Grandpapa, may we take Pet and Dolly for a spin? I'll bet they'd enjoy some exercise."

"Yes, dear. You may go riding. Better be careful, though. Dolly's frisky. Are you sure you can manage her, Ardith?"

"Oh, Grandpapa! Look how tall I am. I'm as tall as you. And I'm almost fourteen. Sure, I can manage Dolly. And I'm sure Noël can handle Pet."

"Pet's lazy," warns Grandpapa. "She needs a little tickle with a switch now and then."

"Bye," we call, heading for the barn. We get the bridles on the horses and pile onto their warm, hairy backs.

"Pet's as excited as Dolly as we set off down the lane; the horses stretch their legs after being in their stall all week without exercise.

I let Dolly have her head as soon as we reach the range line, and within minutes Pet's left in a cloud of powdery snow. I draw Dolly in on the river hill, turn and meet Noël on Pet, sedately coming along the road.

"Don't make Pet gallop today," begs Noël. "I have to get used to riding her. She's so much taller than Nipper. I feel kinda scared up here."

"How I wish it were spring," I cry. "I'm weary of winter."

"It'll soon be spring," says Noël. "I wish Daddy would come home on leave. He hasn't been back since New Year's."

"I'm giving Dolly her head again," I warn. "See ya at the barn!" And I streak ahead on the spirited animal. Dolly forges ahead and I have my hands full as the horse begins bucking. I turn her into the snowy field where Dolly flounders to a standstill. "There," I laugh. "That slowed you down a bit. You've got plenty of zip!"

We brush the horses down and hang the bridles carefully. Then we scurry to the house.

"Your bum is covered with horse hair and dust," I laugh, as Noël runs ahead.

"You should check your own," retorts my sister.

Meanwhile, Grandpapa is having problems. "Edith, there's trouble with the sheep. Some varmints are chasing them. I don't know if it's coyotes or wolves, but I found the flock cowering in the corner of the sheepfold, all in a tremble. We'll have to keep an eye on them."

"Oh, dear. Something else to worry about! All right, Papa, I'll tell the children. Surely among the lot of us we can guard the sheep."

We agree to keep an eye on the sheepfold, and only a couple of mornings later, I set up an alarm, calling. "There's a wolf in the sheepfold! There's a wolf in the sheepfold!"

Douglas rushes outdoors in his longjohns and rubber boots, while Grandpapa scurries to his bedroom for the gun and all the womenfolk peer out the window. Uncle Jim gets very flustered because he has lost his glasses and can't see the action.

In fact, no one can. We look carefully across the melting snowbanks to the sheepfold. The sheep lie serenely on straw in the fold calmly chewing their cuds. Douglas looks like a scrawny abominable snowman in his suit of white underwear, creeping across the crusted snow to check them. He stands there uncertainly for a minute surveying the flock, and then turns toward the house with a puzzled expression.

I can contain myself no longer. "Ha-Ha! April fool!"

"Och, Ardith," says Mom, shaking her head disapprovingly. "You really had us all going. Don't you know the fable about the boy who cried 'Wolf'?"

But the best joke of all, this first day of April, is played by Daddy, who arrives home unexpectedly on the train. His eyes twinkle as he steps quietly into the kitchen.

"Daddy!" cries Noël, flinging herself into his arms. He nods to Mom, and yanks my braids, winks at Douglas and smiles at Ruby.

"You're a real lady, Ruby," he admires her, and steps forward to shake hands with Grandpapa and Uncle Jim. Then he sits down at the table with Noël sprawled on his knee.

Mom scurries about, getting coffee on. The family has lots to tell Daddy about, so we stay up later than usual to enjoy our father's company. Douglas brings out his Monopoly board, and we play for several hours. I'm thankful when I finally go broke and can stop. Noël and I slip quietly off to bed, leaving Douglas and Ruby battling it out with Daddy. Mom has retired long before and I notice that she looks sad.

Next day, the men have a consultation. "I've been studying new farming methods," says Grandpapa. "And I really believe we have to change our ways. Sowing grain crops every year is depleting the soil, and it's too cold to depend on alfalfa, which seems to winter-kill badly. What do you think of planting field peas to put nitrogen back into the soil, so that we'd get a grand yield of barley the following year?"

"That's an idea," agrees Daddy. "But how do you harvest peas? Surely not with a threshing machine?"

"No, no," says Grandpapa. "We'll have to buy a combine. That's the new movement now, Will. Every farmer works independently and buys more land and larger equipment. Tell you what … you and I can buy a combine together, and continue to operate our farms as one unit."

"Agreed." Daddy offers a handshake." Can you look into the price of seed peas?"

"I'll check with McCabe Seeds," says Grandpapa. "And I'll watch for a combine model that our little Ford can manage."

"Is your brother Jim any help to you around here?" Daddy asks Grandpapa. "I don't see him going outdoors."

"Och, no, Will. He can do nothing at all. I'm afraid he has a drinking problem, and his nerves are shot. He trembles like a leaf. He's really in a bad way."

Daddy's face turns stern. "If he's just a freeloader, I'll have to move him on. I thought he'd be of help to you."

"I don't need more help, Will," says Grandpapa stoutly. "Douglas is a wonderful worker, and Edith does a marvelous job at managing. We're getting along fine."

"Then I guess I'll have a word with Jim and take him back as far as Edmonton with me."

When we learn that Uncle Jim is leaving, Noël's very upset. She loves the old fellow. We all troop to the station when Daddy and Uncle Jim leave.

"Now I'm going to show you a trick." Uncle Jim looks at us kids fondly. "Here's a penny for you, Noël. And a nickel for Ardith. A dime for Douglas and a quarter for Ruby."

Not much of a trick, I think. But there's more to come. "Set your coins on the railroad track," says Uncle Jim. "After the train has gone, have a look at them. Bye-bye now, dears. Take care of your mother."

We put our coins on the rail. We can hear the train rumbling in the distance as we hug Uncle Jim and Daddy. The train arrives, enveloping our group on the station platform with great gusts of steam. Daddy helps Uncle Jim aboard and stands on the steps, waving until the train's out of sight.

"Oh, look!" says Ruby. "My quarter is flat as a pancake! You can hardly tell that it's a quarter."

"Here's my dime," my brother says. "Look how big around it is now. It's larger than a quarter, and as thin as paper! Great!"

"My penny looks like a cookie. I'm going to save this as a keepsake from Uncle Jim."

"I can't find my nickel," I protest. "It should be along here some place."

"Here it is!" shouts Douglas, producing a perfect nickel. "It must have bounced off the rail."

"Murphy's law!" I say ruefully.

Doug moves back into his own bedroom, and things seem normal. Grandpapa's confounded. There's such a confusion of tracks in the slush and muck that he can't make out what's chasing the sheep. But several have bloody scars. "I don't know if the sheep are flinging themselves against the barbed wire, or if they're torn by fangs," Grandpapa fumes. "But this is serious."

Spring's just around the corner. The air is heavy with moisture from the slushy snow evaporating. The glistening crusts change to dingy grey as they settle on the sodden fields. The yard's a muddle and the road's a glistening black ribbon of sticky mud.

The weather remains warm, so the snow melts gradually. The river behaves with no dramatic flooding. It's an uneventful spring. Uneventful, except for the sheep. The end of April is heralded by a full moon in a cloudless sky. Grandpapa checks the flock faithfully in late evening and goes to bed.

When he returns to the fold next morning, chaos and destruction are evident. Grandpapa's entire flock of sheep has been slaughtered, their bodies ripped to shreds. The sheepfold is a gory spectacle. Grandpapa stares in stunned disbelief. Every body lies lifeless. As Grandpapa counts the carcasses, his eyes detect a cowering form slinking toward him, jaws dripping with blood, body plastered with gore—Spotty. The dog grovels at his feet.

Grandpapa turns on his heel and heads for the house. "That dog has gone mad!" he tells Mom. "Spotty was harassing the sheep. Why didn't I think of that? No wonder he didn't bark at coyotes or wolves. There were none. It was Spotty all the time! He may have started to chase the sheep as a game, but with the full moon, that dog went crazy. I'm going to have to shoot him. He's dangerous. If he can kill a dozen sheep, he can kill anything—even the children aren't safe. I tell you, that dog is a rogue. I knew from the start he was nothing but trouble!"

I shudder. Then I turn and rush upstairs to my bed, burrowing my head beneath my pillow.

But I can't block the sound of gunshot, and I can't block the sounds of Mother's wrenching sobs. "Oh, everything's going wrong!"

FIFTY-FOUR

Crack Shot

Bear shot in chicken house. 1948.

I sing

Buttercups and daisies, oh the pretty flowers!
Coming every springtime to tell of sunny hours.
While the trees are leafless, while the fields are bare,
Buttercups and daisies spring up everywhere.

It's true. An unseasonably cool spring delays the leafing out, although buds swell along the bare branches of the poplar trees. The orchard looks lifeless, twisted black apple trees naked against the sky. Yet the first hint of green shows in grass, weeds and wildflowers. And with the moisture, an invigorating feeling of freshness fills the air. May is such a promising month, pregnant and peaceful. The silence is broken by a cacophony of high-pitched yelps that announces the passage of lesser snow geese, taking refuge on the Paddle as they head north for their summer nesting grounds.

"They are the most vocal of all waterfowl," I tell Noël. "I'll be glad when they go. Their call makes me feel unsettled and anxious somehow, although I don't really know why."

May continues cool. Now the low grey sky threatens rain. I slog along the road, black mud squishing under my boots. A thick mist hangs on the tops of the trees and fog drifts across the draw. I shiver. I'm chilly and damp. Sweat stands in beads on my forehead and runs in rivulets down my neck. My glasses have flecks of moisture on the lenses, and my hair, red enough to stagger a bull, feels untidy as a bristle brush.

I'm frightened. My face feels taut beneath my freckles, and I grip my side in terror. I want to get home—to safety. I glance back over my shoulder as my feet smack into the mud. I'm being followed. I smell a rankness, a musky odour. Yet I hate to stop to listen for footsteps and give my pursuer the chance to gain ground.

No, better to keep moving, even though my side aches. I'm almost to our lane. Surely I won't be followed right into the house yard. My heart beats faster and I feel as though my throat is closing. I call out, but manage to make only a thin squeak. Now I'm at the yard gate. I can see a feeble light through the mist. Someone is home.

I pant up the path, pound through the veranda and burst the door open. "A bear is after me!" I screech. "A big black bear is chasing me! It's following me home." I collapse on a high-backed wooden chair, my teeth chattering.

"There, there," says Mom. "You're all right; nothing can harm you here."

"I'll just step outside and check around," says Grandpapa calmly. He is back within seconds. "She's right!" he declares. "I saw a black hulk going into the chicken house. I'll get my gun. It looks like a big one."

"My goodness!" Mom says in surprise. "I guess you're right."

I stare at my mother through my misted, round steel glasses. "You *guess* I'm right?" I say flatly. "I *know* it is a bear." I give a big sniff. "It was so close I could smell it." I shudder as I remember the musky odour that still lingers in my nostrils. Mom never believes anything I say, I think resentfully. She thinks I imagine things. Try imagining a huge black bear running right behind you! Try that!

"No doubt the poor thing is half starved," says Mom. "Just out of hibernation."

Sure, and who is the first person it sees? Me!

"Can somebody bring me the hammer and crowbar?" yells Grandpapa from the doorway. "Hurry! Hurry! I've locked the bear in the henhouse and I must tear a board off the back wall to shoot through."

Mom and I rush to help Grandpapa. We pry one board from the wall and Grandpapa puts his eye to the crack to peer in. He bursts into such a frenzy of choking that Mom cries, "What's wrong? Are you all right?"

Grandpapa uses his handkerchief to clear his streaming eyes. "Phew!" he says. "That bear has halitosis! When I stuck my eyeball to the crack to peek in, there was the bear's eyeball peeking right out at me. Phew! Its smell could knock the stripes off a skunk! I'm going to shoot the wretch, although I hate to do it among your chickens, Edith. But it might be a rogue, chasing Ardith like that. We can't take a chance! Here goes!"

Grandpapa pokes the rifle barrel just inside the crack and fires. All hell breaks loose in the henhouse! The blast of gunfire is deafening; smoke chokes Mom and Grandpapa and me.

The hullabaloo in the henhouse is horrendous. The hens squawk and flutter in fright. Dust and debris fill the air. The dust takes over. Dust rises—dust fills with chickens leaping and screeching—dust fills with feathers—dust fills with lime, which smarts the eyes—dust fills with gun smoke—dust that is choking—dust that is shouting!

I shout, "I can't breathe!"

Grandpapa shouts, "I got him! I got him!"

Mother's shouting, "Oh, my poor hens!" Rooster and hens are shouting. Bedlam in the building!

And lying in the centre of the floor like a lumpy hair rug is the carcass of a huge black bear.

Mother runs to the door to turn loose the terrified chickens. They refuse to budge outdoors in the gloom. They huddle in a heap in the henhouse, half smothering one another. The brave old rooster cowers in the corner, quivering, his tail dragging, his feathers bedraggled. He hides his face in shame, his comb red with embarrassment.

Grandpapa checks around, fearful that he has cleaned out the chickens, but nary a one is shot.

"Maybe it wasn't such a smart idea to kill the bear in here," Grandpapa says ruefully. "How are we going to get the carcass out?" He lifts one paw, letting it drop limply. "This beast is gaunt, but it still weighs a ton."

"Come to the house, both of you," shouts Mother above the uproar. "Let's get out of this dust and noise. The hens will settle down and the bear's done all the damage he's ever going to do. We'll deal with it in daylight."

The next morning I run out to see the bear, to be sure the whole thing wasn't a nightmare. I survey the carcass, examine the cruel claws and long sharp teeth. Would this bear have attacked me? It's a sobering thought. The old rooster has fully recovered and acts as though he's cock of the walk. He has his hens back in line. I head back to the kitchen.

"I don't think Pet and Dolly can handle that bear," says Grandpapa over porridge. "For one thing, it's really heavy. And for another, Dolly is too high-spirited. When she gets a whiff of that rankness and blood, there'll be no controlling her. And it's so boggy around the henhouse that the tractor will sink to the hub caps in that soup. I'll have to ask Granddad to bring his heavy team. Douglas and I will get a chain on the carcass as soon as we finish the chores, so if Granddad will bring Ol' Tom and Charlie, we'll skid the bear out."

"Well, Ardith," laughs Mom, "would you like to run down and tell Granddad the whole story? After all, it's your bear!"

Granddad listens with great interest to my tale of being followed by a bear. "Sure, Honey Child. I'll snake that ol' bear out of there. Must'a been a hot time in the henhouse with all that ruckus!"

"It sure was, Granddad," I agree. "I was really tuckered out last night. I was so scared that my heart bounced in my chest like a catfish in a wet sack."

Granddad just laughed.

"Gotta get to school. See ya."

When we return that afternoon, the bear's gone. One long skid mark in the mud across the yard and field to the cut bank tells of its demise.

"Wasn't the hide any good?" asks Noël. "Didn't you save some meat for the chickens?"

"That bear was shedding and his hide was patchy. And it was so rank that even the chickens wouldn't touch that meat. No, Mr. Bear went over the bank," Mom says. "The coyotes can fight over him."

The coyotes make a real banquet of the carcass. I hear snarling and snapping for several nights down at the cut banks.

"I'm *bearly* over it," I laugh with Granddad. "That old bear almost scared the stuffing out of me! Grandpapa is sure shooting up a storm these days," I continue. "First Spotty, and now the bear. Lucky for us he has guns!"

"Yep! And he has a good eye for a man of his age. He's a real crack shot."

FIFTY-FIVE

Tutoring

*Ardith helps Dad mix cement for foundation
of new chicken house. 1948.*

A strange car parks in our yard. "Can I hire one of your girls to teach Toby his lessons by correspondence?" asks Mrs. Peterson. "I'm trying to home-school him so he'll catch up a bit. He's missed so much he's really behind. But now that he's got leg braces, Mrs. Warnock says he can come back to school this fall. He's just got to practise walking at home for a while. I've been trying to teach him a little every day, but he really needs more, and I'm so busy with the garden, and feeding the men and stuff. And he don't listen good for me. So I thought of your girls, Mrs. Ray. Surely, you can spare one?"

Mom glances at us. I catch her eye and nod slightly. "Why, yes, Mrs. Peterson. Ardith may go. When would you like her to start?"

"Right away," says Mrs. Peterson, her pretty blue eyes appraising me silently. "I know school's not out yet, but if you'll come for a couple of hours right after school, it will be great. Then, if you do good with Toby, you can teach him three hours a day all summer. I'll pay you a dollar an hour."

"All right, Mrs. Peterson. I'll be down right after school tomorrow."

I ride my bicycle to school every day and whiz on over to Petersons' for a lesson with Toby. The little fellow is bright and cheerful, with sparkling pale blue eyes and a pointy dimpled chin. He has a summer shave in Scandinavian style—keeping a completely bald head so his ears stick out like the handles on a soup tureen. But his body is strangely still for a child. He's sadly handicapped by polio and wears solid-steel leg braces.

Toby's sunny disposition pleases me, and I enjoy my tutoring sessions. I'm proud of his progress, and Mrs. Peterson is delighted.

"I declare, you do get the best out of that boy," she says to me. "I do want him to be able to hold his own when he starts school."

I don't tutor on Sunday, and am glad to have a whole day to myself; I've several things in mind that I must get done this day.

"Oh, for the love of the Lord!" I exclaim, "I don't think … "

"Ardith!" interrupts Mother. "Don't you dare take the name of the Lord in vain."

"Sorry." I feel guilty. "What I mean is, for the love of heaven, I don't even feel like going to church this morning. I have things to do."

"Aren't you feeling well, Ardith?" asks Mother with some concern.

"Sure. I'm okay. I just don't want to go to church, so I'm not going. I have other things to do."

"I can't bear insolence. You're scarcely thirteen, and you're rude and insubordinate. You're going to church with the rest of us and that is that." Mother snaps her mouth shut firmly. I say no more, but sulkily put on my Sunday clothes and flounce off to the service.

Back at school the next Monday, all this is forgotten. I have found a little time to study and I write my grade nine departmental examinations with confidence and ease. Mrs. Warnock has been a conscientious teacher and I never regret my decision to skip grade eight. I also receive a book for perfect attendance, *Wild Animals I Have Known* by Ernest Thompson Seton, which makes me very proud.

"Now that school's out, let's celebrate by going on a hike," says Douglas. "Shall we scout along the cut banks of the river and see if there's going to be lots of berries this year?"

"Oh, yes," I say. "Let's do that." I'm always glad to find a new berry patch.

"Count me in," calls Noël.

It's the beginning of a July heat wave and we're restless. Armed with a canteen of water, sandwiches in a lard pail, matches, hot chocolate mix, and three tin mugs, we three kids set off through a green kingdom of shadow and sunshine among the thick bushes along the Paddle. After we climb the steep banks we're drenched with sweat, which attracts hordes of mosquitoes that sense tender prey.

I find a profusion of saskatoon bushes along the ridge. There's also a tangle of dogwood bushes with waxy white berries along its red branches. Wild honeysuckle's in bloom. The air drones with bumblebees doing their business of pollinating. Little gnats join in with the mosquito clouds, so a high-pitched hum fills the air.

"Let's find an open spot and eat lunch," I suggest. "Then we'll have both hands free to swat these pesky little critters!"

"All right," Douglas agrees. "I'll just veer south." It requires lots of energy to scramble up and down the wooded ridges in the humid July heat.

We stop at a natural clearing on the very edge of the cut bank where we can view the Paddle's dappled water flowing beneath us.

Douglas builds a small campfire of cones, dead branches and twigs, dry enough to catch fire on the first match. Soon the flames crackle. We lie in the grass. We empty the lard tin so we can heat water in it, and stuff our mouths full of jelly and peanut butter sandwiches while the water heats, stacking more cones and twigs around the pail.

"Oops! I forgot a spoon," I say.

"I'll fix a stick." Douglas peels a green poplar branch to stir the chocolate powder with. Before the water even boils, we drink the brew. "It's too hot for hot chocolate anyway. We should have lemonade," Noël says.

"I'll douse the campfire with the last of this water."

Douglas dumps the water and we lie on our backs for a time, relishing our freedom, enjoying the twitter of birds, buzz of insects and scurrying sounds of unidentifiable creatures in the bushes.

"Let's slide straight down this bank into the river," says Douglas.

"Dare you," I challenge.

"Is it deep?" Noël wonders.

"Here goes!" Douglas slides down. We follow. Splash! Splash! Splash!

"Not too deep," shouts Douglas, standing in the shallows. "It's nice and cool!" The river is thick with mossy plants laid flat by the current.

"This'll cool you off." Douglas stoops to scoop his palms against the surface, spraying us.

"Pay you back." I dip the bucket and fling the water over Douglas, drenching him completely. His streaming glasses blind him. "Gotcha!" I chuckle.

"Let's walk the stream all the way to the bridge," Douglas suggests. "It's much cooler here than up on the banks." The reeds stand silent on the shore beneath the shade of willow trees.

"All right," I agree. "Where are the mugs, Noël?"

"I thought you had them," she says. We look at one another with dismay.

"We must have left them by the fire. Mom will be mad if we've lost three tin mugs."

Douglas says without enthusiasm, "I'll scale the cut bank and bring them back. Wait here."

He toils up the cliff and slides back, clawing at the bank. Dirt clings to him. He has no cups. "We must've lost them when we rolled down the bank."

"Never mind. Let's get you back into shape." I use the bucket to sluice him down.

We spend the whole afternoon following the riverbed to the bridge, exploring the beaver dam, marvelling at a structure that allows trickles of water to overflow the dam while raising the water level by at least four feet.

"Here's a beaver slide," Noël cries. It's a well-worn mud track ending with an abrupt drop to the water.

"Look!" Douglas points. We stare in awe as a large blue heron slips silently from its nest, flaps flat wings, and glides through the shadows shed by Balm of Gilead trees lining the bank.

"What a magnificent bird," I whisper.

"And huge," Noël adds.

"We'd better move on," Douglas advises. "We're disturbing its nesting site." A tiny frog splashes from the bank.

"Look at these freshly fallen trees," Noël says. "The beavers have been busy." Douglas balances all the way up the trunk as he ascends a steeply angled log.

He checks the stump. "Beaver all right." Their distinctive tooth marks are plainly visible on the pointed stump. Freshly peeled limbs prove that beavers inhabit the area although none are in sight due to our noise. The cry of a fleeing killdeer fills the valley.

"There's the bridge," Douglas says. "Let's walk home on the road. This has been quite a hike."

"I'm all tuckered out," Noël sighs. A wide dusty road welcomes us home. Wagons are giving way to cars and pickup trucks that pack paths in two parallel lines along the dirt grade, making easy walking.

Sweet buttercups and daisies bloom in profusion along the verge, tossing clouds of scent. Tiny winged insects flurry from the green grasses.

"A wild rose!" I cry. "The first this year. What a perfect way to end our day!"

FIFTY-SIX

Fourteenth Birthday

Ardith rides Dolly to tutoring class. 1948.

M y fourteenth birthday is almost unnoticed. Mom and I spend early morning in the garden, pulling and leaving weeds to wither in the scorching sun. By noon, we seek shade. Mother reads on her bed, and then slips out to the shaded flower bed on the north of the house. "No matter how tired I am, I can always tend my flowers," she confesses.

I freshen up, tidy my plaits and glide off on my bicycle to the Petersons'. My thoughts whiz in time with my flying wheels. I'm pleased to have a summer job and I'm earning money. Ruby has gone to Jasper for the summer and earns a good wage as a waitress, hoping to enroll in college this fall. This will be Doug's last year at school. He'll graduate in the spring and I'll start high school. It just doesn't seem possible— no more Rochfort Bridge School days. I've been there for eight years, and now I'm going to Sangudo. What will that be like? I'm not sure that I want to face a strange bunch of kids in a strange school in a strange town. I really don't feel grown up. I wish everything could stay the same so I'd feel safe and secure with what I know.

Mom lays a linen cloth in honour of my birthday. I automatically count the plates and raise one eyebrow to Mom. "Six?"

"Well, there are you three young people," explains Mom. "And Grandpapa and I. So I asked Granddad over, too. Happy birthday, dear."

The meal is festive—chicken and dumplings, mashed potatoes and dandelion salad. Then Mom produces a real treat: strawberry shortcake, piled high with rich whipped cream and sprinkled with bright fresh berries, the first picking from the new patch. Four candles flicker atop the sculptured cream. "I thought 14 candles might burn the house down," Mom teases. I make my secret wish—that high school will be fun, with no teasing—and make it come true with one mighty puff! Mom presents a large package. I rip it open and find my first pair of blue jeans! "Oh, thanks, Mom. I can wear jeans to high school."

Now I'll look like the other girls. I wonder if any of them will have braids. And will any of them have freckles? Will they tease me about mine?

August brings a wave of sultry heat, and I'm weary of tutoring. Toby is weary too. The poor little fellow tries to concentrate, but the heat in Petersons' front room is stifling. The air lies stiff as a painting, with utter stillness everywhere.

"If you'll finish this page, I'll read you the funnies," I bribe.

Toby scowls with concentration as he struggles with his lesson, then smiles with satisfaction and begs, "Read about Wimpy. 'Cause I love hamburgers just like he does."

I tousle the short hair on the little fellow and unfold the funnies. We read together.

The weather's stifling, suffocating. But a storm's brewing. The sky changes from clear blue to sullen grey, as thunderheads form in the west. Then a wall of solid black looms above. The grasshoppers and other insects swell in volume from a whisper to a surge of sound. The quivering aspen tremble in a rising wind. Suddenly a great gust of cool air brings instant relief from the heat.

Large raindrops freckle the dust as I pedal swiftly down the road. I welcome the cooling rain although I'm drenched by the time I reach home.

It's too muddy the following day for me to ride my bicycle. The steady downpour had continued far into the night.

"I'll ride Dolly to Petersons'," I say. "And I'll take the light chain to tether her in their orchard." I use one of Daddy's shoulder duffels and ride off to my job. Dolly plods along the muddy road. Toby and I have pleasant lessons in the cool living room.

Dolly is eager to get home and sets off briskly, her narrow hoofs smacking the mud. I have the tethering chain stuffed into the backpack where it rattles and joggles. The strange noise spooks the horse. One end of the chain works loose from the bag and slides out in ever-increasing lengths, and as we move faster, it flogs Dolly's flank. I try to retrieve the chain with one hand, while controlling the reins with the other. Then my glasses slide down my nose but I've no free hand to raise them, so I fling my head back, balancing my spectacles while calling, "Whoa, girl! Steady now! Whoa!" But the chain continues to flog the horse at every leap.

Dolly bolts. Taking the bit in her teeth, she gallops full blast; mud splatters and water sprays in our wake. Startled birds flash across our path and further excite the horse.

The smells of hay and colours of flowers flash past in a blur so I have to close my eyes to the dizzying scene and concentrate on the power of the horse.

The flogging chain inches its way completely free of the bag and slithers onto the road. This gives me a chance to control the runaway. "Whoa, now! Whoa, Dolly! Whoa!"

I draw Dolly to a halt. The pony stands, wheezing and blowing while I adjust my glasses.

I guess I'll go home and walk back for the chain. I hope no one finds it meanwhile, but I'll never control Dolly if she hears that rattle again.

"Come on, girlie. Let's go home." We continue sedately up the lane.

It's only a short distance back, and I claim the chain before anyone finds it. I'll use a rope next time, I decide ruefully. I'll give the horse lots of rope. Wish Mother'd give *me* a little more rope!

FIFTY-SEVEN

Starting High School

Ardith's first pair of blue jeans. 1948.

Douglas and I catch the school bus on Rochfort Bridge's main street. Very few students climb aboard—most teenagers consider themselves sufficiently educated when they reach grade eight or nine, so the academic route isn't very popular.

The squat orange bus collects more students along the route to Sangudo.

It's a cool, crisp September morning. Frost fringes the crimson and brown bushes that edge the highway. The freshly gravelled grade is rough and I feel every jolt when the bus hits the chuckholes. I'm nauseous by the time we pull up to the high school.

I tumble from the bus in front of an oversized two-room building of weathered clapboard. At one time, it was painted white with dark green trim. Now most of the colour has scaled from the withered boards. The building is built on a very steep bank, facing east. Spacious windows face east in one classroom and north in the other. All the windows fit poorly, which provides unwanted ventilation. A long narrow hall connects the two separate buildings pulled adjacent to one another. This hall is a cloakroom with a door at each end. The west door leads to a sidewalk and the street, and the east exit leads to the toilets, screened in bushes. Both biffies stand on the steep slope.

I'm surprised by the number of students—I count forty-six desks in grade ten and I hurry to choose one near the back, to remain inconspicuous.

It's my first experience of having only one grade level per classroom. And my teacher, I see with misgivings, is a man. My heart plummets to my heels. I furtively study his face. He has a hawk nose, swarthy complexion and beady brown eyes with a neatly trimmed moustache that matches his wavy black hair. He's really tall with angular arms and legs, beefy hands and a barrel chest. He stands very straight and looks confident, capable, and stern.

"You must be Ardith Ray," he says. "You're so much like Douglas. Welcome to grade ten. My name is Mr. Howard."

I smile slightly and nod as he moves on, speaking to every student.

"Isn't he scary?" whispers a voice at my elbow. I turn and see a pretty girl with an elfish face and curly black hair.

"Hi! I'm Mugs."

"Hi, Mugs! I'm Ardith. I've never had a man teacher before."

"I've had a man teacher all my life!" laughs Mugs. "My dad. He taught me in a one-room school right up to grade nine. So here I am, trying for high school. I come on a bus."

"So do I," I say, "from Rochfort Bridge."

"I'm from the opposite direction—Cherhill."

I settle back to study the group. The girls all wear jeans, pant legs folded in wide cuffs across their calves with baggy white socks stuffed into penny loafers. I hastily fold up my jeans, carefully creasing them into cuffs around my calf. "I left so early this morning, I didn't have time to dress," I explain casually to Mugs, who's watching me with amusement.

Mugs nods. "I know what you mean."

I tuck my running shoes under my desk, hoping no one will spot them. I'll use my tutoring money to buy penny loafers and white socks, I decide. Then I'll look like the other girls.

I continue to study my classmates. Oh, oh. I'm the only girl with pigtails. Mom says these French braids are really stylish, but I feel like a skinned onion. The other girls have puffy hair, curly and frizzed out. And I don't see a single soul who's plastered with freckles like me. They'll all tease me and call me Turkey Egg. I just know it. I cringe.

Mr. Howard rings a handbell to settle the class and we choose desks and watch him, his face twitching in much the same manner as my mother's, I notice. He really flinches. I guess he's human, after all.

"Good morning, grade ten students," he begins. "I'm Mr. Howard, one of your teachers, and I hope you'll enjoy your term here. Mr. Morgan, the principal, will be teaching you social studies, English and French. I teach physics, chemistry, algebra, geometry, trigonometry and music. There's a

*Doug and Ardith ride bikes before catching school bus
to Sangudo. 1948.*

small laboratory at the back of this room that is strictly out of bounds unless a teacher is present.

"We will have an hour and a half noon break to allow the dormitory students to return to the dorm, eat, and do their kitchen duties. I would suggest that the bus students utilize that time to do homework because you'll be getting home much later than you formerly did. You are welcome to write on the blackboards and help one another with your assignments.

"Now a word or two about dress code. Since the Wartime Prices and Trade Board Consumer Branch restrictions have recently been lifted, we have decided to allow the young ladies to wear blue jeans to school." He chuckles as he glances around the group.

"This is the first year we have allowed slacks at school—on young women," he hastens to add, causing a ripple of laughter. "We discourage the use of make-up and nail polish. We want you to wear comfortable and modest clothing.

"There will be no smoking on the school property. Those of you who smoke may bring a pass from your parents allowing you to go downtown at noon. No one may leave the school premises without a pass. Are there any questions?"

That about covers it, I think.

Then Mr. Howard outlines the course of studies for each of his subject areas.

Later that day, our grade ten group goes into the other classroom, where Mr. Morgan teaches. I look around curiously. His classroom is larger, and more crowded. Fifty-two desks, counts my compulsive mental calculator. Grades eleven and twelve are housed here, but the eleventh grade kids must switch to Mr. Howard's room, emptying desks for us grade tens. As I sink into a seat, I glance around, spotting Douglas with the grade twelve students.

Mr. Morgan looks the extreme opposite to Mr. Howard. Our principal is short and slight, wearing heavy glasses that dominate his delicate face and fine features. His thinning grey hair is trimmed closely around his shell-shaped ears. He walks with a limp and carries a cane with which he lambastes a desktop to emphasize his point when speaking. Worried grey eyes peer through his heavy lenses and he blinks rapidly like an owl in sunlight. Mr. Morgan is soft-spoken and kindly.

"Don't let him hornswoggle you with his complacency," Mugs whispers. "My dad says Mr. Morgan can read the riot act and really take a strip off your hide with his tongue, but he gets Mr. Howard to do the dirty work with the strap. That's the ultimate disgrace."

I shudder, hoping I'll never provoke such wrath that I need a strap. After listening to Mr. Morgan's course outlines, we are dismissed.

"I look so different," I complain to Noël as we exchange experiences about our first day at school. "These pigtails! I hate them!"

"Why don't you ask Mom to braid your hair up, instead of down?" Noël suggests. I check with Mom.

"Sure, I can make French braids from the back and wind the braids around your head like a crown," Mom says. "It'll be tidy. You know, Ardith, there's so much electricity in your system that your hair will stand straight up like Raggedy Ann on the rampage if you loosen it. Braids are really best for your crowning glory, dear, and you must know your hair truly is outstandingly beautiful."

So I have my hair restyled and am happy when no one comments about it. I also buy penny loafers and white socks, and feel more like the other girls.

FIFTY-EIGHT

Unorthodox Crop

*Grandpapa shovels manure from slowly moving stoneboat
to fertilize the field. 1947.*

Mother is excited when we kids get home from
school. "You'll never guess what we did today," she
says as she pours Grandpapa a fresh cup of coffee.
"Grandpapa and your Dad are going halfers on a new combine, and today we drove to Mayerthorpe and picked up an
orange Minneapolis-Moline combine that can be pulled by
our little Ford tractor."

"So whose combine is it?" asks Douglas.

"I'll square up with your Dad when he comes home," explains Grandpapa. "I put the combine in my name, but of course, it belongs equally between us."

"As you can see," Mother continues, "the entire half-section is sown to field peas from McCabe Seeds. Now that the vines are withering and curling, we must combine before they shell out."

"Or freeze," Grandpapa adds. "We'll start tomorrow morning if the weather holds. The sooner we harvest those peas, the better it'll be."

The good weather holds; conditions remain perfect. Douglas keeps up the chores and helps gather the garden with us girls while Mom is everywhere: in the garden, at the barn, doing errands, making meals, carrying lunches to the fields and helping in every possible way to hurry the harvest.

The peas in the field stand curling and dry, ready to burst their pods and blow the profit unless the harvest proceeds. The weather is cooperating with a dry Indian summer. Luckily too, there's very little dew to mildew the vines. Mom and Grandpapa might revolutionize the district with their unorthodox crop.

Grandpapa keeps the combine humming from the first rays of dawn until blue twilight gathers and a sickle moon appears. He hasn't been so busy in donkey's years. Pulled by the Ford, the new combine sidles up to the granary, where it disgorges round green peas from the hopper—piles peas high and higher, with still more to harvest.

Grandpapa comes to the house so tired that he has the blind staggers, his weathered face is drawn, and his skin has turned a slick green colour, so he appears to wear a Robin Hood mask.

"Edith, we've finally finished the harvesting," reports Grandpapa. "If we can just plough those vines under, they'll enrich our soil ready to crop next spring."

"Yes," agrees Mom. "But you must be on your last legs, Papa. How'd it be if you take over the chores, and Douglas and I'll do the ploughing? If I plough all day, he can take an evening shift. Then I'll plough through the night, until I get too chilly. We'll get those vines turned under, as long as the weather holds."

The Indian summer continues warm and dry with light night frosts.

FIFTY-NINE

I'll Take Over

Noël and Ardith walk Edmonton street. 1950.

Every Saturday night, there's a dance at Rochfort Bridge Community Hall. I beg to attend. "All the kids from high school go," I plead. "Douglas can take care of me. We'll be all right!"

"Nonsense," Mom says. "If you must go to the dances, Ardith, I shall go with you. But I have one rule you must obey: *never leave the hall.*"

The rule is easy to obey. Although the biffy is outdoors, I have no need of it, since these are *dry* dances. No beverages or refreshments are served. Outside, young people drink beer. Outside, they sit together in parked cars. Outside, kids smoke. Or tell jokes, or … or … Mom never says what else happens, but it sounds like vultures circle outside, waiting for fresh meat. So Mom's rule holds: never leave the hall.

The music plays from nine till twelve and then breaks for midnight lunch, served in a nearby café. But Mom never indulges us with a lunch. She can't afford it. And I'm not permitted to go for lunch anyway, because that involves leaving the hall.

So whenever I sit quietly through the lunch break, I check the clothing worn by others. Styles sure have changed since the clothing restrictions were lifted. No more fabric conservation program, with skimpy skirts and women's suits made from their husband's old suits. Mom used to salvage worn clothing, figuring and cutting and creating smart new outfits. But now she can buy new material or even ready-made clothes.

"Mom," I begin on the walk home, "I'd love to have a real Gibson-girl outfit, with a black velvet bow tie on a long-sleeved white blouse and a long, full black skirt."

"You're too young to wear black, dear," says Mom.

"But the Gibson style is better than those peasant outfits with gaudy cotton skirts and drawstring-necked blouses decorated with coloured braid."

"I agree," says Mom. "But they're more expensive."

"Lots of women are wearing fabric shoes, too," I say. "I notice they look quite stylish, although some are tacked onto clunky wooden soles."

"There's still a government leather restriction, you know. It's hard to get good leather-soled shoes. Plastic shoes are coming in, but they're stiff and unwieldy."

"Oh, I'd love a pair of those velvet shoes to match a Gibson-girl outfit," I say. "The kind that you bind with ribbons tied around the ankle like a ballerina." I dance a few graceful steps in the moonlight, gliding lightly along the dirt path. Mother brings me back to reality by saying, "I wish you didn't always have your head in the clouds. You're a young lady now."

But at school, I feel gauche and self-conscious. I long for the natural ability Mugs has to create an atmosphere of gaiety. Mugs is always the centre of attention and adoration. Her vibrant personality charms the gathering, bringing fun and laughter.

I feel like a fish stranded on the shore, separated from this sea of spontaneous good fellowship. I have nothing to contribute to conversations about boyfriends, dates, romance and love. None of this is within my experience.

I'm like a rabbit in the headlights, my brain paralysed by uncertainty and inhibition. My vocabulary becomes monosyllabic and I stutter banal remarks. Only during classroom instruction can I speak with confidence and assurance.

When I'm alone with a boy, I get wary, guarded and unsure of myself. I can't relax. I'm afraid all the boys consider me stuck-up, but really, I feel idiotic.

In time, I enjoy the trips to Sangudo and am no longer sickened by the motion of the bus. The kids joke and clown in the old clunker, and a light-hearted driver joins our hilarity.

The trip takes an hour between towns. Douglas and I still have to walk home when the bus reaches Rochfort Bridge, so evenings are shot.

"Lucky we do our assignments at noon break," I tell my brother. "I'm tired as it is, and you have to hotfoot it out to do some ploughing, Douglas."

That evening, and for many more to come, I can hear the whine of the Ford tractor on the fields, far into the night. I picture Mom, rolled in a Hudson's Bay blanket, ploughing in the dark.

It's a grand, open fall, dry and calm, with gradually heavier frosts. The cranes that cross the sky on their migration have a cloudless track. The Canada geese sample the green peas at the edge of the field and quickly move on. It seems they prefer small, hard kernels of barley.

"Now there's another plus for our pea crop," chuckles Grandpapa. "Water fowl don't like peas. I think we've really hit on a good thing, Edith. If we can just turn under the fodder, we've got it made." He chuckles again as we eat a late supper.

Mom surprises us a couple of weeks later, when an Eaton's parcel arrives. "How will this outfit do for the dances?" she asks me.

"Oh, Mom!" I'm overcome. "I love it!" I smooth a green flowing skirt, feeling the weight of yards and yards of material cut on a bias to provide a billowing flare which reaches almost to my ankles. And there's a green velvet bow tie to match the skirt fabric. I laugh in delight. "It exactly matches my eyes!" Then Mom presents me with a shoe box. Nestled inside are velvet shoes with smooth composition soles and long laces to lash around my ankles. "Try them on, dear. And here's something your Granddad bought you." Mom slips a package of nylon stockings into my hand.

"Oh, Noël," I cry. "Now I'm just like a ballerina—and the latest of stockings, too. Real nylons! Thank you so much, Mom. I'll run down and thank Granddad. What did you get, Noël?"

She shakes out a voluminous skirt that drags to the floor. "Oh, dear," says Mom. "That's much too long on my little girl. It looks like one of Cinderella's stepsisters' gowns. I'll have to order you a petite size. Don't get it dirty, Noël. I must send it back."

She and I run down to thank Granddad for his gift. I can hardly wait for the Saturday night dance. I fairly fly through my chores, have a sponge bath and stand dressed and ready to go by eight o'clock.

"Aren't we a bit early?" asks Douglas, who agrees to go dancing.

"We have to wait for Mom," I tell him. "She insists on coming, although I'm sure she's tired." Mom emerges from her bedroom, all spiffed up, and we trudge across the field in the shivery evening moonlight.

"We're lucky to have talented musicians living right in our neighbourhood," I claim. "We have the best band around."

"That's what the kids at school say," agrees Douglas. "Do you realize they draw a crowd from as far away as Blue Ridge and Cherhill?"

"Of course it helps to have a wonderful dance floor. The community worked like beavers laying a hardwood floor and getting it polished," Mom explains. "Now they just spread it with waxing powder and it's ready for action."

"So am I," I cry. "Here we are at the hall." I find a place on the high-backed benches (which serve as church pews the next morning) with the other women and girls.

Douglas stands near the back of the hall, gathering courage to ask a young lady for a spin on the slick floor. He isn't, of course, afraid of the floor or of the dance steps, but rather of being refused by the young lady.

Mom tells me the etiquette of refusing a dance request: never refuse, unless there's an obvious problem, such as drunkenness. Secondly, if I refuse to dance with one, I must refuse them all for that round. Otherwise, it's not a social grace, and might crush or anger the first fellow, giving me the reputation of being a snob. I understand the logic of this rule.

So I sit demurely watching the young men milling around at the back of the hall. They keep awkwardly roughhousing, horse-playing and gawking at us girls along the benches. When one makes a lewd remark in a lowered voice, they all burst into reedy laughter, putting on manly airs one minute, the next picking their pants from their crotch like kids at kindergarten. One or two guys wear zoot suit pants, drawn snugly by cuffs to the ankles, flaring from the pleated waist with ample material draped to form baggy legs. Only the bold wear faddy slacks. More reserved guys are satisfied to loop a chain from their belt to their flat leather wallet and thrust that into their hip pocket, leaving the chain dangling across their hips.

"I guess that looks hip!" I giggle with Anita.

"And I think they look manly."

Douglas and I aren't bashful about dance steps, since we learned the basics as children during Grandpapa's concerts. We often dance together. Douglas also includes Mother as his partner. She faithfully chaperones me to every dance, and sits visiting with friends during the evening. Then the three of us walk home under the stars.

I continue to excel in my studies and am accepted good-naturedly as *the brain*. Never once am I teased about my freckles. These kids simply take me at face value.

Sometimes I feel as if my childhood beliefs are sucking me down, that I'm caught in a whirlpool, a kaleidoscope of blurring colours, made-up faces, fancy hairstyles, faddy clothing and slang jargon, which confuses me.

Where's the real world? Is it the fast pace set by this ambitious school of teenagers, or is it the strict and rigid regulations set by Mom? Or what?

Sometimes Douglas prefers to skip the dances and stay home to study, since he eats encyclopedias like most kids eat chocolates.

On one such occasion, I attend a dance with Mom alone. As midnight draws near, Mom disappears to the café with a friend, leaving me in the hall with a handful of people. I'm sitting quietly on the bench when Archie McGee, a school friend, sits down beside me and we chat. He's so clumsy his shoelaces could strangle him, but he has a great sense of humour. I talk with him easily enough, and we're soon engrossed in conversation.

I'm flattered when he says, "May I walk you home?" He stands uncertainly, hovering over me. I smell his manly aftershave, and the faint musky odour from sweaty armpits.

"Sure," I say airily. "I'll just leave a message for Mom." I speak to our neighbour, Mrs. Schmidt. "When Mom gets back, would you please tell her Archie is walking me home?"

We leave the hall together. As Archie and I stroll along the ribbons of silver paths under the pale moon, we laugh and talk until I hear a rapid tap-tapping coming from behind us. Mother arrives, completely out of breath from exertion and anger. She got my message and quickly overtook us.

She says sternly, "All right! I'll take over. You get back to town," in a voice as heavy as doom. Archie turns a stricken face toward me, his eyes agog, and then he dissolves into the darkness.

Mother escorts me home. All the way, she admonishes about the dangers of disobedience. In vain, I protest, "But none of that happened, Mother! Archie never even touched me. We were just talking and walking each on our own path."

"Don't you pussyfoot me!" Mother's voice escalates. "I'll have no more escapades of disobedience. I absolutely won't tolerate it."

Mother is like the Black Plague. Once she grips onto an idea, there's no escape. She gives me a blistering lecture. Arriving home at last, I'm taken right past the house to the barn, to conceal Mom's action behind closed doors.

Using a harness strap with a buckle on the end, she thrashes me as I scuttle across the floor. Mother grabs me by my braids, yanks my face down across a manger, and lashes and lashes. With each blow, she screams, "I'll teach you to disobey. Don't you ever disobey your elders."

The dispassionate cows watch my trouncing. The lashings and screaming aren't heard from the house. But I find scars on my body from this brutal whipping, and scars from Mother's harsh punishment imprint on my heart.

SIXTY

Love Is Where You Find It

R.A.F. boys help with harvest. 1950.

I'm searching for a rainbow
With love the pot of gold
I'll know that I have found it
When his heart I can hold.
'Cause love needs no abusing
or painful disillusion.
I'll end my sad confusion
by finding my true love.

I sing this composition while I strum on my guitar. It's my first attempt at putting verses to music, and I'm pleased—but I don't dare sing it at home. Perhaps I'll share it with Marian.

I enjoy music-making with Marian, a new friend who's living in a tiny shack at Rochfort Bridge so that she can attend high school. "It's cheaper than boarding at the dorm," Marian tells me. "We can't afford that. When I go home on weekends, I stock up on food, so I'm managing to get my high school education."

Marian really values education, I realize, to live in this miserable shack. "Doesn't your fire go out when you leave for school?" I ask her.

"Sure! I have to start another every afternoon, and pray it warms up the shack enough for sleeping," Marian says.

"Brrr-r! That's worse than when we lived in the cabin!" I laugh. But I enjoy visiting Marian at her shack, where we giggle and sing songs together. If I bring my guitar, Marian tunes up her fiddle and we spend wonderful carefree hours in music.

Word spreads throughout the high school that my mother is crazy as a coot. Archie plants that rumour, killing every hope for my having a boyfriend from school. I'm deeply hurt but hide my embarrassment with a smile, living a permanent lie by pretending that everything is all right.

I hang around the fringe of discussions held by girls behind the school. Standing in the lee of the building, absorbing warmth from feeble rays of the sun, we exchange *information* about sex.

"My mother says I must always wear clean underwear when I go out in case I'm in an accident," says Jane.

"Well, who'd wear dirty old underwear anyhow?" asks Ginny. "Especially if you're planning *the accident!*" She rolls her eyes meaningfully, while we giggle.

"Did you know a guy can pull his balls up like twin Adam's apples?" Ginny offers. "He wants you to suck'em!"

"Ugh! Hair in the mouth!" protests May. "Unromantic!"

"But it really turns him on," claims Ginny.

"So what happens when he's *on*?" asks Jane. "Does he do all the humping, or do you both, or what?"

"When he heaves, you haul," explains Mugs. "I think."

"But when you're heaving, does he haul? Or what?" asks Jane.

"Oh, Jane, quit worrying. When the time comes, there's lots of heaving and hauling but you'll get a rhythm going."

"Not me," declares Mugs. "I don't think an hour of pleasure is worth a lifetime of regret."

"An hour?" all the girls exclaim. "How do you make it last an hour?"

"I don't!" says Mugs shortly. "Just a figure of speech. What I mean is, I'm saving myself for Mr. Right. I'm not fooling around until I finish this dumb trigonometry and try my wings in the world. Sex is dangerous. You might get caught and have a kid."

"Not if you do it standing up," claims Marian.

"That's not true. It's safe only if he wears a rubber," says Mugs.

"Those things!" snorts Ginny. "My boyfriend says wearing a safe is like washing his feet with his socks on. He won't use one. But I know a foolproof method to keep from getting pregnant."

"What?" Everyone waits for this gem of wisdom.

"Coke!" says Ginny.

"Just drinking it?" asks Jane.

"No, dummy," snorts Ginny in exasperation. "Douching with it. Right afterwards."

"How?" Marian persists.

"Have a bottle of Coke ready in the cab. As soon as he shoots out, grab the bottle and shake it till it froths up. Then tear off the lid and push the neck of the bottle up deep inside. Coke kills those pesky sperm deader than doornails."

Silence.

We digest this bit of information with interest and embarrassment—it's cutting close to the bone.

"Wanna try my new lipstick?" asks Mugs, suddenly aware that we've strayed into deep waters. "Real dynamite."

Everyone smears it on, pursing pretty lips, stretching mouths to spread the colour. I try some, too, longing to be light-hearted, to be daring, to be included.

The bell rings, bringing us back to reality. We troop into the school, ready to suffer another afternoon of studying.

I wipe my mouth, remembering Mr. Howard's request not to wear make-up. As I sit down, I glance at Neil.

His chin looks like a stubble bun, his Adam's apple rises and falls as he swallows. I'm fascinated, and stare, thinking about Ginny's comments regarding Adam's apples.

Feeling the intensity of my gaze, Neil glances toward me, and I drop my eyes in confusion, covering my mottled arms. He smiles at me, but I dither, reorganize my notebooks, to show that his gaze hasn't fazed me. I sense a fleeting interest from Neil, but I'm too flustered to pick up on it. I feel rattle-headed. Does he know I like him? The very thought sends a tingle to my toes, but when I dare to glance his way again, he's looking elsewhere.

Drat! Why didn't I smile at him when I had the chance? How will he know I like him if I don't show it?

To heck with it! Who needs him, anyway?

I can spit in anyone's eye, I decide, staring into space. My vague expression doesn't pass unnoticed.

"Ardith's a bit teched!" Archie tells everyone. "Must run in the family."

"Not really!" defends Mugs. "Look how keen-witted she is. She's as smart as her brother, Douglas. You're just sore because you didn't score!"

"That's right," agrees Marian. "And if Ardith lacks talent in anything, she compensates with effort and determination. She's certainly not teched. She's just … different."

The days grow shorter, colder. "I'm glad there's no snow for November eleventh services," says Noël. "I always feel sorry for those old guys from World War I, trying to keep in step with younger men although they've been wounded or crippled. It's a long march for them from the Legion Hut to the community hall. Armistice Day is kinder without snow."

Daddy comes home for Remembrance Service, bringing two young soldiers with him. They're chaps stationed at Edmonton to test cold weather survival equipment in the Arctic wilderness.

Noël and I watch these strangers with interest. Jock Black comes from Scotland. He's a gawky young man with sandy-blond hair, a huge hawk nose and buck teeth bursting from his smiling mouth. His features are rugged, but he's kind and thoughtful, with a very winning disposition.

John Browning comes from London, England. He's handsome, tall and muscular; his ready smile exposes straight white teeth. He has wavy brown hair with flashing eyes, and a very friendly personality. Fortunately, he's good-natured too, because we tease him mercilessly over his Cockney accent.

Jock speaks sincerely to Mother. "'Tis a wonderful experience for John and me, sharing the warmth and hospitality from a Canadian family when we're so far fra' home. It's very kind of you t' take us in, d'you ken, and I want you t' know we really appreciate it."

"We'll be glad to help out on the farm," adds John. "This is really great—I've never been farming before."

The men work at any task Dad sets for them. And he warns them, "Touch one of my girls and I'll personally kill you."

Of this, I know nothing until much later. But these mature fellows are my friends; they're partners at the dances the whole family attends, visible proof that I have boyfriends. There's never romance with them, but I talk about them at school—even brag about them! The school girls are impressed, since my friends aren't mere boys—they're men!

Dad keeps them busy around the farm.

He's surprised to find every nook and cranny packed with peas. "Looks like a real bumper crop. How are pea prices?"

"Not good," admits Grandpapa. "They're really low. In fact, pea prices have dropped a bit more. But we can't sell the peas now anyway, Will. There's a quota on them."

Dad shakes his head and turns away.

It turns bitterly cold, with threatening grey clouds, gloomy and dark. When Dad leaves by train with Jock and John, it still hasn't snowed. The ground turns to iron, and Mother fears for the orchard trees. She says, "They need snow cover, or they'll winter kill."

A keen wind shrills over the hills, bringing sleet that plasters sheets of ice on the roads and sheathes trees along the lane. The trees become white on the windward side but remain bare and black on their back.

I feel the blast of wind in my face, keen as a knife blade; it slices my breath as I stumble over the treacherous frozen ground. I clutch my chest and gasp open-mouthed as the wind leaps down my throat, chilling my body from the inside out. I head down to Granddad's.

"Got a message for you," I tell Granddad. "Mother says she'll need a huge turkey for Christmas this year. Uncle Lawrence is bringing his family, and Ruby will be back from college. And Dad is bringing those two young men. So Mom wants you to save us a big bird."

"Sure, Honey Child. I'll do that," says Granddad.

A wan sun shines, melting the sleet until the iron ground turns black again. It seems strange to have no snow.

Grandpapa listens to seed reports every noon, his face furrowing with worry. He grips the edge of the radio with hard, knotted fingers as pea prices plummet more each day.

"They're dropping our peas to no earthly value," he cries in despair. Mother only gazes at him with hollow eyes; she hates to speak of it in front of us kids.

Pea prices continue to drop a few pennies a day and Grandpapa's in despair. The weather remains bitterly cold, but no snow falls.

Now it's nearing Christmastime. Mother draws us aside. "The splurging on clothing we made when school was starting must be considered your Christmas spending, because we still can't sell the peas. Money is tight."

"We understand, Mom," I tell her. "And I really needed the skirt and those shoes during the fall for the dances. Are Jock and John coming for the holidays?"

"I think so," Mom says. "I've invited them—they're really decent boys and must be lonely this time of year."

"It's going to seem strange, having a black Christmas," says Noël.

"Black in more ways than one," mutters Douglas, while Mother gives him a sharp look.

"We'll manage," she murmurs.

Now, as we set off through the cold to meet the train, we sense a change in the weather. The air seems softer. Stars are blotted by a blanket of grey and the first lacy flakes come sifting down.

"Snow!" I turn my face skyward. "Oh, look, it's snowing at last."

Noël says, "A white Christmas after all!"

A muffled whistle warns that the train is near and makes our family hurry down the trail to town.

It's a magical moment, while whirling flakes dance and twirl before the beaming headlight from the locomotive. I hold my breath—snow in the spotlight has the appearance of a Nutcracker fantasy.

But then the engine sends swirling steam and smoke into my face, and a flurry blown from the top of the passenger carriage temporarily blinds me. By the time I've cleared my glasses, Daddy's swinging from the steps, followed by Jock and John.

"Merry Christmas, Jock! Merry Christmas John!" I call. "Merry Christmas, Dad," I add, kissing my father.

"You know, Will," says Mom quietly, after all the young people are off to bed except for me—I'm filling the hot water bottle with heated water to ease my toothache. "Our grocery bill is outstanding, and I'm afraid Mr. Jones will cut off our credit. Can you pay him?"

"Pay him in peas!" Dad sneers. "I warned you about putting all your eggs in one basket."

"Yes," agrees Mom. "But what will I feed this mob? Those young soldiers have two hollow legs!"

"Pea soup," Dad retorts.

But Granddad comes through with a huge turkey, and Grandpapa buys two boxes of mandarin oranges, and our farm provides the rest of the food, so our meal is bountiful as ever. The whole group gathers to enjoy the feast.

"Lucky for you, Edith," says Auntie Martha, watching

Mother prepare vegetables, "that you can grow everything you eat on your farm."

Not just luck, I think, but plain hard work. Mom smiles at Aunt Martha and says, "Have you weaned your son yet?"

"No," says Aunt Martha. "And I'm not going to until he's sixteen!" She winks at Mother. "Nursing him will keep me safe."

"Don't count on it," Mom replies. "I got pregnant again while I was still nursing a baby." But she's too busy to say more, and turns instead to her eldest daughter.

"Och, Ruby, I'm so glad you're home to lend a hand. Set the plates for sixteen."

The dancing snowballs are a delightful distraction during the meal, where jollity seems forced. Aunt Martha tries to keep things lively. "Cracky," she laughs with John and Jock. "Look at the spread on this table. No sign of rationing, like back home."

Jock nods, holding high his tumbler of tomato juice. "Thanks t' this wonderful family for their hospitality," he toasts. "And a prosperous New Year t' you all. Merry Christmas!" Mother eyes her father, who sinks lower into his seat, his shoulders sagging.

"Merry Christmas! Merry Christmas!"

Black boughs of skeletal trees stand silent as the family crunches along the trail on freshly fallen snow. We're seeing the three men off on the morning's train. "We'll not be back 'til spring," warns Jock. "We're posted t' Watson Lake t' test survival equipment in the Yukon."

"Take care of yourselves," calls Mother. "Goodbye. Goodbye!"

It's quiet after all the company leaves. Winter months drag. Windstorms rage frequently, and bitter temperatures hold, although there's very little snow. The air is cutting, and sears the lungs with iciness, yet Grandpapa spends hours at the woodpile, splitting logs and kindling, driven to keep himself busy. He pulls off his hood, the fur whitened around the face from his frozen breath, his lashes whitened too.

"What's the white stuff in this bowl?" Noël asks as she lays the table.

"Margarine," I tell her. "Dad brought some for us to try."

"But what is it for?" asks Noël.

"It's a butter substitute," I explain. "If you're using it as shortening, you mix it with other ingredients, but if you want it for table use, you mix in this yellow colouring to make it look more appetizing, like butter. Want to taste some?"

"Ugh," says Noël. "Thank goodness we have cows that give cream for real butter. This margarine tastes awful!"

I laugh. "Don't worry—margarine will never catch on."

Marian and I continue to sing together every week, our voices blending so nicely that Mr. Howard urges us to sing a duet for the school musical festival in March. We practise faithfully, and are thrilled with the adjudicator's critique. I'm proud to be considered excellent in some way. It makes me feel satisfied somehow.

It's a strange springtime. Meagre snow cover means little run-off and very little mud. The roads dry quickly. The river behaves. Migrating birds wing their way northward through a clear sky.

Sharp air catches at my throat and I tighten my coat as I walk home. There seems an iciness in the atmosphere at home, too, which has nothing to do with the weather. Dad's home on leave, making me feel uncomfortable. I want to escape the house, escape Mother's hollow eyes, escape glaring accusations and Dad's scornful stare, and Grandpapa's humiliation. Something's seriously wrong, stemming from the failure to sell the pea crop. But there's more. Much more. I sense it, and avoid contact with my family as much as possible.

I realize that Mother's heart is breaking, yet her tongue is firmly ruled by unbending pride, so she won't tell me her feelings. This inheritance of pride she learned from Grandpapa, but it's really false pride, I think—a fear of weakness in any form.

Every joy Mother might feel is choked by silence and secrecy. Why must we be always proper? The neighbours have faults. What does it matter if we have, too? Why be shackled with chains of pride?

Daddy is cruel and proud of it. He deliberately tries to shatter Mother's properness and propriety, but he's beaten by her pride. Her values are founded on the approval of her family and friends, and she always puts a face on things. She demands respect. She deserves prosperity. But Daddy cares about neither.

As I look at Mom, I scarcely recognize her. A woman sits in Mother's place, someone who looks like my mother looked, but now looks like she's not my mother. She looks lost. Her eye ticks incessantly. I'm powerless to make Mother come back.

Is it Mother who's changed, I wonder? Or is it me? Nothing seems the same. My head feels as if it were filled with chunks of gravel rattling in a whirlwind.

I seek comfort from Granddad. "I don't know what's wrong at home," I confide. "Mom's lips are sealed. She won't tell me why she looks so wretched. Is it my fault?"

"Now, now, hush up," he says. "Your mother and dad have to work this out on their own."

But I see their marriage disintegrating before my eyes. Dad treats Mom cruelly; Mother sinks into bitterness and depression.

Noël and I trail around uncertainly, trying to distract Dad. We follow him, engaging him in conversation. When he stamps in with full milk buckets and sets up the separator in the basement, both of us go down to talk. He smiles and thrusts a large canister into my hands. It contains fruitcake, crumbled in a cheesecloth. Raisins and crystallized fruit peel lie in musty crumbs.

"Have some," he offers. "Eat it all!" slyly smiling like the serpent in the Garden of Eden. Noël and I both munch a bit, just to please him.

"It's stale," Noël whispers. "Let's go upstairs to get a drink to wash this down."

When Mother sees the canister in my hands, she bursts into tears. We stand miserably, wondering what we're doing wrong.

"That's our wedding cake," Mother chokes, her voice trembling with emotion. "I've saved that can of cake for twenty years. I rescued it from our house fire. I kept it in the cabin. I put brandy over it to keep it moist. It was meant to be eaten on our twenty-fifth wedding anniversary!" And Mother rushes upstairs in a fresh frenzy of grief.

Guilt and shame sweep over us girls as we realize we've betrayed our mother.

I'm confused. To whom do I owe my loyalty? To a father who's deliberately cruel? To a mother who's so rigidly strict that she can't be confided in, and must be treated with a pretence that everything is good? I feel hopeless. I'm in despair.

SIXTY-ONE

Home Truths

Noël and Aster Ray. 1950.

Peas are valueless. There's no market for them. McCabe Seed Company accepts a quantity of seed equal to that which Grandpapa had purchased, squaring him with the company.

But he's stuck with the combine debt, since Daddy refuses to come through with any cash. "Take it in peas!" Daddy sneers. Mother's horrified that her hard-working old father is treated in such a callous manner.

Daylight hours lengthen and sunlight strengthens. First to respond are pussy willows that burst from the tips of branches in delightful buds that smell of fresh sap. But it's a slow spring. Daffodils bloom briefly; the lack of snow cover makes them burst through the ground much too early, so they're repeatedly frozen. Now stunted tulip blossoms stand on stubby stems, blooming brave and bonny in their bed.

Ruby returns early in May from her first college term. "I've got a job in Jasper again," she reports. "I'll be waitressing at the Athabasca Hotel. If I'm frugal, Mom, I can save enough to pay for my next term."

Mom smiles approval. "You're managing well, Ruby. Keep it up."

Later that month, Douglas lines out the garden by floating the stoneboat upside down, leaving a patchwork pattern on the mellow soil.

"Why are we planting such a big garden, Mother?" I ask. "There's only four of us at home now."

"I know, dear. But we'll supply Douglas with batching foods while he's attending university. And we'll have company. But I suppose we can cut back on turnips, parsnips and corn."

Noël and I plant the garden while Grandpapa sows the fields to barley and oats, and Douglas relieves Mom with chores and yard work whenever possible.

At the end of June Douglas graduates from Sangudo

High School and begins a college summer session in Edmonton, with an Alberta Wheat Pool scholarship covering expenses. Mother's proud of her ambitious son.

But she mopes long hours on her bed, and I suspect she's reviewing bitter episodes with Daddy, although she claims that she's reading.

I finish grade eleven at Sangudo High School and Noël completes grade eight at Rochfort Bridge School, both of us doing very well.

My fifteenth birthday passes almost unnoticed until Noël stirs up a chocolate cake and invites Granddad to supper. It's a quiet gathering, and Mother looks miserable, her face twitching in continual motion. The grandfathers discuss the weather and the events of the neighbourhood, but the subject in which they are all most interested, Daddy's plans, remain unspoken and unknown.

A strong wind comes up, rattling the windows and emphasizing the silence during supper. We've almost completed the meal before I speak, "Isn't Dad due home tonight?"

Mom nods, as I turn to Noël. "Want to meet Dad at the station with me?" I give my sister a pleading look.

Noël answers, "Yes." We both need to get out of the house.

The night isn't as black as I expect, since the heavens are dotted with stars and greenish fingers of northern lights twitch across the sky. We hurry along the trail, boughs bending a greeting, bushes billowing in the breeze. The sound of the train whistle catches in the wind and is tossed over the hills with an eerie wail.

Dad's alone this furlough, giving us our chance to have a serious talk with him. "Why don't you come home to stay, Daddy?" asks Noël as we pick our footing along the bush trail. "The war is long over and I wish you were home."

"If wishes were horses, beggars would ride. I'm not coming home to stay while your Grandpapa lives there," Dad says. "We don't see eye to eye on how a farm should be managed."

"Then why don't you tell him that?" I ask. "Or get him to move out?" The solution seems simple to us girls.

"Maybe I will," Dad says. Nothing more is said, but we feel cheered, thinking we understand the problem.

Granddad surprises me by telling me that my Daddy wants to buy his land.

"Where will you live?" I ask in surprise.

"Have you forgotten I have a homestead in Peavine?" Granddad chuckles. "I might move up there."

So many changes, I think in bewilderment. Nothing stays the same. Everything's unsettled.

Daddy doesn't stay home for long; he and Mom bicker constantly. Dad makes cutting remarks—Mother wilts and weeps.

I hate to hear it. And I hate to see Dad's cruelty to Grandpapa's animals—he bashes the cattle with boards; he lashes the horses as he passes their stall. Pet and Dolly get wary and skittery whenever Dad enters the barn. I'm thankful when Dad's leave ends.

A few days later, Noël and I are home alone while Mom goes to her Ladies' Aid meeting and Grandpapa attends a meeting of church elders.

"What can we do to cheer Mom?" asks Noël.

"Let's make doughnuts," I say. "That will surprise her!"

Noël says, "I'll stoke up the fire and get the lard on to heat while you mix the dough."

I soon have dough ready and Noël produces the doughnut cutter. She also has a blazing fire going, and the lard bubbles.

I drop rings of spicy dough into the pot and watch them sizzle and sputter. I turn them with care while Noël lines a tray with paper napkins. As I lay a neat row of doughnuts on the tray, we hear a thunderous roar in the chimney.

We look up in fear, and are horrified to see the stove pipe red-hot, with black smoke seeping around the edges.

"The chimney's on fire!" I cry. "Och, Noël. We're going to burn the new house down!"

"No, we won't," Noël says. "We'll put the fire out. Come on. We've gotta get up on the roof."

"I'll fetch the ladder," I call. "You get the salt bag. And pull that hot grease to the back of the stove."

We lean the ladder against the veranda roof and scrabble up the steep roof to the high peak, where flames and smoke spurt from the chimney like a veritable Vesuvius.

"Oh, Noël, I'm dizzy!" I cry.

"Don't look down," warns Noël. "Or you might faint and roll off the roof. I'll hold your feet. You reach up and sprinkle salt over the flames."

I grope for the salt bag, but keep my eyes on the flames. Bracing my feet against Noël's palms, I manage to reach the chimney top. I shake salt sparingly. It scarcely affects the flames. I try again, shaking a larger quantity. The fire diminishes slightly. More salt. I pause to check results. More salt. More salt. I dump the last of it down the chimney and it quells the flames.

Thank God, I think, and thanks, too, that Mother had such a large bag of pickling salt on hand.

"Now, how do I get down from here?"

"Don't look down," Noël cautions. "I'll brace myself as you slide, until you bump me. I think I can check your slide. I'll move down sideways."

I slide down shingles, hugging the rough surface, and slither along the steep roof while Noël braces sideways. A harrowing business getting down, but at last, we drop to the veranda roof. From there to the ground is easy.

Both of us burst into hysterical giggles after looking at one another. My red hair is now a sooty black, and I look like a chimney sweep.

Noël is bleeding from shingle slivers, and has skinned arms and knees.

"That's it," I laugh. "I'll never make doughnuts again. What a fright!"

When we later confess to Mother, I notice her face is pinched and shrinking, her shoulders bend as though burdened with an unseen load.

July brings sultry heat and sudden cloudbursts. Excellent berry weather. Saskatoons hang like grapes from the bushes along the range line.

"Let's pick saskatoons," I suggest. "It's a perfect day for it. Come on, Noël, you'll feel better in the fresh air!"

Noël allows herself to be coaxed along, although she detests berry picking and really isn't well. Each with an empty bucket, canteen of water and lunch, wearing broad-brimmed straw hats as protection from sunstroke, we leave with instructions from Mom, "Don't come home till your pails are full!"

We find a perfect patch along the blind line and begin to pick. "You know, I have a tummy ache," Noël begins.

"What's new?" I say. "You always pull that trick."

"But it's getting worse," she says.

"You just don't like picking berries," I tell her.

We pick in silence for a time. Noël sits down flat on the ground, holding her tummy.

Moans.

A symphony of insects drones.

I continue picking. "Mom says to fill these buckets."

The groans grow louder.

There's a whirring of busy wings from the bushes. More groans. I pull berries from the bushes, purple stains my fingers and mouth, my pail half full.

Noël's moans grow louder. More frequent. Interspersed with sighs. Then she sobs.

I pick sanctimoniously, saying nothing, but pursing my lips with disapproval.

Finally Noël declares, "I can't stand it, Ardith. I'm heading home."

I glance at my sister. Her face is drawn and she looks miserable. "Go home, Noël," I tell her. "I'll pick both pails full."

"You can have my lunch." She leaves the lunch, leaves the patch taking short, painful steps. I toil on through the humid summer afternoon, quiet with Noël gone.

Finally, both water pails brim with beautiful ripe berries. It's late afternoon by the time I walk home with care so my treasures don't spill.

"Och, Ardith, fly to town and buy apple juice for Noël," Mom urges me. "And hurry!"

Noël must be really sick if Mom is buying her canned apple juice, I realize, as I ride my bicycle to town.

Returning with the juice, I take some directly upstairs to Noël, whose face is drawn and pale.

"Flu," Mom diagnoses. "She needs rest and must drink plenty of fluids."

"Pain just doubles me up," Noël whispers. "I was on hands and knees by the time I crawled home."

"Oh, Noël!" I cry in horror. "I'm so sorry! I should have come with you!"

Noël just smiles and sighs. "The apple juice seems to be helping. Thanks." Then she dozes off.

During the next three days, Noël doesn't recover, and

appears almost greenish, drawn around the lips. The pain persists despite quantities of apple juice, and she looks much worse, weary and wan.

Saturday morning, Mother decides to take her to the doctor. She props Noël on the tractor seat and holds her rolled in a blanket, as she sets off on the ten-mile trip to Mayerthorpe. Mom calls instructions as they leave, "Do your usual Saturday chores. Sweep downstairs, wash the kitchen floor and wash down the biffy. Make up Noël's bed with fresh sheets so she'll have a nice place to rest when we get back. And bake a cake, please. Daddy will be home tomorrow!"

"But Mom," I protest. "What about the dance? You promised you'd take me if I did all the chores."

"Yes, and I will," promises Mom. "But right now Noël needs attention." They drive slowly along the rough road.

I tear into the chores. I do everything Mother asks and more, knowing Mom and Noël will both be tired when they get home. As afternoon turns to evening, I watch and wait for them. But they don't come.

I serve a bite of supper to Grandpapa, when he comes in from haying, stains of sweat on his hat band, his face weary and wrinkled.

"I guess Mom should be bringing Noël any minute now," I chatter. "I've fixed her bed nice and fresh, so you can stay with her while Mom takes me to the dance." I keep glancing out the window, and listen for the whine of the little Ford tractor, but nothing's seen or heard.

"I'll take a sponge bath upstairs." I carry the wash basin with warm water from the kitchen. As I use the soapy flannel to clean each square of flesh, I strain to hear tractor sounds. Nothing!

I dress in my long green skirt, white blouse with green tie, and velvet dancing shoes.

Still Mom and Noël don't return.

Finally, I march down the lane and set off for town alone. As I walk, I rationalize: Mother promised to take me to the dance if I did the chores. I have done all the chores she assigned, so I'm entitled to go. And I will remain safely in the hall. She will pick me up before the dance ends. So I'm not in danger, nor am I disobedient. This last thought brings a flicker of fear, and my steps flag.

I walk, but more slowly, to town, and expect to meet the tractor returning with Mother and Noël.

A pickup truck passes me on the range line road. The driver slows his vehicle and backs up when he sees me.

"Want a ride to town?" calls our new neighbour, Fred Trudzik, a veteran who has settled on a farm only a mile away.

I climb in and smile to the young man.

"Where are you headed?" asks Fred, glancing at my finery. "Going dancing?"

"Mom promised to take me dancing, but she has taken Noël to the doctor, and they haven't come home yet. So I thought I'd go alone. But maybe I shouldn't .... Mom doesn't like me to be out alone."

"Would you like me to drive you to Mayerthorpe to see your Mother? I'll ask her permission to take you dancing."

"What a great idea!" I say, and settle back on the seat with excitement. This guy is really nice!

When we arrive at the hospital, we spot the Ford tractor in the parking lot. We hurry into the building and a nurse ushers us into a quiet room where Mother sits crying.

Noël is dying!

She lies deathly still. I stand beside the bed, and gaze at my darling sister while Mother motions Fred to step out into the hall. They speak together in low tones—I'm not included in the conversation to *spare* me. I hate being treated like a baby, and I creep to the door to overhear their conversation.

Mother explains that Noël has a ruptured appendix. She has had immediate surgery, but is in grave danger of the poison spreading throughout her system. The doctor warns Mother that if Noël dies, Mother will be charged with manslaughter for using a rough tractor to transport her daughter to hospital. As she speaks, Mother's voice chokes with emotion, and her face contorts with grief.

She's crying, too, because she can't return the tractor and she knows Daddy will be furious with her for using it; another wedge between them. But she refuses to leave Noël's side. What can she do? She looks at Fred with doleful eyes.

He's quick to offer a solution. "I'll drive Ardith home," Fred promises. "Then I'll return this truck to my brother here in Mayerthorpe since I borrowed it from him. Then I'll come here for the tractor and drive it back to your farm."

"Oh, thank you!" exclaims Mother. "Thank you, so much! How kind you are!"

All the while, I've been peeking out and straining my ears to hear what's said. I catch enough to realize the gravity of the situation and feel hurt and rejected that Mother excluded me when plans were being arranged.

They're both treating me like a baby, I bristle. I step into the hall and say to Fred, "Since the truck isn't yours, return it now. Then you and I will go home on the tractor. After all, I can ride on the tractor—my appendix is okay."

Fred and Mother are startled by my assertiveness, but they follow through on my suggestion.

I sit beside Noël. "Dear God," I pray, "please don't take Noël."

Fred returns for the tractor key, and I ride home with him. It's a strange trip, me gripping the smooth fender as the tractor bounces along over the gravel, and the moon gives a pale luminous light. We speak very little. Each is deep in thought—fearful for Noël, sorry for Mother, and frightened of the outcome. But we're too shy to discuss such personal thoughts. When we reach home, I tell Grandpapa the whole sad story.

Then I go to bed. But my emotions overwhelm me, and nightmares rob my rest. I feel tremendous guilt for not taking care of Noël.

My breath comes in heavy sighs, shudders. I feel beaten around my heart; my guts hurt. A loathing of life seizes me.

I might as well be dead. I dress myself and begin to walk through the darkness, straight to the river.

It wouldn't be hard to kill myself. I can end this corrosion of my insides—this rotten feeling. I am doomed. Yes, doomed. I don't have anything to say about anything. I'm like Lot's wife.

I'm the one who looks back. I'm the one who dares to see. I'm the one who tries to feel. But my feelings are confused. I cry, as I head straight toward the Paddle. Then I stand stock-still in the middle of the range line. I feel immobile—like a pillar of salt. Fixed and frozen by my thoughts. Second thoughts. Should I end it all? Should I give up my life? What will everyone think? Why? Why should I care? Yes, why?

It won't be hard to kill myself. What does it matter what everyone thinks?

Why go on living on this earth? No one really cares about me. Move on. Move on. Go to the river. Go to the water, where I'll dissolve into tiny grains of salt. Into nothingness.

My fists clench. My teeth tighten. I clutch my arms together. My toes grip the ground. My lips are taut. I move woodenly toward the river. Across the water, clumps of willow bend greeny silver; the skeletons of dead cottonwoods stand dry-boned against the sky. A slight breeze quivers aspen leaves.

Dropping my clothes, I leave them on the shore. Cool air embraces my naked body. The shallow water, tepid to my toes, squelches underfoot. I plod in and feel my flesh contract. Deeper water's icy. My groin clenches. My nipples numb. I wade deeper. Count steps. Deeper, deeper. I take an involuntary gasp, go under. Ears fill. Eyes wide closed.

I turn my head toward the bottom. Dive to murky depths. Arms fold. Hold, embrace the water. This is the end … peace … tranquillity … oblivion … *death.*

My body sinks in dank water. Paralyzing cold enfolds me. I open my eyes. Vision blurs.

Begin to panic. Open mouth to cry. Swallow gulps of sandy water. Long limbs flail. Panic takes over. Clutch with fingers, cramp in toes. Water rushes up my nose.

Burst upward. My arms reach. Beseech release … from a watery grave. My legs thrash. Surface … gasp … cough … spit … drool pools of cool water … tread wildly …. Air rushes to burning lungs. Suspend on surface … sway … wave …. Head spins … body swims … swims strongly … fights death.

Extend toes … touch bottom … tumble. Gain footing … stumble … wade to shore. Death, no more.

A sodden lump of salt … shiver … cold … heart throbs … throbs with life. Life? Yes, life! It's worth fighting for!

Rays of light burst through the clouds; a growl of thunder rumbles in the distance. I shake uncontrollably. My naked body curls into a ball. Shivers. There must be a way. I'll find a way! I'll *make* a way. "Dear God," I pray through blue lips, "Please guide me into a new path, a new life. Help me make a way for myself in this world. I must take control. Please, dear God, show me the way."

With numb hands, I fumble, dress myself, walk home. Slipping silently into the quiet house, I comb my tangled wet hair. It's almost train time. I hurry along the path to town. I must tell Daddy about Noël. Daddy will know what to do.

I meet the train, warn Dad how terribly sick Noël is ... and that Mother's staying at the hospital. Daddy goes to Mayerthorpe on the tractor straight away to visit Noël, furious with Mother for using the tractor to take a sick child to hospital.

Mother is devastated by grief and blame, ashamed of her thoughtlessness.

Noël recovers.

Slowly.

She remains in hospital for two months. Mother stays by her side until Noël is totally well. Mother is not to be trifled with—she knows her place.

And every Sunday afternoon during Noël's convalescence Fred drives me to visit Noël and Mom on his only vehicle, his tractor. I appreciate and respect this quiet man who's so kind.

This hospital experience has stiffened Mother's backbone, and she makes a firm resolve. She decides her job now is to care for her children—her husband can run the farm.

Daddy goes back to the air force base in Edmonton and Mother has a serious talk with her father.

Noël and I lie on our bedroom floor with our ears to the heat vent where we can eavesdrop on their conversation.

"I really appreciate all your help during the war years when Will was away," Mom tells Grandpapa. "But it seems there's not room for two men to run this farm."

"I can see that, Edith," agrees Grandpapa. "And I'm ready to step down. This last year has been tough. I can't keep up with things. I've been thinking, too. I'll move. I've kept in touch with Jill. And I've waited a decent time since your mother's death. Jill and I will marry and move back to my old house. We deserve some happiness. I'm getting old. Why, I can't even manage my horses any more—they seem to have gone loco. I don't know what's wrong with them, but they're dangerous for the girls to ride, especially for Noël after her surgery. You'll have to watch her, Edith. Ardith seems strong, but Noël's delicate."

Noël and I look into each other's eyes. I nudge her with my elbow.

"Yes, Papa," agrees Mom.

"I'm going to sell my horses and cattle. We'll go into chickens. Maybe raise rabbits." Grandpapa continues. "I'll give you a very decent price on the machinery. And you can have the blamed combine. Then you'll be set to continue farming a large holding, since Walter told me that Will is buying him out. If both grandfathers clear out of here, you and Will can farm without family interference. So that's what I'll do, dear."

We shake our heads. Both of us are very serious. If both grandfathers go, will Mom and Dad get along?

"Wise Papa," Mom murmurs. "I hope you'll be happy. How can I ever thank you enough?"

"By being happy," says Grandpapa. "I want to see your bonny smile again."

So do we. Noël and I get up from our crouched position and lie down on our beds. So many changes. Now we'll have Aunt Jill as a step-grandmother. What should we call her?

SIXTY-TWO

My First Haircut

Ardith, Mom, Douglas, Noël (in front) Dad, Ruby. 1951.

It's an ordinary autumn. Migrating ducks gather on the river, their muted gabble drowned by the raucous squawking of the crows, whose voices speak of rotten bodies for scavengers to plunder while they bunch for their long trek south. Starlings wheel in great black swirls that invade the clear sky, and the meadows are vibrant with brilliant dragonflies.

Pesky houseflies are sluggish, and swarm on the warm walls of the veranda, waiting to invade the kitchen, enticed by odours of preserves—jams and jellies that cool in sealers on the counter.

"Tack up a couple of flypaper coils, Ardith, please," says Mom. "You're tall enough to reach the ceiling if you stand on a chair."

I pull long helixes of sappy paper from coils and festoon the ceiling with traps for the unwary flies.

"I'd rather spray the house, Mother," I tell her. "That DDT in the hand pump will kill the flies all at one shot, so we don't have to listen to them buzzing and dying on the coils."

"Yes, but I'm afraid the poison gets on the jams and in the water pails. Besides, every time the door opens, more flies come in," says Mom. "And then there's Noël." Mom's voice drops to a whisper. "She certainly doesn't need more poison in her system."

I nod. Noël, though thin and wan, is home from hospital at last. Mom's very protective of her little girl and still keeps her home from school.

Daddy is discharged from the air force in time to combine the crop. Thanks to the nitrogen from last year's pea crop, we have an excellent yield. Morning air is filled with pigeons fluttering in the clear sky above the hip-roofed barn. The days snail by, with monotonous sameness.

Mom cleans the downstairs bedroom, which is empty since Grandpapa moved out. As she mixes paint on the veranda, the strong smell offends our nostrils.

"Will this paint smell bother you, Noël?" Mom asks with concern.

"Of course not, Mom," Noël smiles. "What a pretty shade of pink. It matches your new bedspread."

"Yes," Mom says. "I'm going to whip up some curtains of

the same material. Douglas and Ardith will bring down my bedroom furniture to set up in here for your Daddy and me."

We soon have the bedroom furniture in place. "There you are, Mother," says Douglas in a soft voice. "My last little chore—I'm off to Edmonton tomorrow. I'll take along a small bag of vegetables."

Douglas catches a ride to the city next morning with the stock truck. "It seems strange having him gone," I say. "He never says much, but he's comforting." I roll forlorn eyes at Noël. "I'll miss Douglas, won't you, Noël?"

"We have Daddy now," she points out.

That's true, but I don't share her blind devotion to Dad. Noël doesn't see his cruel streak. She doesn't see Dad vent his rage by savage slashes at the cattle with his pitchfork. She doesn't see him mashing the heads of newly born kittens to submerge them in a bucket of water to drown. She doesn't see Dad yank the young pigs by their ears and fling them across the pen because they nudge his pail in eagerness to be fed. Noël has to stay in the house while I help with chores, so she doesn't see. Dad frightens me. He has a sadistic streak. I shudder. Does it run in the family? I vow, here and now, never to be cruel.

I help Mother all I can.

"We surely have plenty of vegetables." Mom tosses potato shaws in piles as we clear the garden.

"More than enough." I pause to wipe sweat from my brow, envying a lone eagle that circles on invisible currents high in the sky. Oh, the freedom of it.

But just wait until I graduate next June. My last term at high school! Then I'll be done. I'll be sixteen. An adult! Mother will no longer control me. Nor Dad. Freedom from childhood. I can hardly wait!

Now I hear my parents' constant quarrelling. They hurl angry words at one another like rocks. It begins over the supper table this time. "Do you call this stuff food?" Dad demands. "I'd like to see some red meat on this table for a change."

"Red meat costs money," Mom reminds him through prim lips. "Unless you want to butcher."

"I'll butcher when I'm damn well ready," Dad roars. "I'm waiting for it to get cold. Do you think I don't know anything?" I shiver when I hear Dad speak in that tone; it sounds as if he could strangle Mother. I peek into the kitchen.

Mother's mouth gapes and tiny pearls of sweat appear on her forehead and roll down her cheeks. Her face convulses. She sucks breath into her lungs and tries to explain, "I haven't been buying red meat because our grocery bill is already over the moon. I haven't even been buying bologna for the girls' school lunches. We've always managed on eggs or squab pie, Will, during warm weather. If you want meat, go slaughter a rooster."

Dad draws his heels to attention, gives a mock salute, turns smartly and heads out the door. I watch him march to the chopping block and catch up the axe, march into the henhouse where fowl are chuckling on their perch in the dusky building.

Sweeping his hand across the perch, he clutches Biddie, the barred-rock hen that Noël has raised from a chick. "No, no!" I cry. "Not that one, Dad. That's Noël's pet."

But I'm too late. With one chop, he severs the head from the body, flinging the careening corpse into the air where it veers, convulsing, right into my face. I run screaming to the safety of the house.

Neither of us girls can stomach the chicken and dumplings Mother prepares. She gives us a pitying look, but nothing is said.

Ardith with haircut. 1951.

On Saturday morning, Mom carries the wooden high-stool onto the step and pulls out her shears. "Come, Ardith," she says. "Sit you down on this throne and I'll change your crowning glory." I perch on the stool, thus reducing my height so Mom can reach my head. My hair is a mass of glittering copper in the sunshine. Shears in hand, Mom gazes at the undulating waves reaching my waist.

Snip! The grating sound.

Snip! makes me want to cry.

Snip! Stop! Stop! I've changed my mind!

But I remain silent as long strands fall into a glistening heap on the step. I open my eyes and then fall to my knees to gather the silky strands. Clutching them to my body, I rush to the mirror, my golden eyebrows arching in wonder as I stare at my reflection for a long moment without speaking. Then I smile. Freshly bobbed hair gives me an entirely new appearance. "No more Lady Godiva look!" I laugh to Noël. "How do you like my hair now?"

"Kinda straight," says honest Noël.

"Oh, but just wait." Mom produces a mysterious small pink box. "Come, wash your hair, Ardith. And I'll give you a Toni." It's really worth the smarting eyeballs and sickening smell when the last rubber band is pulled from my curls, and I can see my new image in the glass. I smile at my reflection.

"I'm a woman," I cry. "I look like all the other girls at school! I love it! Oh, thank you, Mother, thank you!"

But I tuck my shorn tresses into a discarded shoe box and hide them in the depths of my closet—it's a jolt to lose my crowning glory.

SIXTY-THREE

What Will the Neighbours Say?

*Fred Trudzik helps Ardith
with school books. 1951.*

Winter winds blow across the land and lay a thin mantle of white. The weather turns bitterly cold. There are flurries of fresh snow and powdery blasts sting my cheeks.

I hate to hear my parents bicker. Constantly. Regardless of the innocence of the topic, it always ends the same. Their remarks snap back and forth like windshield wipers. I dread being in the house, although I no longer enjoy being in the barn either. As my silent feet step into the kitchen, I hear raised voices.

Dad demands, "Why isn't Noël back to school? Why do you insist she stay at home? Are you afraid of me? Is that it? Do you think you've got protection with Noël home?"

"Of course not, Will," says our reasonable Mother. "She's not strong yet. She was so sick. I want her really well before she starts back to school."

"You're mollycoddling her. My kids must stand on their own two feet," growls Dad. "She's starting tomorrow. Do you hear?"

"Yes, I do." Mother's voice is resigned. Noël returns to school the following morning.

I'm afraid to mention Fred to Mother. His very name seems to be taboo. I know my mother disapproves of Fred—not the kind of man he is, but of what he is—a bohunk. And a Roman Catholic. Grandpapa has always said that these things are deadly sins to be avoided at all costs, and Mother sides with his beliefs. And yet, I feel drawn to Fred. After all, I'm not a little girl any longer, I think with resentment. I'm fifteen.

Fred meets me where the school bus stops at Rochfort Bridge on Monday afternoon. He's been waiting for the school bus to let off students on Main Street.

"Can I take you to the show on Saturday?" he asks. "Or are you going dancing?"

"I'm not going dancing. Och, Fred, I don't think I'll ever dance again! Every time I think about going dancing while Noël lay dying, it makes me cry. I'm so ashamed of not taking better care of her. I swear I'll never dance again! Not for a long time, anyhow!" I look directly into Fred's eyes, watching them light up when I add, "Sure, I'd like to see a show."

"About seven o'clock then," smiles Fred. "I'll pick you up. I might have a surprise for you." A lopsided smile pulls up one corner of his mouth.

Now I'm in for it! I'll have to ask Mom if I may go out with Fred, although I've already told him I would. But I'll wait until Saturday before I ask. No use borrowing trouble!

I creep into the house, my cheeks glowing from blowing snow. I'm still stepping out of my winter boots in the kitchen when I hear an outburst from the living room.

It comes from Mother, voice high and shrill. "But Will, what will the neighbours think? You'll be the laughingstock, coming home and instantly switching everything around here. Things are working very well the way I have them. We have a system going. Surely you're not going to disrupt everything at once? Take one step at a time."

Then I hear a snort, much as if Ol' Tom is in the living room. I realize it comes from Dad. I can glimpse Mother's face colour deepening as she sucks breath into her lungs while listening to Daddy say, "I'm sick and tired of this set-up. No matter what I try to do, you think you know better. You think I don't know how to run a farm? Well, I've made up my mind what I'm going to do. I'm tired of your disapproval and your stiff-necked pride. To hell with what the neighbours think! I want out of this and by God, I'm getting out. Do you hear me? Do you hear?" He actually takes a step toward her. "Do you hear me?"

Mother blinks rapidly, her face disintegrating with humiliation. "Oh, Will," she cries. "You can't mean that. After everyone bent over backwards to let you have the land. And now you say you don't want it? I can't believe it!"

"No," howls his savage voice, "I didn't say I don't want the land. I *want* the land. All of it. I just don't want the marriage." His face flushes with an anger that seems to ignite him, and his eyes glow like coals.

Mother shrinks back. Her eyes are as bleak as two holes burned in a blanket. Her face pales.

"Och, Will!" she whispers. "You can't mean it." She holds up a hand imploringly. "Not our marriage. We just got started again. It'll work out. Give us a chance."

"Shut up!"

Grandpapa Black with second wife, Jill. 1951.

Mother draws her chin into her chest. Then her voice bursts out shrill and angry. "How dare you tell me to shut up? After all I've done for you! I worked my fingers to the bone to build up this place so we'd have it together. I scrimped and saved to build this house. I went without decent clothes or entertainment to build up the farm. I put on pants and drove that tractor over every inch of this place, raising crops and keeping things going. I worked like a man. I never once went to the bar like some of these lonely women. I saved myself. For you, Will. For you. How dare you tell me to shut up? I'm your wife. I belong here."

The anger his slur on her management has aroused in her is suddenly thrust aside by her rejection, and again she pleads, "Let's work this out, Will. Think of the children."

"I have been thinking of the kids," he growls. "I stuck it out at Edmonton for years, just waiting for our kids to grow up and leave home. I knew we'd never make a go of it, Edith. I was biding my time until they left. But you begged me to come home. So I came. But I can't stand it. I know we still have Ardith and Noël to raise, but we won't do it together. I can't take your high ideals. Your holier-than-thou attitude. Do you think you have blue blood in your veins? You're a nothing, Edith. A hick farmer from the bush country. You've never seen the world. You don't know what blue blood is. But I do! And believe me, it's not that ice water you've got in your veins. You don't know how to give a guy a good roll. Why, in England ... "

"Shut up!" Mother shrills the command with a violence that tears the air and hangs there in the stillness. Now she bites her bottom lip, as if regretting her outburst. She adds in a level tone, "I was good enough to bear your children, Will. And raise them with respect and dignity in a decent home. But they're not all raised yet, Will. As you said, we still have Noël and Ardith. What'll become of the girls if we separate?"

Mother slumps and suddenly she looks very old. Her back crumples and even her hair looks old, silvered. She closes her eyes and then opens them with a pleading glance. She says, "Please, Will. Let's leave this for now. Let's raise our daughters." She holds out her hand, palm upward, in an appealing gesture.

But Daddy mumbles, "We'll see."

Mother straightens and extends her hand again in the same appealing manner. "Please, Will. Let's work this out."

But he turns from her, shaking his head. "I'll do what I have to do. I'm sorry." He has his back to her now. He passes through to the kitchen and walks out into the stillness of the yard.

I step into the room, go straight to my mother, hug her and kiss the soft creases in her cheeks. But she turns away, shrugging me off. "You're chilly," she mutters. "Go upstairs and get warmed."

SIXTY-FOUR

New Car

Fred buys Meteor car. 1951.

I t's a quiet Friday evening. Noël and I listen to *Fibber McGee and Molly* on the radio while we play checkers, but the atmosphere in the living room is so thick you could cut it with a knife. The strain between our parents is worse than the bickering. We escape by going upstairs where Noël says, "Oh, I'm so happy to be back at school. Everyone is nice to me there and all the kids welcome me back—school is so much fun! It was awful staying home all day, listening to Mom and Dad!" I nod in sympathy.

I hurry through my chores the next day. I wash my hair and set it with pin-curls, perspiration running down my flushed face. And now for the thing I dread—it's two o'clock Saturday afternoon. The sun's slanting rays flood through sparkling kitchen windows into a bright room. Mother is slashing cabbage into slaw, brandishing the butcher knife like a weapon. Chunks of cabbage lie piled on the table, waiting to be packed into brine. Mother is furious, and I realize it isn't the cabbage that angers her.

I stand for a moment, chewing a bit of raw cabbage, thinking, I'll have to bite the bullet.

"Mother, I want to go to the show tonight with Fred," I begin.

"Spend the whole evening with Fred, Ardith? Why?" asks Mother, gathering a pile of cabbage and sliding it into the crock.

"Just because … he asked me. And I'd like to go."

"Really, Ardith. He's too old for you."

"But Mom, when I tried to go with someone my own age, you didn't let me."

"Well, you can't go with Fred either." Mother grabs the wooden lid and presses it over the crock, placing a heavy stone on top.

"But Mother, I have been with him several times already. Visiting you and Noël at the hospital. You never said anything then."

"Ardith, that was different. It was daylight. And I was worrying so much about Noël—I couldn't think straight. But Fred is twice your age. And he's a bohunk. A Catholic too, no doubt. No, Ardith, I forbid it."

I slant my gaze toward my mother. My whole body begins to tremble. I wish I had the courage to defy my mother and break the invisible cord which binds us, but I know I haven't. Yet I dare to speak once more, my voice quivering. "Its just to the show, Mother. I want to go."

"And you shall go," bellows a voice from the basement stairwell. Dad stamps into the kitchen. He stands there in the doorway, glaring at Mother.

She stares back, flour sack in hand, ready to cover the kraut crock. "Will! I have forbidden Ardith to go."

"Maybe so, but I'm the head of the house."

Mother sweeps the towel around the rim and ties the corners with deft fingers. "Don't take that tone with me. I don't want Ardith mixed up with that grown man. She's just a child."

"Ardith is a young woman and *that man* is a decent fellow who served for six years in the army. He's our neighbour and friend. There's not a thing wrong with him." I see Mother's colour rise as Dad sweeps past her and out the back door.

I follow. Standing with my back to the door, I gasp a huge mouthful of air and say, "Thank you, Dad." He turns and winks at me. Our conspiracy makes me feel I'm disloyal to Mom. But I'm beginning to see my mother through Dad's eyes—quaint, with straight-laced ideas. And, after all, I'm only going to the show with Fred.

I dress in clean clothes and stand combing my curls, afraid to show in the kitchen, where Mother is still working. I remain upstairs, cold seeping around the window sash where I stand gazing down the lane, willing Fred to arrive.

On the dot of seven o'clock, a brand new, four-door sedan painted a deep maroon pulls up to the gate in majesty and Fred steps out, grinning like a prince.

"Oh-h, Fred!" I breathe. "Is this yours? It's so shiny and elegant. What a wonderful surprise!"

"It's a Meteor," he says. Fred holds the door as I scramble in. It's all I can do not to bounce on the seat to test the springs. I inhale the newness of leather upholstery and run my fingers over the textured dash. I turn the window down and up. My breath clouds the glass. "This sure beats the tractor," I laugh, watching snow fall in a thin vertical spray on the windshield. "I never dreamed the surprise would be a new car."

Fred watches me with amusement, smiling at my naive delight in his new car.

Our friendship progresses as winter wears on. We meet only once a week to drive to the movies in Mayerthorpe, and Fred occasionally drives me home from the school bus at Rochfort Bridge.

A terrific snowstorm moves in over the mountains, dumping tons of heavy white stuff, followed by winds of gale force that heap drifts that completely block the range line and highways. All roads have drifted in, so the school bus can't operate. I walk with Marian the ten-mile distance to Sangudo, still maintaining my perfect attendance record.

"We're crazy," giggles Marian as we march atop the hard-packed drifts. "We're going to be late. But it wouldn't be much fun staying in my little shack all day either."

"It's no fun at all at my place," I declare. "Mom and Dad fight all the time. I can't stand it."

"Hah!" laughs Marian, making a snort through her nose. "My folks fight too, Ardith. But I have skin as thick as a grapefruit."

"Not me," I say, crunching fresh footprints along the highway. "Maybe it bothers me so much because we never grew up with anyone fighting in our home." At last we reach the high school, late, but proud of our jaunt. Not too many students are there today.

I'm a keen student—I want to be better than the best. Yet when I succeed, it's a hollow victory. I have aspirations to make something of myself. Maintaining my perfect attendance record is only one example of my determination, my subconscious desire to be, in some way, perfect.

By the time Marian and I walk all the way home that evening, it's almost dark and we're exhausted.

"Why are you so late?" Mom demands. From the tone of her voice, I know that she and Dad have been quarrelling again.

My legs feel utterly weary. "The highway is blown in," I say. "So Marian and I walked."

"All that way?" Mom asks. "Och, Ardith, that was foolish."

"No, it isn't," says Dad quickly. Then he begins making strange noises in his throat, as if he'd like to add more.

But Mom glares at him across the lamp-lit room.

Dad draws himself up, and it's a second or two before he speaks, "If Ardith values her education enough to walk that far, good for her." He gives me a wry smile.

"Yes, and if she freezes to death along the road, I suppose you'd still say 'good for her,'" Mother says.

"She's old enough to take care of herself," Dad points out. "Don't mollycoddle the girls. It's a cruel world out there."

Back and forth snap their words, back and forth with the jerkiness of a heavy line of wash snapping in the wind.

"I'm beat," I say. "I'm going to bed." I leave my parents glaring at each other.

And so another week passes, with constant bickering or black silences in the household.

The next Saturday evening finds me again waiting for

Noël, Alvin Bauer, Ruby, Robert Bauer, Ardith, Douglas. 1951.

Fred to pick me up. We're going to the show. I slide shyly into my seat beside him, gazing at his handsome face, his boyish smile. It's good to get away, and exciting to be with Fred.

SIXTY-FIVE

A Perfect Wedding

Ardith and Fred at Legion picnic. 1951.

Noël and I sometimes slip over to Grandpapa's old house to visit him and his new wife. "What do you want us to call you?" we ask her.

"Grandma Black," she answers. "I'm the only Grandma you have alive now." This is true.

I look around her cosy living room. The inside of his old house has been transformed, and they use the old bedroom as a living room and have opened up the kitchen to twice its size. The old couple are happy together.

Christmas brings excitement to the household. It's wonderful to have Douglas home again, and he must have grown a foot taller. Ruby arrives too, looking proud as she draws a handsome man into the room. "This is Robert," she says. I stare. I've never seen Ruby look so radiant. No wonder; Robert never takes his eyes off her.

The dining table is fully extended to provide space for an adult crowd. "Actually, there's only ten of us," I count, "but everyone has such long legs now, we really need the room under the table."

Mother is more flustered than usual, I notice, and tries extra hard with the feast. We three girls all help her, while the menfolk chat in the living room.

Uncle Lawrence appears, bringing Granddad. Uncle split up with Aunt Martha, so there are no little children present. And Mom didn't invite Grandpapa and his bride, Grandma Black.

"I got a card from Uncle Jim," Mom announces when we are all seated around the table. "He has moved into a men's shelter in Edmonton, and sends his love to everyone."

"Well, three cheers for Uncle Jim!" laughs Douglas. "And a Merry Christmas to us all, God bless us, everyone, as Tiny Tim says!" Everyone laughs. It's great to have the whole family (or almost the whole family) together again and the place is very quiet when they leave. Noël and I strip the decorations and things settle into a dull routine.

Christmastime is long past now, as I plod along the muddy street of Rochfort Bridge. Only dingy patches of slushy snow stand on the northern sides of buildings. Spring is just around the corner, but which corner, I'm not sure. Thin rain driven by wind bites like ice on my scalp. Wind always makes my headaches worse, and they're becoming more and more frequent. First I see an aura of dazzling, twinkling light, then pain stabs the left side of my head.

I hurry past the blacksmith shop, the wide open door allowing singey smells of hot iron to waft to my nostrils. Hammering sounds make my ears ring, adding to the flashing lights and pounding in my temples. I long to reach home, to bury my head beneath my pillow and shut my eyes, to close out the light that blinds me. Migraines totally disable me. I lie motionless, nauseated for hours before the pain subsides.

The sun smiles and spring days grow warmer, although it's mucky everywhere.

"I doubt Fred will come tonight," says Noël. "Not with that nice new car. I'm sure he won't want it plastered with this gumbo."

I feel my heart lurch. I can't imagine Fred not coming! He'll surely come. He has to! I watch. What is there about him that attracts me? Is it his face—sharp features, a prominent nose and attractive, lopsided grin? Is it his soft hazel-green eyes that follow my every movement? Is it his short compact body, muscular and strong? Or his gentle hands—stubby fingers making them appear almost square?

Or am I attracted by his maturity? He's twice my age. Worldly, sensible.

Am I attracted by his wealth? He always carries a large amount of cash in his wallet—flashing hundred dollar bills regularly. I've never before seen that much money!

Then, too, he drives a beautiful new car. And he has his own farm, and he's built a brand new house. He owns a new tractor, and machinery too.

Is it a combination of all these things? Yes, yes, that much is true. But it's more—much more!

It's the excitement I feel when I'm with him. It's the adrenaline rush when we kiss—long, slow kisses that build to bursting point, making me yearn for more. It's the feel of his firm, lean body pressing against my own with promise of more to come. It's the glow of possessiveness in his eyes. It's his decisiveness, his caution, his boldness, his kindness, his dominance, his aggressiveness, and his gentleness.

Oh, will he come to pick me up tonight? I long to escape the confines of my unhappy home. To be carefree. To be admired.

A flash of chrome and maroon in the lane makes my heart leap! He *is* coming! Despite the mud, Fred's coming. He must want to see me as much as I long for him!

Late spring brings Ruby's graduation from Vermilion College—a major family event. Fred offers the use of his car, so Noël, Mom and I pile into the back seat, leaving Dad to sit with Fred in the front. I think it's okay to have this arrangement, and it pleases me that my parents are separated during the long drive.

Ruby receives her certificate graciously. She wears a richly brocaded satin gown, perfectly fitted, the pale mauve bringing out the sparkle in her eyes. Robert is her escort, and joins us all in a feast to honour the graduate, after which Ruby chooses to stay on at his home, so we head for home.

The following month I graduate from Sangudo High School with Mother and Dad in attendance. I borrow Ruby's mauve satin gown, and am grateful for it, since there's no money to buy me a grad gown, but even when I wear flat heels, the dress is much too short, since I tower over both my sisters. "Never mind." I must be sensible. "I'll walk with my knees bent, so the dress will touch the floor!"

As I waver across the platform with bent knees, I hear Mr. Morgan announce, "Ardith Ray, Alberta Wheat Pool scholarship and the youngest graduate this term."

But this honour feels flat because I have no dancing escort. Fred confesses that he can't dance, and prefers not to attend. And Douglas can't come because he has a summer job in Edmonton, so he can't escort me either.

"Never mind," I say to Mother, who is sorry for me. "I can't dance for long with my knees bent like this anyway. Let's just go home!" But I'm secretly very disappointed that Fred wouldn't at least walk in the grand march with me.

Then begins a flurry of preparations for Ruby's wedding. Dad has very little money so I again wear the mauve brocade (with flat shoes and bent knees) to be a bridesmaid. Ruby made a plain lilac-coloured gown of the same pattern for Noël, who is the second bridesmaid.

Ruby is beautiful, wearing a handsome white brocade wedding gown, which she has designed in the same style as ours. Douglas is one of the groomsmen, along with Robert's brother, Alvin. Thankfully, Alvin is taller than I, so he makes a wonderful escort.

"Lilacs are my favourite flowers," Ruby chatters. "So I've chosen to carry natural mauve lilacs from Robert's bushes for my bouquet. And the girls will carry white lilacs."

Rain falls in torrents the evening before the wedding.

Great gashes of greenish sheet lightning tear the blackness of the sky.

Robert goes outdoors to check cattle, and sinks into the oozing mud. The rain drums on the porch roof. He returns drenched, his pants sodden to the knees from the wet grass. "It's as black as the ace of spades tonight," he announces. "And still coming down!" He shakes his tousled curls, spraying water on Ruby.

"How will we ever make it to town tomorrow," she frets, "for our wedding ceremony?"

"We'll make it!" Robert declares. "Even if I have to carry you." Everyone chuckles at his enthusiasm, but Ruby worries as we fix our hair. Ruby rolls Noël's hair into nylon curlers, and Mother rolls mine. Then Ruby rolls Mother's hair into steel curlers. She turns to her future mother-in-law and offers, "Shall I do your hair, too?" She uses small steel curlers for her mother-in-law's hair. At last she winds her own curlers and we three girls settle to sleep on a floor mattress. Noël falls asleep almost at once, tired from our long car ride. But Ruby tosses and turns, so she and I have little rest.

Slanting rays of morning sunshine sparkle on the trees, and the leaves lift like elfin faces, shiny with moisture. It's perfect weather for a wedding.

After a hearty late breakfast, we wash up and begin to ready ourselves for the ceremony. Mother searches high and low for the rubber button for her garter. It has vanished! "Now, how will I hold my stocking up?" Her whole face convulses with anxiety.

Ruby comes to the rescue with a shiny penny. "Here, Mom," she laughs. "This will do! Now hurry, everyone, or we'll all be late!"

Then Robert's mother has garter problems. "I can't hook my back garters," she complains. "My fingers just won't reach!"

"Here, I'll do it," says Robert, and in a flash he kneels and fastens his mother's garters.

She gives an embarrassed laugh, and explains, "I have no daughters, so my boys help me."

The corners of her mouth twitch as Ruby says, "I'll be your daughter after today!" And she starts to laugh, a bit hysterically. We all give in to it, and laugh uproariously—the tension broken. We wipe wet cheeks with our hands, and Robert's mother laughs with relief. Ruby dabs at her make-up with a tissue, finally able to say, "It's all right. Years from now we'll still laugh about this garter situation."

Although the ceremony is a bit late, the procession comes together. Ruby chokes up when she takes Daddy's arm. Although he rebelled against the expense, he's proud of his eldest daughter. Now looking his best in his new suit, neatly pressed, his soft hair bleached by the sun, he's still an upright figure.

The bridesmaids move forward, step by step, and just as we reach the altar, the wedding march begins. Ruby advances up the aisle, looking radiant, and the guests rise in her honour. I feel my cheeks burn and know my freckles are prominent, but I have my back turned toward the guests. I concentrate on holding the bridal bouquet. I turn a direct gaze toward the couple as they make their vows, and tears well in my eyes as I hear their strong responses. Rings are exchanged, their kiss completes the ceremony and guests applaud, while I realize that now Ruby is gone from our family.

Thankfully, our parents behave splendidly. No one would suspect they were at one another's throats. Nothing marred Ruby and Robert's wedding day.

The studio portrait we took that day marks the end of our family living under one roof. I sigh when the day ends. It has been a fairy tale wedding, and as I think of Ruby and Robert's embrace, I feel lonelier than ever.

I turn a bright face toward Fred as he drives the family the long road home. "Wasn't that a perfect wedding?" I look ahead as I say dreamily, "and Ruby and Robert will live happily ever after."

From the back seat comes Dad's voice, with a touch of disdain as he says, "They'd better. It sure cost enough."

Mother's voice rasps at him, "I'm sick of your throwing that up to me. She's our eldest daughter and you should be proud she's marrying well."

"Yes," he agrees, his tone deep with anger. "It still cost more than we can afford."

Her next words were weighted, like a threat. "Just you wait. You have two more daughters to see married. So let's hear no more about expenses."

He rounded on her then, bawling more loudly than ever, "That's the last wedding I'm paying for. Without a word of a lie. It's just ridiculous to fork out all that cash for a few hours of frivolity."

We drive in silence for several miles, until Fred, after clearing his throat, says, "Anyone ready for a coffee?"

My voice comes in a whimper, "Yes, please." I feel drawn to this kind and supportive guy at a time when I feel devastated and abandoned by my parents.

SIXTY-SIX

A Change of Luck

I wake on the morning of my seventeenth birthday, stretching my lean body until my toes poke from beneath the sheet and I can feel the coolness of the iron bunk. I stretch my arms upward and grasp the bed head-rail behind my head. Grown up at last!

I know I've grown up more during the past two weeks than I did in the past two years. Now I swing my legs over the edge of my top bunk and get up.

The yellow sunlight peeking in promises another hot day. Before my feet reach the stairs, I hear my parents' voices rise in anger. Oh, no. Not today. As the sounds rise higher, I wonder what it's all about this time.

And then I hear a slap. I burst into the kitchen and take in the whole situation. Dad's standing with his hands over Mother, poised as if to grip her throat.

Mother doesn't utter a word. She just stares. I stand unable to move for a moment. Then I fade from the room. I hear a second slap as I stumble up the steps. Noël stands wide-eyed at the top of the staircase.

"What's happening?" she asks. But I only shake my head. We stare at each other, sadness reflecting in our eyes. We go quietly into our bedroom and remain there until we hear no sound through the register.

Much later, I step into the living room. Mother slumps into a cushion on the couch, her head leans to one side, and she

454

breathes in gasps. Her face is a picture of suppressed fury; rage chokes her. Her eyes glare at Dad.

Then, ignoring my presence, Mom says, "You filthy man. How dare you set up a household right across the range line from us, in Granddad's house! I never dreamed when you bought his land that you'd take another woman into your bed right here, at Rochfort Bridge, in front of the whole neighbourhood. What will *people say?* Why couldn't you have the decency to move far away, so *no one would know?* Now everyone will find out that you've left me, and taken up with that hussy. Oh, what a disgrace! You'll regret this the rest of your life!"

"I'll regret nothing. Only marrying you. We're through. I should have done this long ago. I rule the roost here."

Mom gives a high-pitched hysterical cry and flings up her arms. "Rule the roost? You weren't here to help with one bit of this house. Or the farm either. And now you say you rule the roost? Huh! I tell you, Will, you're despicable! And furthermore, you'll be the laughingstock of the whole neighbourhood. Will and his womanizing."

Dad speaks again, as if he were very tired. "I thought we had an understanding, Edith. I can't stand your hoity-toity behaviour. So I left your bed. But I'm a man, damn it. I need a woman. And by God, I'm going to have one!"

His whole face flames as he shouts, "Why should I get out of this neighbourhood? I'm keeping my land. If you don't like what I'm doing, then *you* get out! I'm finished with you. More than finished. I knew I'd rue the day I ever married you. Get out before I say something you'll regret."

"You've already done that!" Mother bursts out bitterly. She runs from the room, flings herself onto her bed. Her defiance is gone. Her face shows a great emptiness.

I peek through the door crack to be sure she's all right. She keeps wringing her hands, her face anguished. Then she moans, "What am I to do? How can I face this disgrace? What will the neighbours say? And what about our girls? Can we stand having him live openly with that woman—right across the road from us? What am I to do?"

Then I watch Mother stop wringing her fingers and hold them stiffly at arm's length, staring at them. Slowly, she flexes her fingers and draws her hands up, turns them this way and that to examine them, as though she's never seen them before. She feels her rough jagged fingernails, checks each crescent of dirt-encrusted nails, and examines her swollen knuckles. She stares for several seconds at her solitary diamond, which glistens like a tear on her work-worn finger. She feels the callouses on her palms formed from gripping the tractor wheel, and studies the dark lines of her palms. She rubs her rough fingers, weathered and dry. She lies a long while, staring at her hands.

At last I go to her, and she moves to make room for me to sit on the edge of the bed. "I still have a pair of hands," she tells me. "And I know how to use them." She folds them snug under her breasts. "I've still got you girls to care for. To fight for," and her fingers unconsciously form into fists.

I nod to Mom, but don't say anything. She looks so hopeless. She tells me, "I do know one thing. I've got to get away from here. I can't face your dad's living with that hussy— right across the road from us. I'll have to get out! Get away! Go to Edmonton. Take you girls. I don't know what I'll do. But at least I won't have to face the neighbours." She rolls away from me, shoulders heaving.

Later, I step into the kitchen. Dad sits hunched forward, unmoving. Mother sits at her usual place, next to the fire. They must have been speaking, but now all is silent. I feel that I must fill this quiet. I open my mouth to speak when Dad turns to me and growls through clenched teeth, "Your mother and I are parting. Right away. You can stay on with me here, or you can move to Edmonton with her and Noël. But we're through. Do you hear? We're through." And he doubles his hands into fists and bangs them on the table as he stands.

My mouth agape, I answer, "Yes, I hear you, Dad. I hear." Dad turns on his heel and goes outside.

Poor Mother. She's lost everything and there's no strength left in her. I can see that she's incapable of any more fighting.

I can scarcely bear to look at her. The sight of my mother's dejection is so painful it brings tears to my eyes.

Again I watch Mother put her hands beneath her breast and press tightly. When she speaks, her voice is a low moan, "Och, Ardith. What am I going to do? Where shall I go in Edmonton? All I know for sure is that I can't stay here. I must get away. I can't face the neighbours. *It would kill me.*"

There. It's out into the open at last. It *would* kill my mother to stay on at Rochfort Bridge while Dad has an affair with another woman. Yes, yes, I can see that. It *will* kill my mother. This understanding comes clearly to my mind. And what about me?

If Mother is getting out, then I must also. But I can't go with Mother. She has enough to contend with. Where shall I go? And what shall I do?

I must do something on my own. But what? I've finished high school, but I have no money to go to university. That Wheat Pool scholarship I won isn't nearly enough. So university's out. And I'm afraid to step out into the world! I don't feel grown up, even though I am seventeen. Where can I find a little security? As if in a dream, I step outside. I must get away. Now. But where am I to go?

I leave the solid farmhouse. The wind billows my dress, almost lifts me from the ground, but I scarcely feel it. The trees toss in the sky, but I scarcely notice.

I'm just glad to be outside, and strike off blindly down the lane. The bright moon illuminates the path clearly. This path lies like a ribbon of silver, leading me on. I draw a deep breath; the fresh air clears my head. What am I to do? I long to speak to someone, to touch someone's hand, to hear someone speak in a pleasant voice, to see someone's loving smile.

I think of Fred. Suddenly I feel an overwhelming longing. I want to inhale his musky tobacco and shaving-cream scent, to kiss his lips. I long to see his green eyes light up when I speak, and watch that special lopsided smile lift one corner of his mouth. I need to feel the toughness of his corded arm muscles, the solidity of his chest, the softness of his neck as I snuggle my face against him. I always feel a special security whenever I nuzzle my face into his neck.

Security! That's it! My legs go wobbly, and I get dizzy, my mouth goes dry and my knees knock. I've just made an earth-shattering decision. I must act on it. Now. Before I lose my courage.

The wind lifts my hair from behind my ears and blows it into my face. I look up into the sky again, praying, "Dear God, let this be right for me. The right decision, Lord. I need a change of luck."

Then, with a slight smile, I walk quietly along the mile of road to his house. I'm going to ask Fred to marry me.

——•——

MEMBER OF SCABRINI GROUP

Québec, Canada
2007